# FROM SLAVE TO SIREN

# The Victorian Woman

# and her Jewelry

# From Neoclassic

# to Art Nouveau

*DORA JANE JANSON*

May 1971

The Duke University Museum of Art
Durham, North Carolina

The cover reproduction was financed by Home Security Life Insurance Co.
The catalogue was made possible by Harry N. Abrams, Inc.

*IN MEMORY OF H.W.*

# PREFACE

The Duke University exhibition of jewelry from Neoclassic to Art Nouveau was originally planned as a modest showing of some of the objects collected by Mrs. Dora Jane Janson. It was our intention to accompany this by a handlist cataloguing the individual pieces. Luckily, the original date was postponed and plans were being made by which the exhibition would be extended in its scope and placed on a historical footing. What was once a handlist has now emerged as Mrs. Janson's catalogue under the intriguing title "From Slave to Siren." While her own jewels still form the inner core of our exhibition it will become clear to the readers of our Catalogue that the materials displayed come from a great variety of lenders, both private and institutional. In her Acknowledgements Mrs. Janson has expressed the profound gratitude which all who have worked on the Catalogue as well as the Exhibition share toward those who have lent objects and who have given scholarly and technical advice; it goes without saying that often lenders have also been advisors. I feel privileged to have this opportunity to express once more the lasting gratitude of the Duke University Art Museum to all those who have lent a helping hand and a helping mind.

Mrs. Janson's *Catalogue raisonné* is a significant contribution to the history of art. It is also, I believe, an important chapter in the history of late nineteenth century and early twentieth century esthetic and sociological development. "From Slave to Siren" helps to highlight a phase in cultural history which may be said to be the culmination of the *Romantic Agony* which Mario Praz so brilliantly sketched out in his book which appeared under that title in 1933.

Catalogue and Exhibition approximate the *beau idéal* every museum director hopes for. Its realization is due to the unselfish dedication and help both from within and from without our own walls. I wish to record here our gratitude to Mr. Harry N. Abrams and Mr. Paul Anbinder who have been most helpful in our enterprise. Mr. Leonard Kamsler, an alumnus of Duke University, has made the majority of color transparencies of objects in this country. We regret, of course, that it was possible to have color plates for only a small fraction of the total number of illustrations provided in this catalogue. Mr. Henry van Dijk, Sr., of Duke University, has made the black and white conversions.

Mrs. Carol C. Gillham and Professor William K. Stars have been in charge of the installation as well as many other problems which form part of the exhibition and the individual welfare of its objects. It was, however, above all Mrs. Elizabeth C. Sands who has been responsible for the editoral aspects of the production of the Catalogue. In this she was ably assisted by Mrs. Barbara S. Thompson of the Duke University Press who obliged her and us by acting as an outside consultant.

We very much hope that our students and our colleagues, the Duke University community as well as the visitors of our exhibition and the readers of Mrs. Janson's catalogue will profit by this rare combination of profound scholarship and exquisite beauty.

I wish to express our thanks to the following: Mr. Richard A. Bindewald, Mrs. Virginia W. Callahan, Professor Earl G. Mueller, Mr. Earl Wolslagel.

William S. Heckscher

May 9, 1971

## ACKNOWLEDGEMENTS

Had it not been for the astonishing cooperation of the lenders to this exhibition, who have not only contributed objects but knowledge of the period and its jewelry, patience with the various vicissitudes of assembling the catalogue, and encouragement, the exhibition could not have been presented nor the catalogue finished in a year.

First I must thank Mrs. Shirley Bury and Mrs. Lillian Nassau; over the years they have educated my eye and my mind, the former by opening up the vast resources of the Victoria & Albert Museum to a timid amateur, the latter by allowing unlimited access to the ever-changing "museum" that is her shop and by putting at my disposal her considerable library on Art Nouveau.

Joseph Sataloff, who has himself published articles on Art Nouveau jewelry, as well as other lenders whose anonymity is in no way consistent with their contributions, surpassed my hesitant expectations in the generous number of their loans and their willingness to impart information.

My embarrassing ignorance about cameos, those little ideal-images which reflect the ebb and flow of people's perception of themselves throughout the XIX century, was at least partially overcome with the experienced aid of Mrs. Arès Halpin; and to my great good fortune I have had the enthusiastic collaboration of Miss Caroline Karpinski, founder and president of The Victorian Society in America, in preparing the catalogue of the pre-art nouveau entries. She, in turn, would like to thank Mrs. Zenia Cage and Mr. Chris Rohlfing of the Cooper-Hewitt Museum; Mrs. Benjamin Ginsburg, Miss Jean Mailey, and Mr. Joseph Marks for prompt succor with knotty problems.

And yet all would have come a cropper without Mrs. Elizabeth Sands, who not only edited the manuscript, but who has all along served as coordinator between New York and Durham.

To all of them, as well as to the donors who made the color reproductions possible, my thanks.

Dora Jane Janson

# FOREWORD

The only thing that I have never doubted in the course of assembling this exhibition is that it would find interested spectators. Jewelry is fun; jewelry is fascinating; personal adornment is the first art that children practice spontaneously—it is "life-enhancing." If universal appeal were the sole criterion, then jewelry would be acclaimed first among the arts, and toward the end of the XIX century it nearly did achieve what the painters of the XV century in Italy brought about for their art: its promotion from "craft" to "fine art" in the public consciousness. That the attempt failed is perhaps due to the inherently personal and fleeting form in which jewelry is displayed. If one tries to over-step this stricture by making it into a display object, as René Lalique did with unique success in the jewels that he created for the Paris Exposition of 1900, then it can no longer be worn, and thus tends to lose its scale, its purpose, and its very personal attraction.

But if the appeal of jewelry is self-evident, although its destiny in the artistic pecking order seems doomed to fluctuate somewhere below the major level, what need is there for a scholarly catalogue? Let me confess that making one is fun too. Historical research in this tiny field is the equivalent of living in a detective story without corpses; indeed, the minute examination of these entrancing frivolities has breathed new life into the people who made and wore them. It has a tale to tell about the women, both proud and humble,* whose images were enhanced and whose tastes and life styles are revealed with a candor unsuspected by them—a candor that they would have been hard put to express in words. Surely no other social impasse that has befallen mankind, however briefly, has expressed itself in such exquisite forms as the jewelry of the art nouveau period lent to the war between the sexes!

The exhibits, when taken all together, will strike the viewer as a dialogue between France and England, and rightly so. France, the guardian since the late Middle Ages of what we call "taste"—a certain cultivation of the sweetness of life which refines the senses and softens our natural crudity—envies England, the bold and practical innovator; and England in turn seeks to improve its crafts by importing French designers and work-men. That the latter was largely due to a German Prince Albert, need come as no sur-prise. Communications and life style made the decorative arts of the XIX century truly international, and at times lesser nations take the center of the stage, as the U.S.A. in the early '90's, or the Germans and Austrians at the end of that period. Japan has been a constant influence up to our own time from the moment that the commercial treaty with Commodore Perry opened the door to wider importation of its unique arts into

---

* A little affluence must be presumed in this case: for those who have nothing to spare, a ribbon, a flower or a feather must serve. The XIX century, despite its cities of degrading poverty and its dwindling farm population, did spread wealth to an ever increasing segment of the population, including for the first time the business woman as distinct from the servant.

Europe and America; it has been the foremost of the exotic influences to imbue every aspect of Western design, even though Chinese porcelains and oriental textiles had been treasured by the wealthy for hundreds of years before. The Victorians, until recently denigrated for the ecclecticism of their decorative styles, might better be praised for enlarging their appreciation of sheer variety. Although inadvertent, their experiments with modernizing all the styles of the European past surely led to a new evaluation of the so-called exotic and primitive (and a new appreciation for the extra-European civilizations that had produced them) which has been a growing leaven in our continuing adventure to accommodate all of the peoples on one small globe of earth with dignity and mutual respect.

I myself grew up with a half-articulated injunction against prideful self-adornment, especially against the false which seeks to give an inflated impression of its owner. Some of the pieces in the exhibition, however, are heirlooms and not all of them are negligible trinkets: even for those in modest circumstances a small blaze of glory could be sanctioned! However, one must try to distinguish between the jewelry bought as an investment against hard times (or an overt proclamation of good times) and the kind of ornament which could be bought with a leaner purse and a lighter heart. For this reason I have avoided what the French call "joaillerie," as set apart from "bijouterie," in the show.

Diamonds, pearls, rubies, emeralds and sapphires were costly as much for their rarity as for their beauty; for their purchase the cooperation of a father, husband, or other male well-wisher must be assumed in most cases. Thus they tend rather to reflect status than fancy, although a few pieces of lesser "joaillerie" of the end of the period have been included, when the possession of diamonds became a reality to many middle class women, instead of only a dream, due to their increased availability after the opening up of the African diamond mines in the 1870's. The temporary interruption of the flow of diamonds caused by the Boer War in the '90's may have had something to do with the rediscovery of the esthetic possibilities of lesser stones by jewelers of the Art Nouveau period.

In the main, however, the exhibition is devoted to "bijouterie," not only because the lower cost of the pieces is bound to have given more play to women's preferences about the way they wanted to look, but because the designs all along the way are more adventuresome than in their costlier relatives. Where solid investment is the aim the taste for novelty wanes, and precious gem jewelry is more apt during the XIX century to reflect the "safe" taste of a remembered aristocracy than to be innovative. It is one of the ironies of fate that diamonds, if they antedate modern, so-called "brilliant," cut, and pearls which ranked next to them before the Japanese learned to grow cultured pearls, have fallen drastically in monetary value, whereas the lesser jewelry of the bijoutiers is on the rise as fine craftsmanship and design become ever more appreciated.

Moreover, the safe material value represented by gemstones has militated against the survival of the ornaments in which they were set: the stones being used over and over again in more up-to-date settings, few of the old pieces survive, whereas the "bijou" with its far lower material value proved more immune to transformation or outright destruction.

In our time, it seems to me, artificial or "costume" jewelry, as it has been called to take the curse off the pejorative connotations of false show implied in "artificial," has inherited the role of "bijouterie" for an ever-growing consumer public. With a few brilliant exceptions, designers of "joaillerie" tend to substitute massed dazzle for pioneering designs; minor pieces of gold and gemstone jewelry have become trifling in their banality if, indeed, they are not attempting to equal the surface effect of massed diamonds by various techniques that break up the gold and silver surfaces to give them glitter.

It remains to be seen whether the young people, who are now experimenting with all of the crafts in a revolt against the "false" values of an older generation, will come up with a worthy succession in the old art of jewelry. We wish them luck and hope that William Morris, the first passionate advocate of reform in the crafts coupled with a return to a more natural life-style, is smiling upon them from some corner of heaven reserved for the advocates of honesty in art.

# TABLE OF CONTENTS

# INTRODUCTION

## *CAMEOS AND THE IDEAL OF SELF*

Collections of shells and pretty pebbles make up a child's first treasures; and adults, from earliest times, have employed these same materials for seals, signets, or ornaments by incising or carving symbols and decorations in relief upon their surface. Those which have a personal connotation, either because they represent the emblem of one man or of a clan, or which bear the likeness of a face, whether of a famous or an unknown individual, seem to breathe of the original owner's life across time and space. In addition, there is about them the fascination of the lilliputian; a Hercules as big as a fingernail; or a ferocious lion no larger than a bee, cannot help but charm us with the special appeal of incongruity.

Whatever the reason, cameos (and their incised relative, intaglios) have always been avidly collected from the past and, when skill and leisure permitted, produced in imitation of ancient prototypes and with variations to suit the taste of later ages.

The XIX century is no exception; in fact, ever since the Wedgwood potteries brought imitation cameos within reach of the modest purse in the late XVIII century, the vogue for them—going hand in hand with the rage for Indian and later Paisley shawls which were in need of a brooch to fasten them in place—grew by leaps and bounds. In addition, women were employed, both professionally and as amateurs,[1] in the design and manufacture of the new pottery cameos.

With women firmly established not only as the prime purchasers, but as designers and makers as well, one naturally expects to find their tastes directly reflected in the choice of materials and subject matter of cameos. In the early years of the century this is hard to differentiate from the general decorative predilections of the period: the trend in both England and France at the end of the XVIII century was toward a Neoclassicism made light-hearted and delicate by vestiges of the waning Rococo style.

The repertory of subjects included not only the classical heads and mythological scenes which had come down from the earlier collections of antique gems, but also, as time went on and journeys to Italy—the "grand tour"—came to be an accepted part of the well-rounded education of many northerly Europeans, the cameo carvers of Naples and Rome found that there was a ready market for shell facsimiles of the recently excavated Pompeiian wall friezes with their cavorting putti, as well as certain famous paintings of the Renaissance. In time, the English at home produced new variations on old themes in addition to surprising innovations, such as Figure 3. Catalogue number 7, which had nothing to do with classical antiquity but stem from motifs that were English both in inspiration and proto-type (Appendix, Figure 137). As with the major arts of that turn of the century, a Classic and a Romantic strain may be discerned.

For the present study, however, not these but the cameo heads are of para-mount importance. A genuine antique cameo, such as the example in Figure 1, must have been the aspiration of the connoisseur; but failing this a modern copy of the Classical prototype, or even a free interpretation would do. At the beginning of the XIX century the category included quite a number of portraits (Figure 3), used as personal mementos in much the same way as painted miniatures (Figure 9. Catalogue number 13). At the height of his power, around 1810, Napoleon was also the subject of some highly idealized cameo portraits in the manner of the ancient Roman emperors whom he wished to imitate (Figure 2. Catalogue number 4). A fine example such as this was probably a gift from the Emperor to some-body whom he wanted to honor. In the context of this study the two pieces are revealing: both are images of men and both are in profile.

There are few female cameo portraits of this kind, although copies of antique or classicizing female heads are abundant. The most popular subject among the latter, judging by the number that survive, was the profile of the Medusa (Figure 2. Catalogue numbers 5, 6). Perhaps, then, we may point to this as the first ideal-image of the XIX century woman. By this I mean an ideal unconsciously adopted by women of themselves from among the many types that were available at any given time.

By the 1840's the cameo ideal had changed perceptibly. In addition to shells and stratified stones, materials such as amethyst, topaz, ivory, coral, lava and a host of other soft stones came into common use; and toward the end of the century a large variety of materials capable of being moulded (glass imitations of cameos and intaglios have existed since antiquity) were introduced to satisfy a market that appeared to be insatiable, until about 1880 when the shawl went out of style and the cameo with it.

The male profile, dominant at the beginning of the century, has practically disappeared as an innovative type by mid-century. As for the ladies, they begin to turn toward us: the droop of the dying Medusa's head is still echoed, but the down-ward tilt now turns into an expression of coy modesty.[2] Instead of snakes we find flowers in her hair, and the wings that once adorned her crown have slipped down behind her shoulders. She has turned into the good fairy of the pantomimes, with a curtsy to Psyche.

An ideal so meek was apparently not to reign forever: although she was held up in all her ivory virtue as the model woman (Figure 8) throughout the century, it was not only women who rebelled against this saccharine image: one suspects that men, too, found her a bit dull. By 1860 she has raised her head and looks us boldly in the face (Figure 3. Catalogue number 9); the relief carving has become so high that stone cameos such as Catalogue numbers 9 and 10 (Figure 3) are sometimes too heavy to wear pinned to a thin fabric. Not only has our lady become assertive, but the flower wreath of the previous stage has been replaced with the vine and its fruits, hinting at behavior not so docile. The glass imitation (Figure 4. Catalogue number 12) of this popular type of translucent cameo makes a growing agitation explicit, as does the exaggerated pathos of the goitrous Russian example (Figure 3. Catalogue number 10).

Thus, by about 1880, the ideal self that women chose to recognize in these little images had undergone a remarkable change: from a lovely but lifeless chimera, to a saccharine fairy-tale personage of more recent invention, through a brief period of calm self-awareness in the beginning of the second half of the century, which shortly gave way to a more agitated, and finally to a downright self-pitying image at the point where the evolution of the cameo as a popular genre comes to a halt.

When a new type (Figure 3. Catalogue number 11) makes its brief appearance around 1900, after a hiatus of fifteen years or so, it retains the frontality of the Victorian (post-Neoclassical) heads; but in spirit it seems much akin to the early Medusas. The eyes are again half closed, but in this example the face is tilted upward with an air not of deathlike swoon as before, but of an amorous trance—perhaps Wagner's "Liebestod" (love-death). As the word implies, a contradiction is at work here, a paradox that has served as theme for romantic drama through the ages, but never before as a popular precept: in most places and ages erotic culmination is in "living happily ever after," not in semiconsciousness!

The thoughtful viewer will find several other examples that come close to this one in form, if not always so explicitly in spirit, in the art nouveau section of the exhibition. Who is this languishing woman and how did she come to be that way?

## PYGMALION, THE VICTORIAN SUPERMAN

Inheritors as we are of the Victorian experience, perhaps we are inured in some degree to the disappointing outcome of some of the dreams of a better world that technology has engendered. Bent on improving everything around them, and most of all themselves, the men and women of the XIX century were, for the most part, hardly aware of the anomalies and paradoxes inherent in the process.

Let us begin at once by absolving XIX century manhood from any conscious desire to enslave his womenfolk: the dependent position of women had been dictated by biological and economic necessity for so long that it was largely taken for granted. Symbolically speaking, the image of Queen Victoria herself pointed in two directions at once; the very personification of a small nation grown increasingly powerful as the century progressed, at the same time she embodied the womanly and romantic virtues as they were then understood. Brought up during the years when the French Revolution and its aftermath cast a shadow over the European aristocracies, curbing the exuberance—along with the incomes—of the anointed, these leaders of monarchy newly restored were most careful to project an image not too much at variance with that of any hard-working, virtuous burgher or his wife. The German princess who was to become Queen of England grew up in what we call Biedermeier ("solid citizen") surroundings (also known as "Restoration" style in France, and "William IV" in England), a toned-down, simplified variant of the Empire style of Napoleon, unassuming though still graceful. If the women of the post-Napoleonic generation led dutiful lives, the formula for men too was restrictive.

The caution voluntarily assumed by this first post-Revolutionary generation to take power is reflected in the popular Parian Ware porcelain replicas of "Ariadne Riding on the Panther" (Figure 5) which graced many a mid-Victorian parlor.[3] The original life-size statue (1804-14) was the masterpiece of a German Neoclassical sculptor, Dannecker. It should already have been out of date just when it began to grow in popularity (this particular edition is Minton's of 1848), but the combined taming of beast by beauty, and of both by the strictures of style, was indeed the very combination of romantic decorum that ruled the lives of the early Victorians.

In the Crystal Palace Exposition in London, 1851, the hit of the sculpture display was "The Greek Slave" (Figure 6) by the American sculptor, Hiram Powers. She too went through a number of miniature porcelain editions. In spite of her fetters, she strikes us as being far less tame than the "Ariadne," and this must also have been the impression of her first appreciative audience. For them, the battle of the Greeks against the Turks, a cause only recently in the forefront of English awareness due to Lord Byron's involvement, was already beginning to merge with another cause, the abolition of slavery. In this sense she appealed to morality, while in another—the statue was mounted on a revolving base, the better to display it from every side—she catered to emotions less rarified. The troubling combination of demure resignation with fleshly self-satisfaction is akin to the coyness of our mid-century cameo (Figure 3. Catalogue number 8).

It is only after mid-century that divergence between the two aspects of woman, presumed until then to coexist either by tradition or by nature, is manifest. If the frank, assured gaze of the topaz cameo (Figure 3. Catalogue number 9) finds no counterpart in a larger sculpture, we may postulate that such a self-ideal was of short duration and was not upheld by man. Its monuments may well be the type-writer and the sewing machine, both originally brought before the public in the Crystal Palace Exhibition of 1851, and both destined to change the lives of women—the one in the home, the other in the world of business—far more rapidly than any ideological argument.

That a new spirit of independence arose at about this time in the hearts of women, threatening the age-old order between the sexes, is made clear by the sudden and violent rise of misogyny which begins with the poetry of Baudelaire around 1860, and continues in the even more bizarre and outrageous expressions of the "Décadents" until the end of the century. While misogyny has always existed, never before had it assumed the proportions of a secular movement. Even amongst the more placid stratum of the population which continued to read Scott and Dickens (or their equivalents in other languages), one image of woman no longer sufficed. The two small statues, both by E. A. Carrier-Belleuse (Figures 7, 8), a protean designer and able sculptor who was one of Rodin's teachers reveals the split. The virtuous lady of the ivory countenance continues to rule the domestic side of life, and the type was literally enshrined in a late XIX century example (Appendix, Figure 133). But every large city was glutted with surplus women who had wandered in from the countryside in search of employment, and finding none, turned to any kind of adventure that held promise of keeping them alive, at the least, or of vaulting the social barriers, at best. They were "the slaves of men's passions," but a very different kind of slave from Hiram Powers' Greek. Carrier-Belleuse's "Andromeda Chained" struggles most invitingly as she waits for her "deliverer."

That "good" and "bad" women had always existed in real life was no news: only their separate identities, each with its own attributes and attractions, had never before been set up as conflicting ideals. The more daring of the two could also be silently acclaimed as the self-ideal of the poor girl "on the make," as is attested by the glass cameo (Figure 4. Catalogue number 12) which imitates the material of its richer sister (Figure 3. Catalogue number 9) but is more akin to the "Andromeda" in pose and expression. Is she, then, the "siren" of our title? What, exactly, by Victorian definition, is a siren? The temptress of myth and fable who lures voyagers into shipwreck with her song, or something more complex? We turn to an "'eminent Victorian" for the answer.[4]

William Holman-Hunt, the Pre-Raphaelite painter of religious subjects, was passionately involved with a slum girl for nearly a decade. He found Annie Miller living in the tenement in back of his own proper street, made her his model and his mistress and, with a peculiar twist not at all uncommon among Victorian gentlemen,[5] decided to have her educated in both manners and elementary learning so that she might some day make him a presentable wife. He gave her in charge of a gentlewoman of sorts who promised to supervise the girl's education and morals for a small fee. Thereupon he went about his business as a painter which involved him in a long trip to the Holy Land in search of authentic settings and models for his biblical pictures, not to mention shorter trips away from London whenever he was living in England.

To us it hardly seems amazing that after each return to London he would realize that his guttersnipe Galatea had not spent her time and his money in solitary study and chaperoned walks. However, he was always surprised and incensed by her lack of gratitude (as were his right-thinking friends; the wrong-thinking ones, such as D. G. Rossetti, did their best to console her for his absences). Quoting Viola Hunt on one of these occasions, he was "still besotted on Annie . . . she would call in, looking more *syren-like* [my italics], to ask about something or other, saying she could not stay, just when they were sitting down to dinner, and Hunt would jump up and keep them waiting while he put her on a boat to go home to Chelsea."

So that was a "syren": an ungrateful tease, a flirt, a female testing her power over men; deplorable, it may be, but not exactly unusual! But, how did it feel to be in the "syren's" place? For that we have Hunt's own description, taken from a letter to a friend. "I wonder what particular sin of mine it was that brought me into contact with such a girl. That wretched indifference is the most hopeless of all states. Her final answer will be the same so that either yes! or no! would be of equal worth. When I spoke to her last week and induced her to break silence by about five minutes assurance of unlimited—unended interest in her good, she said first, 'I wish I were dead!' "

It is almost a pleasure to add that Annie, after being badgered and harried into becoming someone whom she could not even visualize, for the sake of future marriage to a painter of unsteady fortunes, who did not seem to care enough for her to do more than check upon her progress at times when this interfered with nothing more important, ended up marrying a man of title and some fortune whom she had met in the course of leading life in her own way!

Annie's wish that she were dead has the ring of sincerity, and if a bad girl could be brought to such a pass, even fleetingly, by being forced to lose her own identity in the name of improvement, the situation of good girls could be just as confusing. Although the latter would not have had ready access to the "satanist" writers and artists who contributed to a gathering cloud of anti-feminism from the 1870's on (see Appendix, Figure 131), there can be no doubt that the woman-hating atmosphere which they created influenced many young men. The insidious suspiciousness and disdain of womanhood, as such, was bound to cause bewilderment and feelings of self-pity, such as we find in the cameo (Figure 3. Catalogue number 10) of about 1880. While the battle for women's rights proved eventually effective in the public sphere, women unconsciously also found private ways of striking back. One course open to them was to mock men by playing the role of Temptation Incarnate to the hilt; in this the self-stylization of the great actress, Sarah Bernhardt, showed the way (Appendix, Figure 132). A certain amount of healthy play-acting went into this version of the "syren," but for others the only exit turned out to be a trap—literally a dead end. As images of mermaids and water nymphs multiply in the decorative repertory of the 1890's, the final brief phase of the cameo as an ideal-image occurs (Figure 3. Catalogue number 11). With hindsight and a modern vocabulary of psychological terms, we have no difficulty in diagnosing it as anomie.

## THE SEARCH FOR A NEW STYLE: LOUIS C. TIFFANY

"Because of man's innate love of show, the artistic cultivation of jewelry is of fundamental importance in the formation of taste, and has always exerted a significant influence in the development of the minor arts." Wilhelm Bode, *Kunst und Kunstgewerbe am Ende des XIV. Jahrhunderts.*

The author of the above is best known as one of the greatest museum directors of the museum-minded XIX century, a man whose fame rests securely upon his acquisition of masterpieces for the Kaiser-Friedrich-Museum in Berlin. His *interest* extended to the minor arts, and he sensed the currents affecting them in his own day. His little book, part speculation, part travel account, was begun in 1893 on shipboard, en route to the World's Columbian Exposition in Chicago. His interest in the state of the arts in the United States had been aroused four years earlier at the Paris Exposition of 1889, in which the marvels of international technology, from Eiffel Tower to Thomas A. Edison's new "talking machines," took the center of the stage. Deploring the low estate to which the decorative arts had sunk—an endless succession of revivals of earlier styles, in which he says the French excelled, with a slightly more independent attitude manifest in the English exhibits— he recalls that the entries from the New World offered a hint of something fresh, particularly in the category of books (which he does not detail); in the display of Tiffany's silver and jewelry; and in the stained glass windows entered by Tiffany and John LaFarge. He was perhaps exaggerating the novelty of the American printers' art, which almost surely derived from the renovation of book design already accomplished in England.[6] The innovations in glass, which did indeed prove to be America's most popular contribution to the decorative arts of the turn of the century are beyond the scope of the present catalogue. But it is worth recounting Bode's comments on the Tiffany jewelry and silver: "The jewelry," he says, "may not at first glance strike the beholder as being as rich and sumptuous as the similar displays of the French jewellers, even though in value of the gems alone they are even more costly. This is because they have developed a new style: the selection of stones, their cut and color, are factors to which the American goldsmith gives much attention. The effect of each stone or pearl is cunningly enhanced by their (complementary) juxtaposition; by the silver or gold used for the setting and the toning of these metals. The forms of their jewelry have developed a lush fantasy; in place of the naturalistic motifs of most Parisian jewellers we find weird transformations of animal and plant shapes, according to what seems appropriate to the metal employed. The same respect for the material is apparent in their silver work."[7]

A glance at the illustrations (Appendix, Figures 146, 148) which were incorporated in the report on the Chicago Fair written for *La Revue des Arts Décoratifs*[8] gives a good idea of the idiosyncrasies of the Tiffany silverware that Bode had in mind. If he, and perhaps we, find them more than a little startling, the Arabian style coffee pots in oxydized silver or lightly tinted enamels (Appendix, Figure 147) with which the French critics were more pleased are unexceptionable. Whichever style we may prefer, there can be little doubt that Louis Comfort Tiffany, who designed and oversaw the execution of the stained glass windows mentioned above, and to whose persistence, curiosity and taste we owe the world-famous Favrile glass, was also the ebullient inventor of the bizarre animal style.

Had Bode been describing, instead of prophesying the jewelry style of the next decade, he could hardly have picked out its characteristics more accurately:[9] the selection of stones for their color harmonies; the tinting of metals by chemical bath or, increasingly, by enamels; the lush fantasy and weird transformations.[10] It is as though the seekers of a metamorphosis in art to celebrate the oncoming of the new century had, consciously or unconsciously, turned their vision toward the New World for a portent of things to come, and seeking it there, found it.

## LALIQUE: THE ART JEWEL

The greatest jeweller of the Art Nouveau period—perhaps of any period—was René Lalique. Born in 1860 to a merchant who dealt in the kind of pretty, inexpensive trifles known as "articles de Paris," he spent an uneventful childhood between school in Paris and vacations in the countryside. He showed an early aptitude for drawing (Appendix, Figure 158) and by the age of fifteen he was already earning pocket money as a painter of miniatures on ivory. Proud of his achievements, and fortunate in their timing (the combination of talent, industriousness, and either intuitive shrewdness or sheer luck was to guide him at every critical turn of his career), his talent was already proven by the age of sixteen when his father died and it became necessary for him to seek a trade. As an apprentice in the shop of Louis Aucoc, a respected Parisian jeweller, he learned the basic skills and had the satisfaction of seeing some of his own designs manufactured by his employer.

From 1878 to 1880 Lalique lived in England,[11] and upon his return found employment as a designer of jewelry with a relative, passing from him to another employer for a brief time. Thereafter he became a freelance designer, the better to follow his own ideas. Alas, rapid success found him carrying out the orders of many different manufacturers instead; but he had enough free time to take courses in modelling, which were to stand him in good stead later. He also toyed with the idea of producing, singlehanded, a book of designs for the jewelry trade,[12] and even found a backer; however, in the end this venture had to be abandoned, and he contented himself with providing two designs a month, for about a year, to another established publication, *Le Bijou*.

In 1884 he had his first real breakthrough. In conjunction with an exhibition of the French royal jewels in the Louvre, a little padding (to justify the admission charge) was added in the form of the works of some contemporary makers of both real and imitation jewelry. Lalique had a modest selection of his designs in watercolor in the show, and these came to the attention of the head of a famous firm, Alphonse Fouquet, who praised them greatly. What was of more immediate interest, however, was his introduction to one Jules Destape, the proprietor of a small jewelry atelier of excellent repute and strong financial position. This gentleman, being anxious to retire to some vineyards that he had bought in Algeria, offered to sell his business to Lalique at a reasonable price. After some initial hesitation, weighing the loss of free time that running an atelier would entail against the greater freedom in designing that he would have, he accepted the offer. Although his affairs went well from the start, the changeover from executing work for other more famous houses was gradual. He moved his workshop to larger quarters in 1887, and many of the pieces deprecated by Bode in the displays of other jewellers in the French section of the 1889 Exposition, were actually the products of Lalique's workshop.

In 1890 he moved once again, to Rue Thérèse no. 20, and there he began to free himself of commissions and to establish himself as an artist in his own right. The cost of the larger quarters prodded him to greater production, while at the same time his aroused ambition prompted him to study enamelling[13] with an almost ferocious intensity, experimenting with new processes, inventing others, until he had achieved an entirely new palette of colors—the soft colors of Art Nouveau. His interest in glass, of which enamel is only a variant with a low melting point, also took shape in this 1890-92 period.

From 1891 to 1894 Lalique designed much of Sarah Bernhardt's stage jewelry and this, besides adding greatly to his renown, accustomed him to working in large dimensions so that the pieces could be seen from the audience. This undoubtedly prepared him to design and execute the crowning accomplishments of his career as a jeweler: the oversized, chimerical fantasies which were the wonder of all who saw them at the Paris Exposition in 1900.[14]

Whether admired or hated by his fellow jewellers in Paris, this gifted, secretive, ambitious and dedicated artist nursed the very Victorian ambition to "uplift" the jeweller's craft from "minor art" to "fine art." An occasional writer of verse—like his contemporary, Emil Gallé, whom he admired and recognized as a kindred spirit (see note 13), Lalique declared

> *Et devant l'art infini*
> *Dont jamais la loi ne change,*
> *Lamielle* [sic] *de Cellini*
> *Vaut le bloc de Michel Ange.*

Sole realizer of his dream, his faith in his cause and in his own abilities carried him along at fever pitch for a decade. But although he had many imitators, none of them understood what Lalique was trying to do for their art; it had taken an entire generation of painters in the early XV century in Italy to do it for painting—namely to have it acclaimed as one of the Liberal Arts.[15]

Once the Exposition of 1900 had closed, he found himself drowning in success with more commissions than he could fill, and a host of eager imitators who only debased his style. While he continued to produce jewelry for several more years, Fortune once again intervened in his affairs. A commission to design perfume flacons caused him to turn his attention to glass, a substance with which he had become well acquainted through his experiments with the related enamel compounds. As one of his admirers intimated later, it may also be that in despair of achieving his ambitious goals for the art of jewelry, he providentially remembered the preachings of William Morris: that good design in mass production could bring beauty to the lives of the many instead of the few. The year after he opened his first glass factory, Gallé, the leader in that field, died; once again Lalique found himself the pioneer in another art, sustained by a different ideal.

# CATALOGUE

## I. *CAMEOS*

1. *Roman cameo,* second century A.D., in a gold frame signed *Wièse,* French, about 1860. (1 3/8 x 2 1/2)* While stones carved in intaglio are truly ancient, cameos are of Hellenistic and Roman origin; the finest were made between the first century B.C. and the third and fourth century A.D. The Greeks were the best cameo artisans; Alexandria, the site where the most successful and earliest work was done. Jules Wièse mounted this Roman cameo as a pendant, encircling it in a golden frame of plain bands, rope and running dog patterns. (Figure 1)

2. *Shell cameo of the Fine Arts,* in a golden frame. Italian, 1830's, made for the English tourist trade. (2 7/8 x 2 1/2)

3. *Male head cameo,* profile facing right, marble. Italian, late eighteenth century. (1 13/16 x 2 1/8)

4. *Head of Napoleon,* white onyx in a modern golden frame. French, c. 1810-1815. (2 1/16 x 2 3/8)

5. *Head of Medusa,* shell cameo in a golden frame. Italian, 1815 or earlier. (1 5/8 x 2 5/16)

6. *Head of Medusa,* soapstone cameo. French (?) imitation of Italian Pava cameos. (1 x 1 1/4)

Augusto Castellani in his book on gems (translated by Mrs. John Brogden, London, 1871) regretted that the almost exclusively Roman art of carving shell cameos—seen here in Numbers 2 and 5, fine examples from the first part of the nineteenth century—had, by the time of his writing, conspicuously declined in quality. Shells having strata of different colors like agate and onyx were used in the place of more costly semi-precious stones. Number 2, *The Fine Arts*—here Architecture, Sculpture, Painting, and Music—is set in a golden frame having a Greek key design in granules and beaded on its outer and inner edges. The head of Medusa, Number 5, framed in a beaded and rope-patterned golden oval, and the soapstone Medusa, Number 6, reproduce a Medusa type current in antique cameos: wings

---

* Measurements are given in inches, width preceding height wherever possible. The length, when cited, is designated by *l.,* the diameter by *d.*

above her temples, and among her luxuriant hair coiled serpents which meet under the chin. (See H. B. Walters, *Catalogue of the Engraved Gems and Cameos, Greek, Etruscan and Roman in the British Museum,* London, 1926, p. 333, No. 3542, illustrated on plate XXXVI; p. 333, No. 3545, illustrated on plate XXXVII; and others.) This is a type which was in use among neoclassical artists, notably Antonio Canova in his two versions of Perseus (Rome, Vatican Museum, finished 1801; and New York, Metropolitan Museum, finished 1808), and the less famous Benedetto Pistrucci (1784-1854) in a jasper cameo brooch made in England about 1830 (illustrated in *Nineteenth Century Jewelry from the First Empire to the First World War* (The Cooper Union Museum) New York, 1955, Figure 2).

The head of Napoleon I, Number 4, veiled in the sacerdotal style of ancient Roman emperor portraits, is stylistically close to the cameo on a snuff box given by the Emperor to his jeweler (Vever, I, p. 88, see Bibliography). (Figure 2)

7. *Shell cameo of Ariel* in a chased golden frame. Probably English, ca. 1840. (2 3/8 x 2)

8. *Female head,* full face. Ivory cameo in a golden frame. Italian (?) c. 1845. (1 5/8 x 2)

9. *Bacchante.* Topaz cameo in a frame of gold, twenty pearls and four diamonds. Frame: French, about 1865. Unidentified hallmark on clasp. (1 5/8 x 2 3/8)

10. *Female head,* full face cameo framed in gold with diamonds. Russian (?) cameo; Russian setting, about 1880. (1 3/4 x 2 1/4)

11. *Amethyst glass female head* in silver frame, pendant pearl. Cameo ca. 1900; (2 x 3 1/4) frame, modern imitation of art nouveau (by Bill Tendler, New York).

Joseph Severn (1793-1873), English portrait and history painter, resident in Rome and Venice between 1820 and 1841, and friend of Keats, painted Ariel from Shakespeare's *Tempest*—seated on a bat holding in both hands a peacock feather—in Rome in 1828 (Collection Victoria and Albert Museum, London). An amateur jeweler, choosing a section of the shell which a professional would have scorned, carved the Ariel (Number 7). A similar though slightly less adroit carving of this subject is in the Victoria & Albert Museum.

The ivory cameo, Number 8, picturing a Primavera reminiscent of Botticelli's style (XV century Italian) would have been popular in England in the early years of Victoria's reign. In France under the Second Empire, cameos became popular again and were worn large and bulky and of high relief around 1860 (Number 9). Similar Italian taste of the same date may be seen in Catalogue number 50 while Russian taste for the formidable, coinciding with European style—though lagging behind the French by some fifteen years—produced cameo Number 10.

Lalique's brooch of a poppy-crowned mask surrounded by flowing hair exhibited in 1900 (Collection Calouste Gulbenkian Foundation, Lisbon) inspired this reconstruction using a glass cameo of the period. (The poppy cameo is illustrated on the cover and on plate 1 of *Le Bijou 1900, Modern Style—Juwelen,* Hotel Solvay, Brussels, 1965.) (Figure 3)

12. *Molded glass cameo,* French, ca. 1870. (1 3/16 x 1 5/8) The popularity of colored stone cameos, such as the topaz one (Catalogue number 9), was so great that they were often imitated in both topaz and amethyst colored glass, usually in the form of an agitated head such as this one. (Figure 4)

## II. *POPULAR JEWELRY**

Starting at noon and reading clockwise in Figure 9:

13. *Painted miniature* on ivory in a silver gilt frame. French, c. 1810. (1 13/16 x 2 1/2) Miniatures on ivory and enamel were superseded by the daguerreotype portrait, a process invented in 1839, and later by other photographic processes. In a compartment on the reverse of this painted portrait is enclosed a lock of hair, a conceit which both preceded and succeeded sentimental jewelry made entirely of hair, rampant in the 1840's and 1850's. (Figure 9)

14. *Bracelet in pinchbeck* with a glass cameo. English, late 1830's. (1 3/4 x 1 1/2) Christopher Pinchbeck (1672-1732) made an alloy of copper and zinc which temporarily retained its gold color without tarnishing. Renty of Lille, about 1729, and later Leblanc of Paris produced imitations of Pinchbeck's imitation. Cheaper jewelry of all kinds was made from the material in the eighteenth century; in the nineteenth, chiefly in the 1830's and 40's, it was die stamped into various forms such

* Whenever possible to assemble the pieces for photographing an attempt has been made to form meaningful groups to help the reader grasp the phases and stylistic transformations during the XIX century. Those types which enjoyed the widest popularity were, of course, the least susceptible to the whims of the moment (Sections II, III) and it is consequently difficult to assign them accurate dates.

Toward the end of the century dating becomes easier, but tracing the origin of Art Nouveau ornaments becomes exceedingly difficult as the style overwhelmed not only national differences within Europe, but spread over Asia and the Americas as well.

as this bracelet. (For a bracelet clasp similarly leafed, dated 1838, see Flower, p. 117, Figure 43b, see Bibliography.) (Figure 9)

15. *Gilt filigree brooch and earrings.* English, 1860s-1870s. (brooch: 2 x 1 3/4, earring 1/2 x 1 1/2) The enduring grape and leaves motif (see Catalogue numbers 34, 47 and 225) here expressed in filigree is a technique which, though most fashionable in the 1890's and '30's, carried on a popular existence into the 1870's. (Figure 9)

16. *Silver brooch with pietre dure.* Italian and English, about 1870. (1 3/4 x 1 3/8) This ornamental work in hard stone, which originated in Florence late in the sixteenth century, was widely used henceforth for table tops and other furniture. From the 1830's on, mosaics of glass and of semi-precious stones depicting monuments and views, or butterflies and flowers, were made in Florence, Rome, Naples, and Venice chiefly as tourists' souvenirs. This stone bouquet was mounted in silver by Jo. Michels who signed on the reverse. (Figure 9)

17. *Two enamelled plaquettes* (modern mountings). German or Bohemian, c. 1910. (5/8 x 1/2) The appeal exercized by children and putti, their winged idealization (Catalogue numbers 18, 22, 45, 69), infiltrates all of the revival styles of the XIX century, from Neo-classical to Renaissance. Frankly sentimental, these plaquettes, produced in quantity for sale to jewellers who could set them as they wished, are inferior in technique to number 19 in this group, but accurately reflect the heightened color scheme with the addition of tinsel underlay in turn-of-the-century enamels. (Figure 9)

18. *Plaque of enamel on porcelain.* German, c. 1885. (1 1/4 x 1 9/16) In its sentiment and pastel coloring this bust of cupid is reminiscent of innumerable chromolithographic prints of the period. (Figure 9)

19. *Gold brooch:* opaque and translucent enamel picture over guilloché ground, with pearls. German(?) c. 1870-80. (1 1/2 x 7/8) This brooch, finely executed in three horizontal hollow stemmed bars, with chasing on the reverse of the disk, is an early example of a type which was followed by countless inferior repetitions in the 1880's and 90's. For a twentieth century example having a horseshoe substituted for the cupid, see the catalogue of the Goldsmiths and Silversmiths Co., Ltd., London, 1903-4, p. 41. (Figure 9)

20. *Portrait photograph* in a gold swivel frame, American, c. 1880. (d. 1 1/4)

Descendant of the locket which heads this group (number 13), the ornamental outer frame contains a plain bezel which can be revolved on pivots; thus it can have either side facing outward so as to display either of two pictures, or a picture and a lock of hair. Although the style of ornament is too nondescript to point to the locale of origin, the known family provenance of the brooch in addition to its novel gadgetry (which has always delighted Americans, and never more so than in the prime of Edison) points to this country as its source. (Figure 9)

21. *Hair bracelet* with a lightly-chased gold clasp. English, 1840-1850. (13/16 x 7 1/2) Hair jewelry was often worn as a memento of the dead: it was woven into chains and bracelets, or coaxed into a pictorial or ornamental pattern and mounted as a brooch. When the material was freed from lugubrious associations, it could be an expressive medium for unremarkable drawing room pictures, or for arresting images such as a full length, life size portrait of Queen Victoria (see Flower, p. 21, see Bibliography). (Figure 9)

Second circle, starting at noon:

22. *Ivory brooch:* bust of a child surrounded by rose buds. German, c. 1850. (d. 1) Ivory ceased to be a popular material for jewelry in the 1880's. This charming and dainty brooch may have been made in the middle of the century (for style and material compare Flower, p. 85, Figures 12 a and b, see Bibliography). (Figure 9)

23. and 25. *Two shell cameos* in gold frames. English, before 1860. (left cameo: 1 3/4 x 2, right: 1 1/2 x 1 7/8) Those shells which have in cross section two or three strata of color were used in the making of cameos since the sixteenth century as substitutes for similarly layered semi-precious stones such as the sardonyx. For finer examples of shell cameos, see Figure 2. Catalogue numbers 2 and 5. (Figure 9)

24. *Oxydized silver necklace* with angelskin coral. English, 1880's. (l. 11 1/4, pendants: 3/8 x 1/2) Plain flexible chains with pendants were popular in the 1860's and may be seen in two superior examples in Flower, p. 168, Figure 70b; and p. 170, Figure 72, see Bibliography. (Figure 9)

26. *Coin bracelet,* gold. American, c. 1860. (l. 7, pendants: 1/2 x 5/8) Bangles with pendants of hearts, acorns, medallions, pearls or other jewels and objects were widely used during the 1860's, '70's and early '80's. The coins are California gold dollars, 1858. Though medals and ancient coins have been set like jewels ever since the

Middle Ages, the use of modern coinage as ornament seems to have been another typically American invention (see also no. 20). (Figure 9)

Center

27. *Brooch with a glass cameo* inset with gold and a pearl, mounted in gilt metal. French, about 1860. (1 1/8 x 1 3/8) One material set into another was popular in the 1860's, here illustrated by a so-called *camée-habillé*. The Negro, having been romanticized by the eighteenth century, figured in the nineteenth as a result of travel books, and the abolitionist movement. However, the welcome chance that it gave the cameo carver to reverse the usual order of light against dark layers had already made "blackamoor" cameos popular from classical times on, with a strong revival in the XVI century (four such cameos of various dates can be seen set into one Dutch XVII century covered bowl: *Royal Treasures* ed. E. Steingräber, N.Y., 1968, p. 150).

## III. *THE SYMBOLS OF SENTIMENT*

Although the celebration of true love has always been one of the functions of a gift of jewelry (explicitly so in early Greek and Etruscan jewelry where Cupid, the god of love, was an ever-popular motif), the XIX century developed a repertory of symbols for the various gradations of love unparalleled in earlier times. The locket, portrait as souvenir of a beloved (see Catalogue numbers 13, 19), is of ancient origin; the "Valentine" heart (Catalogue numbers 24, 172) a fairly recent secular version of the Sacred Heart symbol of Christian iconography. On this plate we present those symbols which retained their meaning throughout the century even though most of them were formulated between 1830 and 1850.

Clockwise in Figure 10:

28. *Hand offering a rose.* Ivory, ca. 1850. (2 3/8 x 1 3/16) The hand motif "dressed" in a lace cuff probably derives from Italian coral souvenirs brought home by northern tourists (see M. Flower, p. 83, fig. 10b, see Bibliography), talismans against the Evil Eye. With the addition of the rose, however, it took on the meaning of "sincere friendship." (Figure 10)

29. *Lily-of-the-Valley earrings* (left and right of center). Ivory, ca. 1880. (3/4 x 2) The stiffness of the execution betrays a design copied too often (compare the

freshness of the ivory umbrella handle, Figure 59, center). The origin of this modest lily's meaning as a good luck symbol is obscured in folk iconography; however, bouquets of it are still gathered and exchanged on May Day in many parts of Europe, and a popular perfume still bears the name "Muguet du Bonheur." (Figure 10)

30. *Scottish dirk*. Silver set with agates and cairngorms. Scottish, ca. 1840. (9/16 x 3 7/8) An early example of a genre which was to become the rage after Queen Victoria and the royal family made Balmoral Castle their favorite summer retreat. Royal favor only followed the Romantic predilection for "the sublime" in nature, which raised wild and stormy landscapes to equal esteem with the calm, classical landscapes preferred in earlier centuries. Scott's *Waverly* novels, dovetailing with part nostalgic, part nationalistic elevation of a medieval past, along with a yearning back to simpler ways, lent this pebble jewelry, which had started out simply as souvenirs for a growing tourist industry, an emotional charge which is not immediately apparent. Its vast success was noted, and Irish as well as Welsh versions appear later in the century.

31. *Dove encircled in a frame imitating branches*. Ivory, ca. 1180. (2 1/4 x 1 3/4) A late, slightly dessicated version of a motif that first became popular around the middle of the century (see M. Flower, p. 85, 12b). In this, as well as the example just cited, the Christian motif of the Dove of the Holy Spirit set in the Crown of Thorns is still discernible. However, a curious transfusion took place between this type and the cooing pairs of doves (the bird of Venus, hence symbol of erotic love) popular as betrothal gifts during the XVIII century; during the XIX century doves were recognized as nest protectors. Sometimes they are even shown attacking a serpent who threatens the eggs. Neatly combining the spiritual and the carnal aspects of love, such jewelry made an appropriate gift from husband to wife. (Figure 10)

32. *Cross entwined by ivy*. Ivory, ca. 1850. (1 3/8 x 3) Nearly identical with the one illustrated in M. Flower, p. 85, 12b (see Bibliography), this seemingly conventional Christian symbol betrays a curious—very English—misinterpretation: the vine, which in conventional iconography represents the Eucharist, is always a grape vine bearing clusters of grapes. Here it is rendered as English ivy! Perhaps it had come to symbolize the wearer's clinging to her faith. (Figure 10)

33. *Whippet in a frame of twined branches*. (Center) Oxydized silver with copper patina; French, ca. 1845. (1 5/8 x 2) The dog as a symbol of faithfulness forever goes back to ancient Greek grave stones, but was especially striking in its place on late medieval tombs; it often appears, rather like a foot stool, at the feet of the richly clad, reclining funeral effigies—she with her poodle, he with his hunting dog. In the symbolic context of the medieval revival, such a brooch as this one was probably from a lover to his lass. (Figure 10)

## IV. *MID-CENTURY CHANGES*

Beginning around 1845 the scintillating, yet two-dimensional effect of jewelry in the post-Napoleonic generation (see numbers 46, 47, 67) underwent some changes; it took time for these to gather full force because the upheaval of 1848 in France, and the political disturbances all over Europe (with the exception of England, to which many French luxury craftsmen fled for a few years), slowed the tempo. However, the salient marks of change in design were: (a) toward fleshier and more naturalistic forms—accompanied, not unreasonably, by greater emphasis on Renaissance and Baroque revival styles than on the hitherto favored Medieval—and (b) a tendency for the designs to form a predominant central "ball," frequently of inflated appearance, instead of the consistent or only slightly varying bands made up of small elements in repetition such as were common in the preceding years. Massed color, and that of richer tone, also distinguishes the full mid-century style from its predecessor.

34. *Suite set with black and white pearls and emeralds* consisting of necklace, bracelet, and brooch of gold. French, ca. 1845-50. (necklace: l. 18 7/8 x 1 1/8, bracelet: d. 2 5/8 x 2 3/4, brooch: 1 1/2 x 1 1/8) The vine and grape motif, infinitely complaisant in its adaptability, can be found throughout the history of European ornament. (For somewhat earlier examples see this catalogue, number 47, and M. Flower, p. 102 fig. D, see Bibliography). The bracelet heralds the predilection for stiff bangles (instead of the sinuous link bracelets of the previous style), which was to predominate during the latter half of the XIX century. Though not yet pronounced, the massing of heavier elements toward the center of the necklace, as well as the slightly domed structure of the central design of the bracelet proclaim the high Victorian style of catalogue numbers 49, 71, 72.

Although unsigned and without master's hallmark, this set is related in style and workmanship to those of Jean-Valentin Morel (see Vever, I, p. 260 ff., see Bibliography). This gifted jeweller of somewhat mercurial fortunes fled France in

1848 for London, where he remained until 1852. His work, especially the dextrous setting of massed small stones *en pavé,* such as exemplified in the emerald-set leaves of this suite, was especially praised in the pieces which he submitted to the Crystal Palace Exhibition in 1851. The technique, first perfected in XVIII century France, had fallen into disuse in the hard times following the French Revolution, and its revival in 1851 was favorably noted. The absence of French hall marks may be accounted for in this way, though the bracelet is stamped with the owl hallmark, indicating that it found its way back to France some time after 1893. (Figure 11)

35. *Man's silver and gold watch chain.* French or English, ca. 1848. (l. 7 3/4 x 9/16) Morel (see entry above) assembled various other refugee craftsmen in his London establishment, among them a designer-craftsman, Névillé (Vever, p. 266, and ill. p. 276, see Bibliography) who seems to have been known for designs of precisely this sort. Each link is a tiny sculpture, which when they are all assembled form a hunt scene. Hunting, "the sport of kings," was a subject for jewelry as early as the XVI century (a ring of about 1540 with a boar hunt is in the collection of the Kunstgewerbemuseum, Cologne); it continued in favor throughout the XIX century (see this Catalogue number 162), though never before or after Névillé was it rendered on so minute a scale with the same degree of myopic naturalism.

The fob, representing a Mephistopheles, may be of slightly earlier date. Meyerbeer's opera, *Robert le Diable,* first performed in 1831 was a popular hit, and inspired a whole souvenir industry. (Figure 11)

## V. *RENAISSANCE-REVIVAL*

Starting ten or fifteen years later than the medieval revival, the fashion for Renaissance-style jewelry was at its height from about 1840 to 1860. Although it never died out completely during the XIX century, the two examples shown here date from the time of its greatest popularity.

36. *Silver-gilt bracelet,* with sturdy vines supporting fleshy leaves, four music-making angels, and twelve pairs of garnets. The raised outlines of the leaves are echoed in the ogee-shaped collets of the gems. (6 5/8 x 2 5/16) Jules Wièse's (1818-1890) initials on the hallmark indicate that he made the bracelet while still working for F.-D. Froment-Meurice.

That vines and leaves were a popular motif in the nineteenth century is illustrated more than once in this exhibition. Two others, by no means rare, examples of vines as structures for the jewel—as here—are Froment-Meurice's bracelet of 1839 (Henri Vever, *La Bijouterie française au XIXe siècle,* Paris, 1908, I, p. 168), and an anonymous English jeweler's brooch of around 1840 (Margaret Flower, *Victorian Jewelry,* New York, 1967, p. 102, Figure 28d). Wièse's leaves are marked by a "naturalism" present in French, but not English depictions of vegetative themes for the rest of the century.

Froment-Meurice also used the second motif of this jewel—the large and small music-making angels—in a brooch of circa 1847 (Vever, I, p. 158, see Bibliography). The swaying central figure resembles Wièse's own angel of 1850-1862 (Vever, II, p. 213, see Bibliography), while the massiveness of the bracelet indicates *a posteriori* a date in the fifties. (Figure 12)

37. *Silver-gilt brooch,* an armor-clad female figure in an ornamental architectural frame, flanked by two female grotesques with foliated tails. Lacking the hand of the upraised arm, which may have held an attribute, the figure is impossible to identify. (1 5/8 x 2 1/4) Étienne Delaune (1518/19-1583) is frequently cited as a source for such designs. The robust forms of the brooch, however, preclude Delaune and earlier Italian patterns such as the anonymous engraver of *Leviores . . . picturae quas grotesches vulgo vocant . . .* (Rudolf Berliner, *Ornamentale Vorlageblätter des 15. bis 18. Jahrhunderts,* Leipzig, 1925, p. 38; II Taf. 101(1), 102 (1-2)) which were copied by Enea Vico in 1541-1542 (Adam Bartsch, *Le Peintre Graveur,* Vienna, 1813, XV, 361, 467-490). Granted that even a Delaune design interpreted in embossed metal assumes a certain vigor (see the shield of Henri II of France designed by Delaune in the Metropolitan Museum of Art, 34.85, reproduced in Helmut Nickel, "The Battle of the Crescent," *The Metropolitan Museum of Art Bulletin,* XXIV, No. 3, November 1965, p. 110), nevertheless prototypes for the brooch should be sought in more fundamentally rampant ornament such as that of Agostino Veneziano (Bartsch, XIV, see Bibliography) translated into the French sixteenth century idiom in metalwork other than jewelry.

The unidentified nineteenth century designer of the brooch, whose monogram *J B* is stamped on the back of the upper left scroll, probably executed it in the same decade—the 1840's—as did Froment-Meurice the brooch illustrated in Vever, I, p. 158. Indeed, that the French Renaissance style was popular and popularized abroad in the late 1840's and early '50's is evident from the illustration of a Platz-menage für Salz und Pfeffer in the 1848 number of *Zeitschrift für Bijouterie* (Weimar, II, Figure 3) described as being among the "Neuste Pariser Silberarbeiten." Five years later an English version of the style, coming from Messrs Baskett and

Martin, Cheltenham, was featured (Weimar, IV, No. 2, Plate 10, Figure 64) (Figure 12)

## VI. *PLAIN STYLE AND EXOTIC THEMES*

With the fading away of the French court after France's defeat by Germany in 1871, the full-blown floral style favored by Empress Eugenie was overtaken by an undercurrent originating in Birmingham, England, the seat of mass production in silver. According to J. C. Roche, "The History, Development and Organization of the Birmingham Jewellery," supplement to *The Dial,* Birmingham, n.d., pp. 27-8, the year 1872 was one of great prosperity for Birmingham; silver was plentiful, cheap, and fashionable. Victoria, whose taste for boldly plastic jewelry may have its roots in her predilection of long standing for Scottish jewelry (Catalogue number 30) presented the singer Jenny Lind with a silver necklace of flat ovoids on gently flaring stems in 1875 (see M. Flower, p. 174, fig. 76, see Bibliography). A retreat from the excesses of ornamentation in all of the minor arts and the crafts was astir in England already in the '60's, and the search for a new style of ornament was on. One probe was made in the direction of the new marvels of the industrial age: disenchanted with the plethora of meaningless and repetitive flourishes so easily produced by machines, a few hardy designers turned to the machines themselves for inspiration. Other designers looked beyond Europe: Japanese wares, once they began to reach the West in quantity following the treaty with Commodore Perry in 1859, had an immediate impact; and Indian designs, popular since the XVIII century in textiles, received renewed attention as England conquered that land (Victoria was crowned Empress of India in 1878). The vogue for this plain and heavy style was short, but it was the harbinger of the reform in XX century "modern."

38. *Bracelet of gold colored metal.* English, 1870's. (d. 2 3/4 x 1 1/8) Composed of hollow rectangular tables, each indented in the middle, with spheres of the same material set into the hollows. The historian of style has nothing to say about predecessors for this one. For the first time in Western decorative art, great technical skill has been deliberately employed to produce an object of utter geometric simplicity. The wonder lies not so much in that this was possible, but that it was even popular. (Figure 13)

39. *Silver bracelet with a floral panel* engraved and inlaid with copper. English,

late 1870's. (d. 2 3/4 x 1) A hint of Japanese motifs, badly interpreted, may be found in the straight, reed-like stems and narcissus-like flowers, so different from the curly vines and fleshy foliage of mid-century Victorian jewelry. (Figure 13)

40. *Silver linked necklace* composed of alternating triple and double rows of plain, heavy links to form a brickwork pattern. American, ca. 1877 (d. 6 3/8 x 1) Akin to bracelet number 38 of this group in its starkness, the necklace is nevertheless of good workmanship; supple despite its heavy elements, and with a smoothly functioning clasp. (Figure 13)

41. *Tiger claw brooch;* silver, tiger claws, and a glass cabochon with the head of the animal carved and painted in the bottom. English, after 1878. (2 x 2 3/4) Although the use of tiger claws in jewelry had been anticipated in China and Egypt, their popularity in England, though rather brief, celebrated the annexation of India. Though rarely beautiful the widespread vogue for these curiosities is another indication not only of the quest for something new in design on the part of its creators, but of a turning away from the old ornament derived from past styles on the part of a large public. (Figure 13)

## VII. *THE SCINTILLATING '80's*

The jewellers' search for "something new" of vast public appeal accelerated toward the end of the century. If the severe style, discussed in the preceding group, came as a reaction to the hypertropic forms of high Victorian jewelry, its relatively modest price also appealed to a spreading middle class with "sensible" ideals and still slim purses. By the following decade many of them had become rich, and the explosion of new technological inventions as seen at the Paris Exhibition of 1889 (new processes, implicit in such a structure as the Eiffel Tower; new invention, such as Edison's, which bespoke the birth of entire industries) insured an ever-rising tide of buyers for luxury goods. As if in answer to the new prosperity, diamonds had become available during the 1870's in hitherto undreamt of quantities (for a history of this windfall see G. Hughes, *Modern Jewelry,* p. 28 ff.). Massive diamond pieces as well as the fine single stones remained the prerogatives of the very rich; but those of small size, off-white color, or old-fashioned cut came within the reach of many more people—and reach they did. The upholstered look of fashions with bustles ceded to a more natural line by the end of the '80's with tulles and other airy materials in vogue; these were not adapted to the weight of heavy pieces of jewelry, but looked charming dotted here and there with small, flashing diamond fantasies (see also numbers 86, 88).

42. *Enamelled Necklace* composed of two strands of fancifully shaped links, black and white on gold, interspersed with elements of peridots between rubies and enamelled, ruby-centered rondels. (l. 14 1/8 x 3 1/8) The chains are held in position by enamelled honeysuckle palmettes, two where the ends meet, and two on the central axis, from which depends a pear-shaped peridot. Carlo Giuliano, London, late 1870's or 1880's. The Neapolitan Giuliano transferred his workshop to London in the late '60's where his first jewels were in the antique manner already made popular by Castellani. In the 1870's his Renaissance-inspired jewelry reveals a predilection for sensitive color combinations and a delicate linearism (see M. Flower, Pl. VI, VII, see Bibliography) that is already close in spirit to the multiple small element ornament favored during the '80's as well as foreshadowing the subtle color harmonies of the '90's.

The ancestors of this design are XVI century "moresque" patterns, such as those of the Florentine Francesco Pellegrino who worked for Francis I at Fontainbleau (see, *La Fleur de la science de pourtraicture, et patrons de broderie; façon arabique et italique,* 1530, nine plates of which are reproduced in R. Berliner, I, Pl. 79-82, see Bibliography); or those of Jean de Gourmont (Berliner, I, Pl. 99) (1-2), perhaps from *Le Livre de moresques très-utile et nécessaire à tous orfèvres . . .*), patterns which were refined in the XVII century by goldsmiths and engravers such as Jacques Hurtu (as in *Dessins d'Orfèverie,* 1614). (Figure 14)

43. *Coif pin of pearl* decorated with diamonds mounted in silver. French, 1880's. (7/8 x 1 3/4) A floral tracery of tiny diamonds clings to the irregular surface of the large pearl enlivening its sheen with sparkle caught from various angles. It is a sort of capsule statement of the overall effect striven for in the jewelry of the 1880's. (Figure 14)

44. *Chased gold brooch* set with nine diamonds. English or American, late 1880's. (7/8 x 2 5/8) Literal representations of flowers, insects, birds and other fauna are characteristic of late Victorian jewelry. The surface bloom of the golden leaves goes back to the process invented in England earlier in the century (see under number 72) and, as in the mourning suite just cited, it makes a pleasing contrast with the fire of the diamonds, now at last available in quantity. (Figure 14)

## VIII. *THE PARURE*

Even though matched sets of jewelry were fashionable among the very wealthy already in the XVIII century the craze for them did not develop until the XIX; it was probably the Empress Josephine with her pronounced liking for sets of cameo jewelry who encouraged others to wear parures of materials less costly than gems.

Whatever the reason, to own a parure was the ambition of every woman until diamonds became available in quantity in the 1870's. With their sparkle they out-shone even the most elaborate sets made out of other materials; and one could add to one's stock, one piece at a time, without running the danger of clashing colors.

The parures that follow demonstrate that the cameo remained in favor for this purpose from the dawn of the XIX century until the 1860's; however, along with it, especially during the Restoration period, when a prudent and still im-poverished aristocracy resumed some of its pre-1789 aspirations on the Continent, while in England experiments in the mass production of jewelry got under way, a desire was felt to imitate the dazzling ornaments of the vanished era. The fretted surfaces and foil-backed stones of the examples dating from the 1830's and '40's belong to this type.

45. *Sandalwood parure* comprising a necklace, one large and two smaller brooches, a buckle, and a pair of earrings of sandalwood on ebony, mounted in gold; buckle in silver gilt. Plaquettes: Italian, 1810. Mountings: French, ca. 1835. (necklace: l. 16 1/2 x 1 3/8; large brooch; 1 7/8 x 2 1/4; small brooches: 1 x 1 3/8; buckle: 1 5/8 x 2 1/4; earrings 11/16 x 2 1/8) Pure Rococo and sometime Neo-classical subjects are silhouetted in the neoclassical style in these sandalwood reliefs on ebony carved by Giuseppe Maria Bonzanigo (1745-1820) and mounted in their frames by Jules Chaise (1807-1870) in Paris. On one hand floral bouquets, wreaths, birds' nests and a fly in the necklace, the buckle and a small brooch; on the other Venus and Cupid in the larger brooch, Fortuna in the second small one, and Euterpe, the muse of music, and Urania, the muse of astronomy, in the earrings. These prosy subjects are transcended by exquisite carving. Bonzanigo, painter and woodcarver, was active in Piedmont at the end of the eighteenth century where he executed a screen in a manner doubly in reverse to the jewelry: panels of realistic subjects are painted in both illusionistic and in flattened pictorial space. (Torino, Palazzo Reale. Illustrated in Giuseppe Mazzariol, *Mobili Italiani del Seicento e del Settecento,* Milan, 1964, p. 93, Figures B, C.)

In England in the 1770's to the 1790's William Hackwood, John Flaxman and others modelled tiny plaques which were executed in ceramic by Josiah Wedgwood and sometimes mounted for jewelry. (Figure 15)

46. *Aquamarine and topaz parure* consisting of necklace with section of pendant detached, bracelet, buckle, brooch, and earrings. French, 1820's-1830's. (brooches: 1 1/4 x 1 5/8, 1 1/4 x 1 1/2; buckle: 1 3/8 x 3 1/8; necklace: l. 17 1/4 x 1; pendant: 1 3/4 x 1 7/8; earrings: 1 3/8 x 2 7/8; bracelet: 2 3/8 x 6 3/8) This gold parure composed of stamped segments which are set with aquamarines and topazes combines generically Gothic motifs—lancets, daggers, pointed tracery—with seventeenth century scroll cartouches. Seventeenth century also is the girandole design of the earrings and necklace pendant. (See the many girandole pendants in *Liure des Ouvrages d'Orfèurerie fait par Gilles Légaré . . . 1663*, on plates 4, 6, and two unnumbered plates. Staatliche Museen zu Berlin, *Katalog der Ornamentstichsammlung der Staatlichen Kunstbibliothek Berlin*. Berlin u. Leipzig, 1939, p. 122, No. 827.) The openwork which originated in the second half of the sixteenth century, characterized seventeenth century design, and was retained in the eighteenth and nineteenth century. Although stamped work appeared in France during the Restoration (1814-1830) (see *Collection Connaissance des Arts: Le Dix-neuvième siècle français,* Paris, 1960, p. 114; and Vever, I, see Bibliography, the grand parure illustrated opposite page 142), it flourished in the reign of Louis-Philippe (1830-1848) (such as the stamped bracelets illustrated in Vever, I, opposite page 186), and concurrently in England (see Flower, p. 95, Figure 22, see Bibliography, who illustrates a necklet of large gold links of floral and scroll design of c. 1838). The stamped granules on the bracelet's three rows of hemispheres imitate the hand-soldered granulation popular in the '20's and '30's. The long earrings however which became unfashionable in the '40's give the parure a terminus ante quem. (Figure 16)

47. *Aquamarine parure* consisting of a necklace with a pendant that alternates as a brooch, and a pair of earrings. French or English, 1830s. (necklace: l. 18 x 1 1/8; earrings: 7/8 x 2 1/8; pendant: 2 1/4 x 2 5/8) In the necklace of this gold parure six-petalled, stamped rosettes with nestling aquamarines alternate with transverse pointed ovals from which are suspended golden grapes with chased leaves. The pendant/brooch in girandole form has an aquamarine centered cartouche with pendants of here upright, pointed ovals and rosettes. Five and six-petalled rosettes are combined in the earrings. The spreading horizontal cartouche is a seventeenth century form. (See the six cartouches by F. Collignon after Stefano della Bella reproduced in Peter Jessen, *Meister des Ornamentstichs, Das Barock,* II. (1923),

p. 26-27.) The pointed ovals dimly echo the Gothic. The fragile quality of the fabric point to a date in the 1830's.

An unidentified hallmark is on the clasp. (Figure 17)

48. *Demi-parure* consisting of brooch and earrings. French, c. 1830. Delicate wire, filigree and stamped pieces form a nest for the aquamarines in this gold demi-parure. The suite is a hybrid of a declining and of an ascending technique: the filigree popular from the 1820's into the 1830's and the stamped work which gradually supplanted it. The girandole, fashionable in the eighteenth century, in fact "indispensable to real elegance since the end of the seventeenth" (Steingräber, *Royal Treasures,* p. 154), was resuscitated in the third and fourth decades of the nineteenth century (see Catalogue number 67; and a brooch dated 1834, Ouizille et Lemoine, in Vever, I, p. 293). As previously mentioned in this catalogue, the use of earrings in the 1840's was almost totally precluded by the style of hair combed over the ear lobes. (Figure 18)

49. *Mourning parure* consisting of a brooch and earrings. English, ca. 1850. (brooch: 2 1/2 x 4 1/4, earrings: 3/4 x 2 9/16) Gold jewelry flourished in the decade following the discovery of gold first in California in 1849, and then in Australia in 1851.

Coloring gold by means of copper for a red tone, silver for green, iron for blue, and a mixture of copper, silver, lead and sulphur for black (the latter a gold-smiths' technique called niello), although already used in the 1850's and early '60's, became common between 1866 and 1886.

This set of mourning jewelry has golds of two colors, black enamelled golden wire, nielloed gold, old mine diamonds, and, on the brooch, a "blooming" leaf. (For the method of creating "bloom," see Catalogue no. 72.)

The stylistic combination of naturalistic flowers and foliage with geometric forms was popular in the 1850's. John Brogden's and his partner Watherston's designs, shown at the 1851 Crystal Palace Exhibition (some illustrated in Flower, p. 98, Figure 24, see Bibliography) were reproduced two years later in the *Zeitschrift für Bijouterie,* Weimar (II, no. 4, Figures 44-51). Although the French, as well, made jewelry of a similar style (Vever, II, p. 43 illustrates an anonymous brooch of 1854, see Bibliography), this demi-parure is decidedly English and should be dated around 1850. (Figure 19)

50. *Gold Parure* two-colored, with malachite cameos. Italian, Rome, 1860's.

(necklace: l. 18 5/8 x 2; brooch: 2 1/8 x 2 1/2; earrings: 3/4 x 1 1/4; bracelet: 1 3/4 x 7 7/8) The bust of bacchante, largest of the cameos, mounted in the brooch, dominates the parure. Ten cameos of bacchantes variously wreathed in vines and flowers compose the necklace, while in the bracelet the Olympian Jupiter is flanked by four bacchantes. Busts of two amorini form the earrings.

The decade of the 1860's witnessed a new revival of the Etruscan, Greek and Roman styles in jewelry. The Roman workshop of the Castellani which had closed in 1848 during the upheavals of the Risorgimento, reopened in 1858. (The activities of the Castellani during this period have yet to be documented. According to Mary Peter, "Italian Influence on Victorian Jewelry" *Auction,* III, no. 1, September 1969, p. 26, the family may have been refugees in England in the late '40's. According to H. Clifford Smith, *Jewellery,* London (1908), p. 334, Alessandro Castellani was a revolutionary imprisoned in Castel San Angelo in 1852.) The Campagna collection of ancient jewelry, acquired for the nation by Napoleon III, was installed in the Louvre in 1862.

The bracelet, hallmarked on the clasp with a papal tiara and crossed keys, with its cameos framed by cylinders, is similar to Castellani's bracelet, circa 1865, in which scarabs are set between the two heads (illustrated in Flower, p. 190, Figure 92c, see Bibliography). Both reflect such Hellenistic forms as a ring with a revolving scarab between two cylinders capped with hemispheres. (Rodolfo Siviero, p. 28, No. 69, illustrated on plate 88, see Bibliography). The motif of the amphora with voluted handles which appears in Hellenistic jewelry (earrings of the third century B.C., Siviero, p. 39, No. 118, illustrated on plate 122a) was widely imitated in the nineteenth century.

The parure, dating from the 1860's, is of a marked plastic vigor in design. Although some other Italian work of a generically antique revival style is less restrained in details (see drawings by Salvatori in the Cooper Hewitt Museum such as a brooch (1938-88-6332) and bracelet (1938-88-6325) of 1680-1875), none other but Italian appears to manifest these decisive plastic qualities. (Cf. an Italian parure in the Egyptial style of c. 1860 reproduced in Claude Frégnac, *Jewelry,* New York, 1965, p. 117, plate 126.) (Plate 1)

## IX. *HAIR ORNAMENTS*

51. *Myrtle coronet* of silver; Italian, ca. 1810-15. (3 1/4 x 7 3/8) Of classical Greek inspiration, (see R. Higgins, *Jewelry from Classical Lands,* British Museum pub., 1969, p. 19 and Pl. 5) the workmanship is less flimsy than it appears to be

and imitates the end wiring of ancient wreaths of this type very accurately. A golden rose bush in the Secular Treasury, Vienna (See E. Steingräber, *Royal Treasures,* 1968, p. 63, no. 18), made by Giuseppe Spagna, and given to the Empress of Austria by Pius VII in 1819, set off a simultaneous vogue in Austria for such floral imitations (see number 52, this Catalogue), which later spread to France (see Vever, I, pp. 104-5). Drawing on classical sources very different from the heavy imperial style of Napoleon's reign, pieces of this sort mark the last flutter of Neoclassicism before it gave way in the same decade to romantic Medievalism, to reappear only after mid-century in the Etruscan revival style of Castellani and his imitators. (Figure 20)

52. *Hair ornament of gold;* aquamarines, pink and yellow topazes, garnets, turquoises; green enamel. Perhaps Viennese, 1820 to 1830. (3 x 7 3/16) Gold stamped petals, leaves and grape clusters, some chased, others smoothed, with gem-set flowers and wheat stalks are mounted on gold wires bound in a fascis which terminates in a bird's head, cast, and set with a garnet eye and encircled with a collar of garnets and turquoises alternating. An aquamarine-set flower trembles.

An asymetrical, seemingly random arrangement of stalks, feathers and flowers would appear to spring from the rococo, but does not seem to have thrived until the end of the eighteenth century (see an English hair ornament of silver with brilliants illustrated in *Collection Connaissance des Arts: Le Style Anglais 1750-1850,* Paris, 1959, p. 148, Figure 1; an Italian drawing inscribed *Fiore per testa* in the Cooper Hewitt Museum 138-88-811; a tiara and aigrette of diamonds and white sapphires made by Duval, the Genevan jeweller settled in St. Petersburg, for the Empress Maria Feodorovna, pictured in Claude Frégnac, *Jewelry,* New York, 1965, p. 101, Figure 111 and 112). In the early nineteenth century, jewelry of such fragile construction was being made in Vienna, and, in 1840, imported into France. That the groundwork for accepting the Viennese style seems to have been laid by Parisian jewelers is indicated by the hair ornaments of a figure dressed for a ball drawn by Pierre Numa in 1836 (Metropolitan Museum of Art, 53.664.40, illustrated in *Metropolitan Museum of Art Bulletin,* XXVI, Number 3, November 1967, p. 145). (Figure 21)

53. *Tiara and brooch* made of natural coral branches and studs. Italian, ca. 1850. (tiara: l. 18 3/8, brooch: 2 1/2 x 1 7/8) A popular purchase in Italy with northerners making "the grand tour," these sets, though fragile, made a graceful ornament for the sleek coiffure that found favor after the towering poufs and curls of the 1830's and '40's. (see M. Flower, p. 86). (Figure 22)

54. *Spanish comb of tortoiseshell,* early 1870's (?). (6 3/8 x 10 1/2) Giving an exact date to a comb as traditional as the Spanish comb is risky. However, the ornament of the border is not out of place in this period, and the functional shape of the whole places it before the second wave of popularity of this hair ornament which took place in the early 1920's, when fancifully pierced and fretted shapes, often garishly set with colored rhinestones, show a marked deviation from the more sober variety.

The early '70's experience a romantic fad for things Spanish. (Bizet's *Carmen* was composed at this time, although the novel antedates the opera. It was first performed in 1875.) The hair styles of those years, featuring an elaborate pile of thick braid (often false) toward the rear of the crown with corkscrew curls descending at the nape of the neck was suited to these out-sized combs, which were often worn with lace mantillas (see M. Flower, p. 125). (Figure 23)

55. *Bonnet brooch* in silver repoussé with hammered (martelé) ground. George Cayley; England, ca. 1870. (2 x 4 1/2) The '70's in England astound us with new forms in jewelry (see Figure 13) even in common mass production. Vanishingly rare today are the jewels produced during the same decade by amateur jewellers of prophetic talent, and of the painter, Dante Gabriel Rossetti, who is known to have designed some jewelry in the early '60's and whose paintings attest to his continuing interest in its design.

Similar in outline to the fantastic red and gold diadem worn by Rossetti's "The Bride" (see Appendix, Figure 142), to which it is very close in date, this bonnet brooch by a maker otherwise unknown, must serve as representative of a lost phase of incalculable importance to the development of jewelry during the 1890's and after, not only in England but in France. Art Nouveau jewelry is unthinkable without it, even though its production must have been tiny, limited to a small circle of friendly patrons, and consequently slow to have any influence on the mainstream of design.

The brooch with its bold, curvaceous lines and unusual motif of crossed dolphins (a subject not unknown in the XVI century, but occurring rarely) is faintly reminiscent of the "fleshy" style of the 1840's in England (see M. Flower, p. 89, fig. 16C). However the allusion to the earlier style is unstudied and almost certainly unconscious; and the dolphins probably have their ancestry in nautical iconography—which must have been familiar to almost every Englishman during the XIX century—instead of in design books and jewellers displays. The effect, however awkward from the professional's point of view, is singularly striking. Although there could have been no knowledge of this particular piece, it marks the start of an exploration of marine animals (other than shells, which have always been popular as jewelry) as subjects suitable for jewelry. By the turn of the century the "sea monster" of deliberately frightening aspect was an accepted theme in Art Nouveau (see Cover; Figure 59. Catalogue number 100; Figure 68. Catalogue number 125). (Figure 24)

56. *Gold and enamel comb* set with eleven sapphires. Signed, *Lalique*. France, ca. 1902. (3 3/8 x 6 1/2) A spin-off of the cock's head comb (now in the Gulbenkian Museum, Lisbon) which was the most astonishing among all the astonishing jewels that Lalique exhibited in 1900 (Appendix number 162), this splendid jewelled and enamelled hair ornament seems, at first glance, to be a variant of the same subject. A closer look, however, reduces the similarity to the dentate outlines of both. This piece, with its enamelled ivy leaves substituting for the crenellations of the cock's comb, is derived from a medieval bishop's crozier, although it (like Number 80, which has a similar ivy leaf border) shows an admixture of classical components. After the super-realism of his 1900 pieces, one feels in this case that there is a tentative being made in the direction of the abstract: the leaves with their exaggerated gold veining, are carefully graduated in size and intensity of color, but they march with a formality reminiscent of the earliest of his works included here (Number 157), and I believe that Number 169 also illustrates this search for a simplicity that he felt was lost. (Plate 2)

57. *Tiara-comb* of gold with rose enamel, pink glass sweet peas, and three facetted oval golden topazes (?). Signed, *Lalique;* ca. 1902. (6 3/4 x 7 1/2) In 1902—just about the time when his jewelry designs begin to reveal signs of restlessness and slight disorientation (see under number 56)—Lalique, whose admiration for the great Nancy glass maker, Emile Gallé, has been previously noted (see Introduction) began his own experiments in glass. By the time of the World's Fair in St. Louis, 1904, his exhibit must have contained a large number of pieces with moulded glass elements such as these. The Walters Art Gallery, Baltimore, has a number of striking examples purchased by Mr. Walters at the Fair (among them the curious piece, Vever, III, p. 765, lower); the Gulbenkian Museum in Lisbon contains others (see G. Hughes, *Modern Jewelry,* p. 99, especially fig. 162). A sculptured horn comb set with silex, obsidian and trimmed with black enamel and gold insects ("Modern Design in Jewelry and Fans," special winter number, 1901-2,

*The Studio,* London, Pl. 2) presages the shape of our tiara even though it has no hinge that would make it possible for wear on the brow.

The sweet pea tiara is designed to be worn on the front of the head; this, in conjunction with its early place in his glass-set jewelry (as well as other new forms in glass which appear about this time, cf. numbers 169, 172) have led me to some speculations which are worth mentioning. Never a slavish imitator, Lalique, once he was on his own, still paid attention to newly published designs in fields other than jewelry (see Number 158, and Appendix, Figure 183). The indications are that he continued to get ideas from illustrations seen at random (e.g., Catalogue number 138; and Appendix, Figure 169). During the 1890's, to judge by the number of new publications on the subject, the Pre-Raphaelites and their paintings first came to international attention (for a bibliography, see R. Watkinson, *Pre-Raphaelite Art and Design,* London, 1970); H. C. Marillier's profusely illustrated *Dante Gabriel Rossetti: an Illustrated Memorial of his Art and Life,* London, 1899 was such a success that a second edition (abridged) came out in 1902. Perhaps because of interest aroused during his youthful sojourn in London, perhaps because his display in 1900 had awakened interest in his work across the Channel (he had a successful exhibition at the Agnew Gallery in 1905), his interest in Rossetti seems to have been aroused. Along with numbers 171 and 174 going back to different Rossetti motifs in glass or crystal, this tiara with its rosy hues (a spectrum which Lalique had not been fond of before 1900) makes one think of the floral fantasy with gold insects that Rossetti's "The Bride" (Appendix, Figure 142) wears in her hair. (Figure 25)

58. *Comb of carved horn* with a pattern of crocus plants on the upper edge. Small clusters of rose diamonds for the stamens. Signed, *Lalique;* ca. 1905. (4 3/4 x 3 1/2) Changing hair styles, which made the tall combs of the preceding decade obsolete, help to date this one (for another of nearly identical shape decorated with carved butterflies with diamond bodies, see Vever, III, p. 754). The flowing lines of the 1900 style have become stiffer and more formal, though Lalique retains some of the organic naturalism of the past in making each tuft of blossoms grow out of a "root" that is a tooth of the comb. Lalique was the first to make fine jewelry of carved horn; a bracelet of horn with silver ornament was admired in his exhibit at the Salon of 1896; the reviewer (Vever, "Les Bijoux au Salon de 1898," *Revue des Arts Décoratifs,* Paris, 1899, pp. 1-10) recalls that the nacreous surface with its resemblance to certain Japanese lacquers was already present in that early piece. Such combinations of materials of little intrinsic value with precious metals and

stones to achieve a desired artistic effect is a characteristic—one might call it a tenet—of the Art Nouveau period. (Figure 26)

59. *Comb of blond tortoise shell,* partially tinted brown and black. Stamped *L. Gaillard;* Paris, ca. 1900. (3 7/8 x 5 5/8) For an account of Gaillard's late initiation to jewelry after fifteen years as a silversmith see under Number 153. The comb with its rather conventional swallow (see number 87) probably antedates his successful debut as a jeweller. (Figure 27)

60. *Comb finial* of gold, silver wire, translucent and *plique à jour* enamels, set with moonstones and a topaz (?), and hung with fresh water pearls. C. R. Ashbee; England, 1903. (4 1/16 x 3 3/8) Quite the antithesis of all his early work (see Catalogue numbers 218, 219) it would be impossible to deduce the authorship of this bird of peculiar feather were it not documented (see, *The Studio,* London, XXVII, 1903, p. 207, also J. Hoffmann, Pl. 49, no. 4); it may be assumed that Ashbee, forsaking his usual somewhat austere style, wanted to try a piece in the French style using the intriguing *plique à jour* enamelling process which had caused more than one jeweller to change course (cf. number 182) after seeing the French jewelry display at the Paris Exposition, 1900. Yet—with the possible exception of works by Boutet de Monvel—no French jeweller represented at the Fair made use of such amateurish devices as the bent wire scrolls or the multiple pendant pearls. These seem to have filtered to Ashbee through the work of a Hungarian, Prof. Paul Horti, whose work (including a brooch which is similar in outline, as well as workmanship to the comb finial here) was included in The First International Studio Exhibition (see, *The Studio,* XXIV, 1902, p. 245 ff.).

The next volume (XXV, 1902, p. 141) helps to explain the esteem of the English for this art school teacher from Budapest: he had been commissioned by the Austrian government to revive the dying native ceramics industries by submitting new designs, in line with traditional patterns, to small local potteries to bring their wares up to date. Since this was the purpose of Prince Albert in founding the South Kensington Museum and the network of government supported art schools in England half a century earlier, the newcomer to the ranks of reform in the crafts was bound to find a warm welcome. (Figure 28)

61. *Comb of blond tortoiseshell,* the finial decorated with a silver openwork head of a girl with flowing hair whose strands merge with the tendrils of a lily, a morning-glory, a rose, and an iris on the right, leaving the shell backing apparent

in all of the interstices. French boar's head mark for silver; master's hallmark illegible. France, 1900. (3 1/8 x 4 3/16) The silver is exquisitely chased, even simulating the fresh texture of the girl's skin. This remarkable technique, coupled with the resemblance of the face, with its wide cheekbones and pointed chin, to the "twin" pendants, number 131 and 183, makes an attribution to the same master, Zorra, tenable. (Figure 29)

62. *Gothic coronet of gold* in the form of an open arcade of five arches, each containing a bush composed of branches and minute golden leaves studded at intervals with diamond and sapphire "fruits," all resting on a circlet rising to a point over the brow, enamelled with a laurel wreath and its berries that meets in the center at a pear-shaped topaz, under the central bush. Below the stems of the smaller flanking bushes are four red enamelled bosses with flower-shaped cloisons; these continue at intervals, and in diminishing gradation toward the back of the circlet. The colonettes of the arcade, terminating in acorn-shaped capitals, are enamelled with overlapping blue and green ivy leaves. English, ca. 1910. (d. 5 x 2 1/8) As in number 225 we find here an incongruity of styles ranging from Neoclassic (the laurel wreath) to Medieval (the Gothic arcade, similar in form to number 64, an earlier stage of Gothic-revival), to vegetation in the illustrator Walter Crane's more formal manner. The overlapping ivy leaf motif on the colonnettes will remind the reader of the similar ornament used in Number 80 by John Brogden.

The formalized, heart-shaped leaves also appear in Viennese work of roughly the same period, where they ultimately derive from the enamels of Margaret MacDonald Mackintosh (Figure 203). The coronet may have been designed by Henry Wilson or one of his pupils (a decorative panel with a similar alternation of columns and formal vegetation in St. Bartholomew's Church, Brighton is illustrated in G. Hughes, *Modern Silver,* New York, 1967, p. 149, no. 255). Trained as an architect, Wilson set up a workshop for metalwork and jewelry in 1895, and from 1901 on taught metalwork at the Royal College of Art (Hughes, p. 252). (Figure 30)

## X. *VICTORIAN JEWELRY*

63. *Earrings of gold filigree.* English or French, between 1820 and 1835. (1 x 3 13/16) Each earring consists of a hollow, slope-sided octahedron, the frame filled with filigree in a pattern of whirls and palmettes. At the axes are golden globes, and at the corners basket-shaped pendants suspended from twisted wire. The pins are hidden by rosettes and palmettes set into a square form.

Filigree was used in Greek jewelry at least from the third-second century B.C. (see a pair of earrings in Rodolfo Siviero, p. 40, No. 120, illustrated on plate 124, see Bibliography), reappeared in popular art in the Middle Ages (in which domain it is still used), was extensively employed in Europe in the eighteenth century, resumed in the 1820's, and waned towards the end of the '30's.

Hair dressed in curls over the ears, especially in the '30's, was thought not incompatible with long earrings such as these, although a hair fashion of covered ears in the '40's was. (Figure 31)

64. *Bracelet composed of five ogive arches,* inspired by a small medieval metal work such as a reliquary. Two arches are outlined in gold and filled with a trellis; three are framed in carnelian supported by malachite columns with leafy capitals. (l. 5 3/4 x 2) In the center of each arch are five variously colored agates. At the top of each arch two rubies in a floweret on an amethyst foil alternate with three groups of three aquamarines. The structure is supported by two mouldings: one with a running tendril pattern, one with intersecting arches. On either side, echoing the larger foliated bosses, are three compartments (of an original four, one of which—part of the clasp—is lacking) : two have aquamarines in their centers, one has a ruby.

The complex plasticity of this bracelet points to a mid-century date, yet the kaleidoscopic polychromy and the mincing quality in the details indicate the 1830's when indeed Gothic revival was most pronounced. The bracelet's size and its exaggerated architectonic character suggest that it may have been made for a costume ball or for the theater. (Plate 3)

65. *Enamelled bracelet* of gold, diamonds, peridots, moonstones, topazes. French, ca. 1840. (3 3/8 x 4 1/4) In the central elongated oval of this gold bracelet are mounted a peridot, two moonstones, and six diamonds surrounded by black enamel leaves set into a scalloped enamelled outline. Two oblong scallop-ended forms in graduated sizes flank either side: each of the larger has three diamonds, and one pink topaz and one brown; each of the smaller has a moonstone. The lively projecting gold and green-enamelled leaves are in contrast to the sober heavy links.

The Gothic revival, after having been a political tool of the reactionary restored Bourbons, became about 1830 a broadly-based movement fashionable among intellectuals of the right and left.

The date of the jewel is presumed from the boldness of its forms in contrast to the mincing quality of Rococo-Gothic examples of the previous decade (See Catalogue number 64). (Figure 32)

66. *Chatelaine and watch* in vari-colored gold and silver. French, 1840's. (1 1/4 x 5 1/8) The shield-shaped center piece has the monogram *LP,* standing for Louis Philippe, king of France who reigned from 1830 to 1848. The habit of putting the monarch's initial or monogram on possessions which had no connection with the royal family was begun as a token of loyalty earlier. Under Napoleon I the initial N surrounded by a laurel wreath appeared on all manner of objects belonging to lesser beings. Under Napoleon III, who succeeded Louis Philippe, the same N, only surmounted by a crown, was put to similar use.

From it are suspended a seal and a fob; between them is a medallion from which the watch is suspended.

The maker's name, Leroy et Fils (115 Palais Royale), inscribed inside the watch case, belongs to a firm which was already in business in the XVII century, when the chatelaine watch was introduced at the court of Louis XIV.

Having many occasions to speak about the revivals of various earlier ornamental styles in the XIX century, it may come as a surprise that there was also a "survival style." Grown somewhat uncertain and clumsy, it nevertheless is a continuation of the flowery Neoclassicism of Louis XVI, well suited to the spirit of uncertainty of the newly restored aristocracy and the clumsy efforts of a rising bourgeoisie to imitate the royal forms of yore to which it secretly aspired. (For a chatelaine of similar proportions, see Vever, I, p. 294.) (Figure 33)

67. *Brooch with pendant* of gold and aquamarines. French or English, 1840's. (2 3/8 x 4 1/4) Suspending a pendant from a brooch on a fine plaited-wire chain, as in this example, seems to have appeared in the 1840's, and to have been fashionable at least into the '60's. (See a sketch for a brooch in the Etruscan style by Alexis Falize, Paris, 1860-1865, in the Cooper-Hewitt Museum, reproduced in Steingräber, *Royal Treasures,* p. 180, Figure 329.)

In this jewel of highly animated chiaroscuro and spatial complexity, smooth scrolls are foils for the finely chased strapwork cartouches with polished edges. Strapwork, which is of sixteenth century Italian origin, came to fruition at the Fontainebleau of Francis I. A horizontal expansion of the cartouche occurred in the seventeenth century; this form as used in the nineteenth century may also be seen under Catalogue No. 47, 48. (Figure 34)

68. *Coral cameo pendant* of a bacchante set in a gold Renaissance style frame with one fixed pearl and three pearl drops in silver mountings set with brilliants. No marks, but the set (including two earrings, not shown) came in a fitted box

marked F. D. Froment-Meurice. French, 1840's. (2 4/5 x 4 1/10) The frame with two sirens flanking the cameo, and a putto head with spread wings at the bottom has the same design derivations enumerated under number 36 and number 37. A coral brooch of oval shape, showing the head and armless torso of a Diana and framed in strap-like scrolls (a XVII rather than late XVI century ornament) is shown in M. Flower, p. 102, fig. 28a. The cameo type, having a very long torso, derives from late XVI century examples such as one in the Kunsthistorisches Museum, Vienna, attributed to Jacopo da Trezzo (E. Steingräber, *Royal Treasures,* p. 109, fig. 183). (Figure 35)

69. *Garland-like bracelet* of gold, silver, enamel, pearls, precious pink topazes. François-Désiré Froment-Meurice, French, late 1840's. The bracelet is composed of golden vines with green enamelled leaves which are studded with pearls and interspersed with golden grapes. In the center, in heraldic fashion, two silver putti flank a pear-shaped briolette of precious pink topaz. On either side pearl-centered golden leaves alternate with oval-shaped precious pink topazes.

The sprightly effect, arising from sprouting leaves, pearls and gems, is distinctly reminiscent of Franco-Burgundian jewelry of around 1400 as may be seen by comparing the bracelet with Appendix, Figure 135. The fully-rounded putti, however, derive from South German or Upper Rhenish jewels of the thirteenth century such as the Schaffhausen Onyx (Allerheiligenmuseum, Schaffhausen. Erich Steingräber, *Antique Jewellery,* London, 1957, Figure 24-25, 27) from whose jewel-studded wreaths peer eagles and lions with cast heads. Similarly, in the so-called St. Heinrich's crown (Hans Thoma, *Schatzkammer der Residenz München, Katalog,* Munich, 1958, No. 13, Figure 10), cast figures of angels surmount the golden leaves.

The predilection for the Middle Ages was in decline among the vanguard in the late 1840's when this bracelet was presumably made. The cult of romance and emotion—which peaked around Rousseau and Diderot in the second half of the eighteenth century—had a nostalgic attachment to the Middle Ages and to the Gothic style as corollary effect. These romantic concepts were linked under Napoleon with aspirations for a Bourbon restoration which was accomplished in 1814. Subsequent political disillusionment notwithstanding, the national past in art, architecture, history and literature continued to stimulate the art of jewelry well beyond the middle of the nineteenth century. (Plate 4)

70. *Mermaid brooch,* enamel, emerald, rubies, pearls. French, 1840's. (3/4 x 1 1/4) The symmetrical gold brooch has a central cartouche with a large carbochon

emerald above a small diamond, and two flanking red and green enamel-tailed mermaids seated on scrolls which terminate above and below in rubies. Three pearls depend and one crests the whole.

This, and three other examples in the exhibition—number 36, 37, and 69—illustrate the course of the Renaissance revival which, in these cases, appears more French, though ultimately it is Italian, in derivation. Like the Gothic style, the Renaissance style in France was introduced in the first decade of the Restoration (1814–1824).

Unlike such tense, bizarre, frenzied ornament etchings of the School of Fontainebleau as those of Antonio Fantuzzi (Henri Zerner, *The School of Fontainebleau, Etchings and Engravings,* New York, 1969, A.F. 40 for instance) or Jean Mignon (Zerner, J. M. 36), this brooch rather approaches Jacques Androuet Ducerceau in its uncomplicated expanse and lack of intensity (Félix Herbet, "Les Graveurs de l'École de Fontainebleau," *Annales de la société historique & archéologique du Gatinais, Fontainebleau,* 1900, IV p. 300, IV, 5; and p. 303, VI, 3).

In its execution it betrays a craftsmanship less perfect than that of Froment–Meurice (see Number 69), although it lies within his stylistic ambient. By comparison with his bracelet of 1841 (Vever, I, p. 166), this brooch may be dated in the same decade. (Figure 36)

71. *Gold bracelet,* chased, blue enamel and diamonds. French, 1850-1860. (d. 2 5/8 x 2) The reign of the Empress Eugénie (1852-1870), in contrast to her predecessor Marie-Amélie's, is marked by sumptuously elegant jewelry such as this bracelet. The comparatively restrained and meager effect of similar floral and ornamental elements from the last years of Louis-Philippe's and his queen's reign (1830-1848), may be seen in Vever, I, unnumbered plate opposite p. 328, top. Enrichments of enamel and diamonds are evident immediately in the next decade (see plate 6 in an album of drawings by the Maison Mellerio, dated 1850-1860, in the Metropolitan Museum, 57.662.3). (Plate 5)

72. *Brooch in the form of a branch.* (2 1/8 x 3 1/8) Contrasting textures of gold is the theme of this jewel: the irregularities of the bark, the smooth, highly-polished ends and tendrils, and the granulation on the leaves. The granulation or "bloom" was obtained by etching the metal with hydrochloric acid; the acid corroded alloys leaving a minutely pitted surface.

The calculated choice of the deeply-colored, translucent cabochon garnet, and the luminous but opaque pearls extends the theme of contrasts.

The motif of natural wood was greatly popular from the early years of Napoleon III's reign, and found favor in England where this brooch was made in the 1850's. (Plate 7)

73. *Chased gold bracelet,* blue and white enamel, diamonds. French, 1850-1860. Garter and ribbon forms were favored in both France and England in the 1840's through the 1860's (see a striped bracelet made by Jules Chaise in 1845 to 1850, illustrated in Vever, I, p. 296, and his other designs from the same years, I, p. 304, 305, 319). Closely comparable to this example in design, materials and execution is a hinged bangle of English workmanship of c. 1855 (Flower, p. 107, Figure 33a). The taste for Victorian inflexible bracelets spread in Germany through the *Zeitschrift für Bijouterie* (Weimar) which in 1851 showed a garter (III, part 4, plate 48), and a ribbon (plate 47). (Figure 37)

74. *Equestrian bracelet* with obverse of gold-inlaid steel, reverse of gold; diamonds. French, about 1860. (2 1/8 x 5 11/16) Three figural high reliefs—Neptune in a horse-drawn shell-shaped chariot, the shaft of his trident concealed by the diamond-studded scroll, and mermaids recumbent on either side—are each enframed in oblong egg and dart patterned borders; the compartments' corners are filled with fine chasing and diamonds set in roundels; a triton's head forms the clasp.

Although Neptune and his retinue were an ubiquitous theme in the sixteenth century, baroque designs are the ancestors of these nineteenth century reliefs with their space-absorbing, weighty forms and Neptune's dynamic outward thrust.

Steel, used in the eighteenth and nineteenth century in France, Russia, and elsewhere for buttons, brooches, watchchains, and other forms of jewelry, is a brittle material, hard to work. Rarely is it inlaid with gold. Examples may be found in the work of Tissot between 1865 and 1880 for the Maison Boucheron (Vever, I, on p. 457 and p. 458), and in that of Froment-Meurice (illustrated in Flower, p. 120, Figure 46b, dated c. 1850). On stylistic grounds, the bracelet may be seen as a late work of Jean-Valentin Morel (1794-1860), or may be attributed to Eugène Julienne (1808-1875) whose heavy, assertive bracelets are illustrated in Vever, II, p. 239; or to Louis-François Cartier, one of his pupils.

On the clasp is an unidentified hallmark. (Plate 6)

75. *Band-shaped cast-gold bracelet* swelling in the center to accommodate a classical carnelian intaglio of a laurel-crowned male head in profile which is flanked by hollowed-out palmettes outlined with inset corded wire. A golden cast of the intaglio is mounted beneath it on the inner surface. (Figure 39)

The deliberate imperfections in the casting, the intentional choice of a cracked intaglio, indicate that the designer, Jules Wièse, who signed the bracelet, repudiated here his own impeccable craftsmanship which may be seen in Catalogue number 36 and 84, in a contrary gesture against both the overly cultivated and overly commercial work of his contemporaries. Wièse's contemporary Félix Duval's geometric jewelry of rivets and screws of 1861 is close to its esthetic (see Vever, p. 267 e.g.). While Wièse too embraced simplicity, he reverted in this bracelet, perhaps in the same decade, to a design which was prevalent in Pompeii in the first century B.C. to the first century A.D. (Rodolfo Siviero, p. 64, No. 236, illustrated on plate 173b). (Figures 38, 39)

76. *Necklace of multicolored enamels* set "en cloison" in gold. The circular flat choker is composed of segmental plaquettes joined by links concealed beneath gold flowerets. From the five joints at the front depend rondels in graduated sizes (the largest at center front) enamelled on both sides and framed in narrow beaded gold bezels. Alexis Falize; France, ca. 1865–70. (l. 6 x 1/2, pendants d. 1 3/10) This necklace poses some interesting problems: misfiled for many years under "Japanese" in the Victoria & Albert Museum's jewelry collection,* the perfection of its imitation of far eastern cloisonné could have no better testimonial.

In Vever's account (III, p. 484 ff., see Bibliography) of the Falize firm, all of it dictated by the son Lucien, the latter takes credit for working out the Japanese enamel technique. Inspired, he says, by the Japanese wares to be seen in quantity for the first time at the London Exposition of 1862 whither his father had sent him ("unaccompanied" is the implication), he succeeded in the 1870's in producing enamel work that rivalled the Japanese. These were first put on public exhibition in the Paris Exposition of 1878 where they met with immediate success.

On the face of it, this account seems plausible, since it was during the '70's that the vogue for things Japanese gathered force among the cognoscenti (especially the circle of the Goncourt brothers in France), and by 1878 Tiffany also displayed work in the Japanese style (see Introduction; and also Number 89). However there are indications that Vever doubted it; too tactful to say so verbatim, he implies as much by illustrating the account of Lucien Falize with some lockets and pendants (pp. 491-2), of rather coarse workmanship, which he labels "Lucien Falize." However at the beginning of the same volume, in the section devoted to jewellers of the 1860's, four others appear, labelled simply "Falize" and without discussion in that part of the text. I have had occasion to see examples of the son's work, and

---

* I am indebted to Shirley Bury for this information.

not only is the enamelling inferior to that of the necklace here exhibited, but the palette of colors is much lighter, with a predilection for opaque white and azure blue, imitating in its lack of tonal gradation the Japanese print rather than oriental enamels.

The design of this necklace accords well with one in the Indian manner, illustrated p. 353 (by Riffault, for Bourcheron, and one of the earliest examples of the *plique à jour* technique which was to become so popular ca. 1900) as an example of the mid-60's. Since the date of accession of the Falize necklace is recorded as 1871, and was preceded in 1869 by a gift from Alexis Falize to the (then) South Kensington Museum, consisting of a demonstration kit showing how he did his Japanese-style enamels (see Appendix, Figure 138), one can only conclude that the father must have accompanied his son in 1862, and that it was he who did the basic research in Japanese techniques and motifs.

Considering that the first clearly Japonizing work by a major artist, Whistler's "Caprice in Purple and Gold" (Appendix, Figure 137) is dated 1864, this shows a degree of artistic initiative on the part of the elder Falize deserving of recognition. (Figure 40)

77. *Necklace composed of seventy-six amphorae-shaped pendants,* gold with blue enamel, ending in a pearl drop, which radiate from a chain of gold rings. (l. 14 3/4 x 7/8) That necklaces of little mobile pyramidal pendants were widely popular in the Greek world is evident from the diversity of the sites where they have been found. (See a necklace of the 4th–3rd century B.C. from a Greek tomb in southern Italy in Rodolfo Siviero, *Jewelry and Amber of Italy, A Collection in the National Museum of Naples,* New York, 1959, p. 32, No. 85, illustrated on pls. 100 and 101.) The revival of jewelry in the Greek, Etruscan and Roman styles was due to Fortunato Pio Castellani (1793–1865); his sons Alessandro (1824–1883) and Augusto (1829–1914), carried on a tradition of pride in the perfect imitation of ancient works. (Alessandro Castellani, *Antique Jewelry and Its Revival,* Philadelphia, n.d., p. 3)

A stimulus to the revival in France was provided by the Campagna collection of ancient jewelry which was well known before its inauguration at the Louvre in 1862. Eugene Fontenay, French master of the genre, won a gold medal at the Universal Exposition, Paris, in 1876, for his "bijoux Campagna."

Works comparable to this necklace were made by the Castellani, by Fontenay, and by Carlo Giuliano—comparable not for the use of ancient motifs though Giuliano also designed in that mode—but for the free-swinging pendants feature. Mrs. Flower illustrates two such necklaces: one by Castellani of circa 1868; the other by Giuliano of circa 1867. (Margaret Flower, *Victorian Jewelry,* New York, 1967, p. 172, Figure 74; and p. 173, Figure 75. For Fontenay see Vever, II, p. 169 and p. 173.) The persuasive argument in favor of an attribution to Giuliano, however, is his undated necklace of slim inverted pyramids inset with blue enamel identically to the necklace on exhibition. (M. L. D'Otrange, "The Exquisite Art of Carlo Giuliano," *Apollo,* LIX, June 1954, p. 145ff., unnumbered illustration) (Figure 41)

78. *Gothic initial M* standing for the Virgin Mary who is framed in the intersticies with the Angel Gabriel in the scene of the Annunciation. Between the enamelled figures is a ruby vase holding pearl and white enamel lilies. Cabochon rubies and large pearls embellish the jewel. The linear feature of the rope moulding which outlines the face is echoed on the reverse by wire tracery of leaves and figures engraved. (1 13/16 x 2 3/8)

The jewel is a copy after one of the mid-fourteenth century, of French or English workmanship, left by William of Wykeham to New College, Oxford, in 1404. (Erich Steingräber, *Antique Jewellery,* London, 1957, p. 44, illustration p. 45, Figure 52) It was made about 1870 by the Roman jewelers Augusto and Alessandro Castellani who signed twice on the back. Both the limited favor for the Medieval revival in Italy, and the English prototype of the jewel indicate that it might have been made for the English market ca. 1850–60. A. W. N. Pugin had designed in the 1840's a brooch in the initial M—letter brooches having been not uncommon in the Middle Ages—among a set of Gothic jewels for a private client. (Margaret Flower, *Victorian Jewelry,* New York, 1967, p. 73, Figure 20) (Figure 42)

79. *Brooch of gold* with emeralds and diamond. The Castellani, Italian, circa 1860. (2 3/8 x 2 3/8) The gold quatrefoil brooch, inspired by a morse, has a triangular emerald in each of its foils outlined with moulding and five rows of gold rope. The central projecting pyramid, decorated with lancet-shaped mouldings, is capped with a diamond. Rope-patterned mouldings outline the whole, and eight bosses mark the points and intersections.

The Castellani monogram, stamped twice on the reverse, identifies the brooch as having been made by the Roman jewellers usually associated with the antique revival. (See Catalogue number 78) The Gothic style had been imported into Italy, and the Gothic revival remained an alien mode. In the crisp and cold precision of its handling—mitigated in part by the richness of color—this brooch recalls the manners of A. W. N. Pugin (1812–1852), and Eugène Viollet-le-Duc (1814–1879) and may have been made around 1860 for the English or French markets. (Figure 43)

80. *Indian brooch.* A tri-lobed plaquette of Indian origin, backed with mother-of-pearl, and framed in a beaded and granulated gold moulding decorated with a band of overlapping ivy leaves. Signed, *Watherston & Brogden;* English, ca. 1860. (2 3/4 x 2 1/8) Although the great vogue for Indian jewelry only took place after Victoria became Empress of India, 1876, exotic styles in jewelry were already "in the air" during the previous decade (see number 176). Brogden, himself, made a specialty of near- and far-eastern styles (M. Flower, p. 30). The plaquette, which at first glance resembles European *en résille* enamel, a rare and difficult technique, is actually of green glass, poured into a mould on which the pattern of gold foil has been spread. When the glass has set, the surface containing the foil figures is carefully polished until they are flush with the surface. The technique is known as "Indian pitch." (Figure 44)

81. *Gold cross on chain,* John Brogden; English, 1846. (2 1/16 x 3 7/8) A Celtic revival formed part of the early Romantic movement in the second half of the eighteenth century, and was reborn around 1850. To the Crystal Palace Exhibition of 1851, West of Dublin sent jewels inspired by the Tara brooch made during the summit of achievement of Celtic art in Ireland—the late seventh and early eighth century (Flower, p. 104, Figure 30a, see Bibliography; and Ludwig Bieler, *Ireland,* London, 1953, illustration p. 111).

John Brogden, who signed this cross on the reverse, was in 1846 a member of Watherston and Brogden at 16 Henrietta Street, Covent Garden, an address at which he stayed for approximately forty years although he became independent by 1860.

This gold cross is based in its form and in its interlaced pattern of decoration which includes the monogram of Christ—IHS—on Celtic stone crosses of the ninth century or earlier. The manner of relief decoration, however, is a corruption of a more elaborate metalworking technique such as may be seen on a processional cross of the eleventh century in the National Museum, Dublin (the Cross of Cong, illustrated in Flower, p. 140). Crosses of this latter type were embellished with gems as is Brogden's: twelve diamonds, and a garnet cameo of the head of Christ. The cross is suspended from a chain of uncertain authorship in a design of a wholly different sort: the pattern of open-work wheels was one used in Roman jewelry of the first century A.D. (Figure 45)

82. *Snake and dove brooch,* glass mosaic set in a jet plaque with gold frame, ca. 1870. Italian mosaic jewelry which had been popular since the 1940's here shows a motif which is the predecessor of our cover siren. The dove, however, does not even have a chance to struggle. (Figure 46)

83. *Enamelled chatelaine,* French, late 1860's. (2 x 4 1/4) This chatelaine represents the high phase of the French Renaissance revival style, earlier manifestations of which may be seen in Catalogue numbers 37 and 69.

The bracket-shaped upper part has in the center a shell-crowned mask enframed by scrolls and foliage. From a chain depends the lower part which consists of a watch on whose outer cover is an enamel picture of Cupid holding an hour glass and the motto AMOUR DÉROBE LES HEURES. Winged, fish-tailed females flank the watch, and a small grotesque male head supports the whole.

Multi-colored enamels cover approximately one-half the gold surface. Diamonds are set into the bracket's shell and around the black, white and gold enamel picture.

Frédéric Boucheron (1830–1902), who had this piece executed, established himself independently in 1858. Nine years later, when exhibiting for the first time and winning a gold medal at the Paris Exhibition, he was bored by the Renaissance and was seeking new styles. Thus it is probable that he designed this chatelaine in the late 1860's in what he considered by then a retardataire style. It seems unlikely that a client with conservative taste would have commissioned at a later date so flamboyant a design. (Figure 47)

84. *Gold eagle* set with diamonds; sapphire. Austro-Hungarian, 1870–1880. (3 3/4 x 2) The golden eagle, chased on all surfaces, holds a diamond in its beak and a cabochon sapphire in its claws.

This massive bird with its feathered haunches and shrouded head is menacing yet unvigorous, of a realism mitigated by the decorating gems, heraldic and symbolic. (Figure 48)

85. *Gold dragon brooch,* Jules Wièse, 1870's. (1 3/16 x 1 11/16) This furled golden dragon precedes by a decade the two dragons of Japanese inspiration in the exhibition (See Catalogue number 87). Three-clawed, like its Japanese kin, it is enveloped in a wave pattern. Star opals serve as eyes. The brooch, signed by Jules Wièse on the reverse, probably dates in the 1870's (he retired in 1880).

Within a few years of the opening of Japan to western trade in 1858, Japanese prints and objects of decorative art—ivories, bronzes, porcelains and embroideries—were imported into France and England. A new exoticism piqued the taste: japonaiserie remained in vogue through the 1880's and slipped in the '90's into the Art Nouveau. (Figure 49)

86. *Necklace of hollow gold links* attached to rectangular plaquettes stamped in the center with denticles. A shield-shaped locket with a lobular center motif enamelled light blue, embellished with beading and granulation. English, ca. 1880. (necklace: l. 19 1/8, locket: 1 3/8 x 5, earrings: 1/2 x 1 3/4) A pair of hollow drop-shaped gold earrings decorated with simple designs in granulation which echo the outline of the pendants. French, ca. 1860. Both items illustrate the techniques pioneered by Castellani in his successful revival of ancient goldsmithing. The earrings, with their graceful simplicity, have a certain originality although their construction bespeaks mass production. The necklace, on the other hand, may serve as a paradigm of both the mechanical perfection (in the chain) and the vulgarization of the Etruscan revival style (here combined with a shield shape more akin to the Medieval-revival style) that had taken place in the cheap but showy mass produced gold jewelry by the late 1870's. If this was the only alternative, then it is understandable that the even less expensive jewelry of the period (Figure 12) should have found preference, for it at least has the virtue of simplicity and solidity. (Figure 50)

87. *Swallow brooch* of diamonds and rose diamonds set *pavé* in silver on a gold base; ruby. French, 1880–1890. Jewelled swallows, large and small, were very fashionable in the 1880's in both France and England. Flocks in gold and one of diamonds still appeared in 1903–1904 in the catalogue of the Goldsmiths and Silversmiths Co., Ltd., London (pp. 40, 54), which attested to their continued popularity (see also number 59). Whereas in the English jewelled version the treatment of the feathers is summary, in this French example primary and secondary feathers and wingbars are distinguished.

The jewel is hallmarked with an eagle's head on the clasp. (Figure 51)

88. *Gold dragon pendant and chain;* diamond, opal. French, 1890's. (3 3/4 x 4) The spiraled dragon of the center pendant (whose tail disappears in a floweret from which depends a diamond and an opal) was originally a brooch and bore an earlier, different relationship to the miniature dragons rampant on the chain. The tension in the spring-coiled form darts into the wings and glides into the arabesque, yet the sculptural plasticity subordinates itself to the linear archetype of the Art

Nouveau. Like the three-clawed dragon of Catalogue number 85, it is of Japanese inspiration. (Figure 52)

89. *Double heart brooch,* enamel on gold, diamonds, ruby and pearls. English, 1880–1900. (1 3/16 x 1) On the red enamel covering a golden ground which was engraved with a rose engine (*fond guilloché*) are mounted two hearts outlined in diamonds, one with a ruby center, one with a diamond, above which is a diamond-set ducal coronet. Pearls surround the oval.

Current at the end of the nineteenth century, brooches and rings of a single or of double hearts, surmounted by lovers' knots, presumably for commoners, and coronets for peers, were given on the occasion of betrothal or marriage at least as early as the eighteenth century (see Cyril Davenport, *Jewellery,* London, 1905, p. 113, and plate XVII for an English eighteenth century diamond wedding ring; and Erich Steingräber, *Antique Jewellery,* London, 1957, p. 146, Figure 262 for a German ring of c. 1700. Neither heart, however, is cusped at the top). (Figure 53)

90. *Silver coffee pot,* parcel gilt; *martelé* background from which dragonflies stand out in relief; the lid handle is a perching dragonfly. Engraved on the bottom, *From L.S. 1882;* American, ca. 1880. (6 3/4 x 9 3/4) The dating of Tiffany & Co.'s artifacts has remained a problem largely unsolved; therefore one is grateful to find a piece with an inscription such as the one above, to help resolve the chronological sequence of styles. The Japanese inspired decoration was that which was much admired when Tiffany displayed it in Paris, 1878. Edward C. Moore Sr., for many years the company's chief designer, and later director of its European stores, was the one responsible for this phase in the firm's stylistic development. The equivalent style in jewelry is probably represented by a brooch in the form of a Japanese fan (Gr. Hughes, *Modern Jewellery,* London, 1964; p. 114, fig. 199; n.b., this plate does not appear in the American edition of this book, otherwise referred to here) in gold of four different colors, set with opals. The execution of such vari-colored metal work as this was probably the result of Moore's importation of Japanese artisans about this time. (Figure 54)

91. *Dragonfly brooch;* the execution is mainly in gold, but the wings are covered with a thin sheet of platinum, empty spaces being cut into it so that the gold will appear through them as wing markings. The body is meticulously modelled, with all of the insect's legs and thorax markings present on the under side where they cannot be seen when the brooch is worn. The eyes are set with small

diamonds. Stamped *Tiffany & Co.,* American, ca. 1880. The relationship between this brooch and the Tiffany coffee pot of the previous entry is self-evident. The quest for mastery of Japanese mixed metal techniques (as well as other Japanese crafts: see under numbers 76, 98, 185), that so obsessed various jewellers in the West beginning in the 1860's has here found a happy solution—whether with the help of Tiffany's imported Japanese artisans or not is hard to tell. They probably had as little experience as their American colleagues in working platinum, which had been available as a jeweller's metal since about 1800; the difficulties presented by its ductility, however, prevented its widespread use as it did not handle well. Here the problem has been overcome by shaping the thin sheet cold, and only heating it at the last moment in order to fuse it to the gold.

The painstaking rendering of all parts of the insect relates this piece to no. 111; however it is superior in its simplification and stylization. (Figure 55)

92. *Silver coffee pot with baroque pearls;* martelé background with raised design of wild rose blossoms and leaves on lower level and lid; the upper band of the pot has a design of bizarre tentacles curled around baroque pearls, interspersed with tendrils of unidentifiable foliage. Chalcedony bead on lid. Stamped, *Tiffany & Co.,* 6652M5143, Sterling Silver, 2212. An inventory number, 12/10, is scratched next to this. American, ca. 1890. (5 x 7 7/8) This is the style which met with so much critical dismay (see Introduction) when it was exhibited in the Paris Exposition, 1889. By 1893, however, a more developed version (Appendix, Figure 149) was being bought by European museums at the Chicago Columbian Exposition, and the Kunstgewerbemuseum in Berlin still has those purchases. (*Werke um 1900,* Berlin, 1966; no. 26, and no. 27, which has inset pearls with a seaweed pattern.)

The rosette motif and the swing of the curved elements is quite usual in American design of the late 1880's (see Appendix, Figure 173 for examples of similar ornament in pressed brick), which differentiates it from both English and French equivalents, although ultimately the source is European. This, and the unusual pearls in their wavy bezels, is probably what caught Bode's eye (see Introduction) when he decided that the Americans, strange as their jewelry now looked, had hit upon something really new. (Figure 56)

93. *Brooch of irregular form;* silver, embossed and glazed (not enamelled) in green, set with one large and six smaller baroque pearls; the entire plaque is set in gold. Stamped, *Tiffany & Co.,* on the back; the letters are much worn. (1 3/8 x 1 1/8) Looking more modern than any other piece in this catalogue, the

brooch resembles a small piece of nature immobilized and framed. Yet the curious soft "prongs" in which the pearls are set exactly resemble those of coffee pot number 90. The piece has a simple hook fastener—something that is replaced by more refined closings by the end of the century—confirming its early date.

Louis C. Tiffany, who had begun his experiments with glass in the late 1880's was, I am convinced, the author of the bizarre designs that crop up at this time in the firm's silver and jewelry. There is little documentation for this supposition, but there is one piece: a necklace frontal of gold set with an opal and other green and red stones that take up its colors. It too curls into tentacle shapes and sea colors. (Appendix, Figure 150). This strange work was acknowledged as his own by Tiffany (Charles DeKay, *The Art Work of Louis Comfort Tiffany,* Garden City, 1914), although he does not say exactly when it was made. Formerly in the Walters Collection in Baltimore, the piece can no longer be traced; perhaps it was acquired about the same time as the Lalique pieces, from the St. Louis Fair, 1903, which are still in the Walters Art Gallery. It was exhibited in the Paris Salon, 1906.* (Plate 9)

94. *Necklace made of Favrile glass scarab beetles* in gold settings interspersed with clusters of three gold beads, all suspended from a segmented tubular gold chain. Stamped, *Tiffany & Co.,* on back of center beetle. American, ca. 1900? (l. 17 x 1/2) Beetles of Favrile glass were also sold by the Tiffany firm for use by other jewellers. This necklace, however, is a more durable counterpart of one made of real beetles of the same size and color (now too fragile to be exhibited) which was in the possession of the Tiffany family (now Lillian Nassau collection).

The style of the necklace is reminiscent of Castellani's or Giuliano's (see number 77), which L. C. Tiffany probably knew. (Figure 57)

95. *Necklace and earrings;* gold with baroque pearls, diamonds, and green and red translucid enamels. No marks (except backs of earrings, which have been altered). Possibly Tiffany & Co.; American, ca. 1910? (necklace: l. 13 x 1 5/8, earrings: 3/4 x 1 3/4) The pairing of the dragons which decorate the individual elements of the design, held together by chains, seem rather conventional at first; yet there is great variety, for no more than two of each cluster design are used. The green and red enamels are one of L. C. Tiffany's favorite color schemes (Appendix, Figure 150), especially in juxtaposition with the irregular pearls which take up the same spectrum. A late version of the "soft" begel used in numbers 92, 93 is apparent in the earring buttons. (Figure 58)

* I am indebted to Robert Koch for this information.

### XI. *CANE AND UMBRELLA HANDLES FROM VICTORIAN TO ART NOUVEAU*

96. *Ivory parasol handle,* ca. 1875; probably French. (1 1/2 x 11 3/4) Originally attached to a tiny black lace over blue silk parasol. In the form of a slender bouquet of lilies-of-the-valley terminating in a cluster of small tulips, it is of the same genre as the earrings, Figure 10. Catalogue number 29, but of far finer workmanship. The seashore scenes of the French painter, L. Boudin, are dotted with such parasols carried by women in bonnets and hooped skirts. (Figure 59)

97. *Ivory umbrella handle,* late 1870's. (13/16 x 5 1/4) The carver has imitated the form of a common walking stick made from a tree branch; but by adding the dolphin he has given it a touch of the exotic along with the outlines of a Japanese bone handle (see Catalogue number 105). The first popular assimilation of Japanese to western art began at about this time (see Catalogue number 39). (Figure 59)

98. *Silver umbrella handle* with a brownish patina. French, ca. 1890. (1 5/8 x 5 3/4) The jewelry museum in Pforzheim, W. Germany, has an umbrella handle bought from Lucien Gaillard at the 1900 Exposition in Paris which has many similar features: the same smiling girl, silver gilt with brownish patina, and a similar way of making the transition from the head to the shaft. Although the master's mark at the base of our handle is that of a jeweller named Quercia, it is also stamped lightly with the monogram *LG* made with simple punching tool on both sides. According to Vever, (III, pp. 636-7) Lucien Gaillard, the son of a well known jeweller, became enamoured of Japanese mixed metal techniques (e.g. Catalogue numbers 106, 108) and after an apprenticeship in his father's workshop, he worked in the ateliers of other specialists in metal work in order to learn as much as he could about patinas. His first public exposition was at the Paris Exhibition of 1889; one may assume that this umbrella handle was made not much earlier.

The juxtaposition of an old man and a young woman also appears as the decoration of a wooden archway in an early water color by the Czech artist, Franz Kupka (on extended loan to the Museum of Modern Art, N.Y.C. from the L. Avnet collection). Perhaps these faces were part of a public building—a saloon or restaurant, at a guess—where both artists might have seen them. (Figure 59)

99. *Silver cane handle.* German, ca. 1904. (4 3/8 x 2 3 /8 x 3/4) It bears the

inscriptions "J. Schmidt (worn) T. Triepel 5.5.04"; the silver content and hall marks are both partially obliterated by solder. Probably designed by Patriz Huber (see *Deutsche Kunst und Dekoration,* XIII, 1903–4, p. 41, for similar handles). (Figure 59)

100. *Massive silver cane handle,* Russian, ca. 1905. (4 3/8 x 4 7/8 x 1 1/4) This monstrous handle stands half way between the chimeras of Lalique and those of the modern Italian film director Fellini, who constantly symbolizes evil and innocence by the juxtaposition of horrible sea creatures and young girls. The monster is close kin to the dolphins of a footed bowl of the same period (pl. 63 in *Fabergé and his Contemporaries,* pub. Cleveland Museum of Art, 1967). It is unfortunate that Russian hallmarks often leave some doubt about the initials stamped on objects, otherwise one might identify "I.A." In all likelihood, however, they are the initials of the chief of the assay office. (Figure 59)

## XII. *JAPANESE WORK FOR THE WESTERN MARKET*

As Tiffany & Co. had done in the late 1870's (see Catalogue number 92), so Lucien Gaillard in 1900 imported Japanese craftsmen to work in his atelier in Paris. They were experts in carving and lacquer work. We cannot tell whether the same artisans later branched out into independent businesses, or whether the craze for things Japanese encouraged others to settle in France. However, the hundreds of carved horn pendants still surviving from the period of about 1910 bear unmistakable signs of Japanese design sources, and a freedom in the carving that can only come of long practice.

101. *Carved and tinted horn "Fly" pendant* with Venetian glass drop, and cord necklace strung at intervals with amber (?) beads. Signed on the back "Gyp." (2 7/8 x 4) One of a pair of prolific carvers (see number 104) of these horn pendants, the prototypes of which go back to XVII and XVIII century Japanese inro (Appendix, Figure 171). (Figure 60)

102. *Comb of carved and tinted horn* in wild-rose motif, set with one sapphire. (3 5/8 x 5 3/8) It would be impossible to tell that a Japanese had anything to do with this piece, which is rather conventional in its western style of naturalism, except for the fitted box in which it came; this has "Hosaka, Paris" stamped on the lining of the lid. (Figure 60)

103. *Transparent vase,* in a multicolor maple leaf pattern, executed in a variant of the cloisonné enamelling technique. (3 3/8 x 4) The silver base is stamped with Fabergé's Latin alphabet initials, as used on objects destined for sale in Western Europe. Yet the design is traditional Japanese, and the curious technique of the transparent enamel work unlike anything of similar effect produced in Europe: the cloisons (metal dividers) were apparently attached to a metal core, and after the enamels had been filled in, the core was etched away with acid. The evolution of transparent (*à jour*) enamel in XIX century France, although equally mysterious, led to a different method: the pierced or shaped metal cells were backed with a piece of mica or isinglass, to which the liquid enamels will not adhere, and this back could be moved as soon as the enamel in a cell had cooled.

The production of these vases (bowls of the same type also exist) seems to have lasted only a very short time, suggesting that the process was known to only one family; and the fact that a member of the staff of the Museum of Modern Art in Tokyo whom I consulted had never seen anything like it in Japan suggests that the entire output was destined for Europe, either through Fabergé or other buyers (not all of the pieces bear his stamp). They were probably introduced to the west in the Japanese exhibit in Paris, 1900 at which time one reviewer grumbled that the Japanese had "stolen" this technique (however, similar complaints were made about Russian transparent enamels that were introduced at the Exposition of 1889, and it is still not clear whether the technique originated in the Orient or not (see Vever, II, p. 164 ff.)). (Figure 60)

104. *Carved and tinted horn pendant* of Lunaria leaves, with a necklace repeating the leaf motif, alternately with white beads. Signed on the back *Bonte.* (2 3/8 x 4 1/8) Similar to number 101, above, but cruder in execution. (Figure 60)

## XIII. *EAST-WEST CROSS CURRENTS*

Having devoted some study to the preceding plate which demonstrates the influence of Art Nouveau, after 1900, on Japanese works made for western consumption, the reader may enjoy testing his discrimination on the objects included in this group (Figure 61). East or West?

105. *Japanese carved bone handle* attached to a western magnifying glass. Head of a bearded, laughing man with an exaggeratedly high domed cranium on top of which crouches a monkey. Glass stamped *B & L Opt. Co.* (1 1/2 x 7 1/4)

This "laughing philosopher" occurs frequently in Japanese art, albeit without the monkey, as an embodiment of happiness. It is not within the scope of the exhibition to delve deeply into Japanese iconography; however, the bizarre juxtaposition of man and beast is the very sort that would have appealed instantly to Europeans on the lookout for metamorphosis at the end of the XIX century (see Appendix, Figure 159). (Figure 61)

106. *Japanese paper knife;* patinaed brass handle in the shape of a gourd, embellished with a curling maple leaf in copper partly gilt, half concealing some gilt blossoms (one of which has drifted to the end of the handle), toward which two minute frogs, one copper the other gilt, ascend on either side. The brass blade has a lightly etched surface (see number 89) and is pierced with two butterfly motifs, completed with engraved heads and antennae. Unlike number 105, above, which is a signed and probably unique piece, this paper knife was duplicated (I have seen two other identical specimens) for export. Work of this sort was vastly admired in the West (see discussion of Catalogue number 98). (Figure 61)

107. *Korean ivory box,* the lid exquisitely carved with the figure of a howling monkey stung by an insect, which has alighted on his left ear. (2 1/4 x 3 5/8) Despite the popularity of monkeys (see also above, number 105) in the Japanese repertory of motifs reaching the West, they were never taken up in European or American design with the same enthusiasm as other orientalia. Apparently the psychic discomfort caused by their similarity to man was too deep-rooted in western tradition (see H. W. Janson, *Apes and Ape Lore in the Middle Ages and the Renaissance,* London, 1952). (Figure 61)

108. *Japanese miniature brass box* with stamped plaquettes in vari-colored metals soldered to sides and lid. (1 1/2 x 1 3/8) Similar in technique to number 106 (above) and produced in quantity, small pieces of this kind which were both available and affordable to large numbers of people in the West helped to disseminate understanding, and with it general acceptance, of Japanese elements as they increased in European and American design during the latter part of the XIX century. (Figure 61)

109. *Comb of blond horn,* in the shape of two highly stylized, overlapping peacock feathers, each with a green enamelled "eye" in gold setting. Stamped *L. Gaillard;* after 1905? (2 x 5 1/4) For Gaillard's early attempts to master Japanese

techniques, Catalogue number 98; for his later efforts to work in authentic Japanese manner, see general remarks heading XII. *Japanese Work for the Western Market*. In comparison to his comb (Number 59) of ca. 1900 this one has shifted from florid design and elaborate technique to a purposeful simplification of both, reflecting the shift from sculptural to linear emphasis which took place generally shortly after 1900. (Figure 61)

110. *Hairpin carved with a cluster of violets* (front and back), in dark brown wood, set with a grey pearl "dew drop." Stamped *Vever*, ca. 1902. (1 1/4 x 5 5/8) Although the quality of the carving if compared with a work such as number 107 (above) reveals it to be of European workmanship, the silhouette, so closely in accord with the two Japanese handles (numbers 105, 106) leaves no question about the japonizing intention of its designer. (Figure 61)

111. *"Locust" brooch;* gold with ruby eyes. French, ca. 1890. (1 3/4 x 5/8) This brooch, or one almost identical, is used repeatedly as a vignette in *La Revue de la Bijouterie, la Joaillerie, et l'Orfèvrier* during the five years, 1900–05, of its publication; as also in *La Revue des Arts Décoratifs*, XV, p. 64, and *L'Art Pour Tous*, Paris, 1892; "Motifs Japonais," no. 776. However, there is no caption to explain its presence in the journals, and though the choice of this insect as a jewelry motif undoubtedly goes back to Japanese art (Appendix, Figure 171), it is impossible to tell whether the hand that fashioned it was French or Japanese. Indeed, the insect is so perfect in every detail (including the under side), that one suspects it of having been cast in a mold made from a real locust, a technique used today for minor jewelry (usually reproducing leaves), but apparently novel enough at that time to merit the use of 18 K gold Eagle's head stamp. (Figure 61)

112. *Purple glass pendant* with two lizards moulded in relief, suspended from a matching necklace of knotted silk strands, and with a pendant tassel of the same silk. Engraved on the back *Lalique,* ca. 1912. The shape of the pendant, based upon Japanese sword-guards, along with the cord necklace relate this to the two carved horn pendant of Catalogue numbers 101, 104. However, though merely of glass, the special refinement of Lalique's work is present in the suppleness of the silk cord, and in the fine proportions. These glass pendants were to continue popular for more than a decade. In most cases the signature "Lalique" in block letters is built into the mold; in this instance the deviant form of the signature might either indicate later forgery (unlikely, since the price charged the present owner was not

a Lalique price!); or an early experiment in glass jewelry (compare Catalogue number 156, one of Lalique's first pieces as an independent jeweller, which also has a signature engraved, rather than stamped in the usual manner). (Figure 61)

113. *Round silver brooch,* the top showing a carnation and its foliage silhouetted against a blackened background; the reverse pierced by four butterfly shapes. Perhaps originally a button. German (?) ca. 1900. Even though stamped with the German assay marks for silver, this brooch leaves room for uncertainty as to its provenance. The pierced butterflies, so reminiscent of similar work on the paper knife (no. 106), indicate a more easterly source, as does the workmanship of the front, partly executed in niello, a technique for which the Russians were famous. (Figure 61)

## XIV. *BOXES*

114. *A gilt metal box lined with wood,* with an enamel on copper plaque set into the lid. Signed *AF* (Alexander Fisher), and dated 1899 on the enamel. (8 9/10 x 3 1/5 x 2 2/5) As in the box by Liberty's (number 115) this lingering on of romantic medievalism in England is due to the belated impact of Rossetti's paintings, which were not known to the general public until the first posthumous exhibition of his works in 1883. His picture, "The Day Dream" (Victoria & Albert Museum), 1880, which also depicts a woman perched in the boughs of a tree, is the source of this enamel.

Fisher, who exerted an enormous influence on his many pupils at the Central School for Arts and Crafts in London, studied in France. By concentrating on the painted enamels of Limoges in the XVI century he seems to have entirely missed contemporary developments in French enamelling, namely the pale harmonies and *plique à jour* technique which dominated the jewelry display at the Paris Exposition in 1900. The lavish use of strong, deep colors relates his work to the coloristic preferences of the mid XIX century rather than of the XVI, although the otherwise somber scheme is often enlivened by the use of paillons (bits of silver or gold foil underlying a layer of translucent enamel). (Figure 62)

115. *Pewter box and silver belt buckle,* 1900. (box: 5 1/4, buckle: 2 x 2 1/2) Liberty's of London introduced two new lines around 1900: pieces marked "Tudric," such as this pewter box with blue-enamelled leaf ornament, encompass what might be properly termed bibelots (boxes, clock cases, platters, etc.) made of the base

metals. "Cymric" was the name invented for smaller objects executed in precious metals, such as this silver belt buckle.

The intention of appealing to a public still enamored of a romanticized national past is implicit in the choice of these two trade names of murky origin; and the designs themselves merely allude to true historic styles. In what might be termed a revival of the medieval revival, their roots go no farther back than Rossetti (Appendix, Figure 141), and such illustrators and designers who continued in that spirit (Appendix, Figure 170). The new shoots growing out of this older stock are the sharply linear recurved patterns, such as the stems of the enamelled leaf border of the box ca. 1905.

A hint of the coming tug-o'-war between naturalistic and abstract pattern occurs in the background of the picture by Rossetti, cited above; but the breaking point occurs only a generation later, and not only in English ornament, but in the paintings of Gustav Klimt in Vienna (Appendix, Figure 134) wherein a vibrant tension is set up between the meticulous realism of the portrait and the artful abstraction of the shapes that suggest the room.

While it would be foolish to equate the importance of the box and the painting, Liberty's designers, among all the craftsmen in England at that moment (see below), most accurately walk the razor's edge between the old and the new. (Figure 63)

116. *Cigar humidor of silver,* the lid set with an enamelled copper plaque. Hallmarked G. o H. Ltd, with the London assay hallmark for 1902. The Guild of Handicraft, of which C. R. Ashbee was founder and chief designer, removed its workshops from London to Gloucestershire in 1902, retaining only two salesrooms in London. The hallmark (subsequently G. o H. or, in the earliest years of operation C. R. A., or none at all) just antedates the translocation. The move to the country was at least partially inspired by John Rudin's preachings of brotherhood and a return to a simple way of life.* Refurbishing the old houses at Chipping Campden and starting a farm seems to have had an extremely sobering effect upon Ashbee's style. One senses that he took the village life to heart, for the design of this box is reminiscent of the tankards of country pubs, minus the handle, but keeping the painted pot lid—in this case a peacock with spread tail, a motif which he had previously done as a brooch. (See "Modern Design in Jewellery and Fans,"

---

* See Shirley Bury, "An Arts and Crafts Experiment: The Silverwork of C. R. Ashbee," *The Victoria and Albert Museum Bulletin,* Jan. 1967, pp. 18-25.

*The Studio,* special winter number, 1901–1902, London, Pl. 20 and Catalogue number 226) (Figure 64)

117. *Ormolu box* set with delicately carved ivory panels, seven of them on the hipped lid, and six around the sides of the receptacle. Erhart, Paris, 1900. (5.2 x 2.6 x 2.2 cm.) The central panel of the lid represents Venus and Cupid; the auxiliary panels contain a sparse but tasteful assortment of floral swags and twiglets that seem to grow out of the rose bush stems articulating the metal framework. Here, as in number 118, the designer of the box has a large-scale model in mind: the typical Parisian building of the XIX century, with its hipped roof. The style and subject matter would easily fit into the XVIII century French repertory; yet the softness, as well as the freedom of the carving relate it to what is most traditional in French Art Nouveau. (The little figures of number 133 also fall within this category, although the treatment of the enamelled tresses betrays its end of the century date.) (Figure 65)

118. *Silver box with flower motifs* in repoussé on the pseudo-hasps and -lock of the lid, where the ground of the design is filled with blue-green enamel. The ornament is repeated in openwork backed by similarly enamelled copper plaquettes, on the four feet (one plaquette missing). London assay office marks, 1903. Master's hallmark *KK*. (12 5/8 x 5 1/2 x 4 3/4) S. Bury has suggested that this may be the mark of a Scandinavian, Karl Karlsen, who settled in England. The floral design is commonplace for England at that time; however the shape of the box with its flaring legs betrays an ages-old tendency on the part of designers of ornamental boxes to refer, consciously or not, to architecture. It recalls nothing so much as the lowest level of the Eiffel Tower. (Appendix, Figure 172)

A copper casket of similar shape antedating this one was exhibited in the Home Arts and Industries show at Albert Hall in 1900. The design, by H. Maryon, was carried out T. Spark and C. Clark, suggesting a teacher and his pupils (*The Studio,* XX, 1900, p. 79). (Figure 66)

## XV. *PEACOCK FEATHERS: THE COLORS OF ART NOUVEAU*

This Catalogue includes many examples of this most widespread of Art Nouveau design motifs: Plate 25, Catalogue number 221 with strong linear tendencies derived from English book illustrations of the '90's; the other, Figure 61, number 109, an even more advanced form of abstraction denoting the stage where naturalism in art is about to yield to a new kind of formalism. This group with its wide variety of styles shows both the diversity of Art Nouveau and the thread holding it together that makes it recognizable as a period style. The common denominator is color.

119. *Brass buckle;* cloisonné enamel in shades of muted brown and green, with a translucent blue-green center, set with a blue glass "eye" in high relief. Designed by *Stalin* for Piel Frères, 1900. (5 x 3) This manufacturer was designated as the best of those producing well designed jewelry at low prices. The perfect imitation of natural forms having been the strength of French goldsmiths throughout the XIX century, it is not surprising to find the tradition still strong at the end of this period. Only the massiveness of the buckle, along with the (literally) visionary of styles shows both the diversity of Art Nouveau and the thread holding it together effect of the raised glass eye in the center relate it to the protosurrealism of the period (*Revue de la Bijouterie,* etc., II, 1901, p. 68 has an illustration of this piece). (Figure 67)

120. *Three small peacock feather brooches;* varicolored enamel over incised or modelled gold. Tiffany, ca. 1910? (large brooch: 3/4 x 2, medium brooch: 3/8 x 1, small brooch: 1/4 x 1) It comes as a surprise that Tiffany whose jewelry in the Paris exposition of 1889 was the bellwether of a radical change has reverted to a rather tame naturalism by 1900, just when success for the new style was assured. Such is the case, however, in even some of the costly pieces that the firm showed in 1900 in Paris. Excellent in workmanship and not calculated to offend by excessive novelty or price, this kind of product catered to a wider market than either the severe style of the English crafts movement, or the more florid and expensive French products. (Figure 67)

121. *Link bracelet;* gold with dark blue opaque enamel paired scrolls centered with a pear shaped opal. English, ca. 1905. (l. 5 x 1) Catalogue numbers 221, 222, 223, along with this bracelet, reveal an English weakness for the heart shape. Whether they were conceived as wings, shields, peacock feathers, or scrolls, and no matter at which end of the naturalism-to-abstraction spectrum, the essential romanticism underlying the entire Arts and Crafts movement in England inadvertently turns a good many of the jewelry designs into valentines. (Figure 67)

122. *Pendant;* semi-abstract scrolls enamelled in green, ending at the lower right in a golden blossom from which sprouts the central motif, an inverted tear-

drop shaped bluish-green pearl shell. E. Colonna, ca. 1900. (1 1/8 x 2) For similar Colonna design see Appendix, Figure 151. The refined and complex hybrid style of Colonna while he was working for S. Bing's "Maison de l'Art Nouveau" in Paris (for an example of his later style, turn to Catalogue number 139) represents a balance between English linearism—probably filtered through the great Belgian designer, Henri Van de Velde who also worked for Bing around 1897 (see Appendix, Figure 167) and French surrealism. The element of metamorphosis is subtle here, yet unmistakable: the flowing forms suggest grasses or pond weeds ending in a blossom; but the central pearl, ballooning like a gas bubble from behind the flower, transforms the composition into something that we "read" as a peacock feather. In complexity of thought Colonna, at his best, is the equal of Ashbee (Catalogue number 219), and a piece such as this, which suggests several things at the same instant is not unlike a Rorschach test (a psychological testing device which was conceived at just about the same time as this jewel).* This piece is illustrated in M. Battersby *Art Nouveau,* Feltham (England), 1969, p. 43 (plate reversed). (Figure 67)

## XVI. *THE FORMS OF ART NOUVEAU*

When color is absent, as is usually the case with buckles because they are subject to more wear and tear than enamels can endure, one realizes how much diversity of form and subject matter Art Nouveau includes. Some designs are good, others poor; yet, even if the more conservative ones do not immediately reveal their period, the interested eye will usually be able to detect some telltale feature that gives it away.

123. *Silver cape clasp;* a knot of foliage connected by means of a large chain of twisted links to a foliage "nest" of interlaced design, in the middle of which sits a large beetle. Engraved signature on the bottom of the insect. French, ca. 1900. (l. 4 7/8, 2 7/8 x 1 5/8) Everything except the beetle is reminiscent of late Gothic ornament (see Appendix, Figure 136) so that the piece in reality is one of the last of the medieval revival that started much earlier in the century. Yet one would not be apt to mistake it for any of the previous stages (e.g., numbers 64, 65), for that it is too bold of form. The popularity of strange insects in Art Nouveau finally leads one to the correct diagnosis. (Figure 68)

* This piece appears in *Dekorative Kunst,* VI, 1900, p. 423; and *The Architectural Record,* XII, 1902, p. 68. I am indebted to Professor Martin Eidelberg for these references.

124. *Brass belt clasp;* the two scrolled halves are identical but one has been turned upside down to lend variety to the composition; center plaquette showing three crocuses sprouting from their bulbs is soldered to one half of the clasp. French, ca. 1905. (4 7/8 x 2 3/4) The rapid degeneration of the French curvilinear style after 1900 led to its being nicknamed "the noodle style"; revulsion against this flabby growth was already under way when this piece was manufactured (see Catalogue, no. 202). (Figure 68)

125. *Silver buckle in the shape of a fantastic fish head* with outspread fins. French, ca. 1900. (3 1/8 x 2) Of high quality workmanship, this rather frightening design is closely related to the frame of a large clasp by Lalique (Appendix, Figure 182) exhibited in 1900. The choice of so bizarre a motif has been discussed; it was one of the ingredients of Art Nouveau that made it "new" in the 1890's. (Figure 68)

126. *Brass clasp with green enamel flowerets* and two oval chalcedony stones. German, after 1900. Executed by the firm of Th. Fahrner whose display at the Paris Exposition in 1900 caused favorable comment, the design is probably by Patriz Huber who was their chief designer at that time (see Appendix, Figure 168). There is about the piece a disquieting hesitation between the draughtsmanlike assurance of the swirls and the rather fussy flower elements. Perhaps he was already influenced by a Darmstadt designer, Rudolf Bosselt (see *Deutsche Kunst u. Dekoration,* VII, 1900–01, p. 131) who seems to have anticipated the Viennese craze (Catalogue number 203) for all-over small pattern. (Figure 68)

127. *Gold buckle set with four amethysts;* Scandinavian, ca. 1910? In one particular sense Art Nouveau was much akin to the early stages of Medieval art; so diverse were the contributing traditions which went into its formation that it was easily adaptable to various national styles and predilections. Though guardedly, it advances the same taut-curve principle of design already discussed above in relation to Catalogue number 122, deriving from Van de Velde's influence on the other designers of Bing's staff at "La Maison de l'Art Nouveau." Nevertheless the interlacing meander ornament is of Viking inspiration. (Figure 68)

128. *Pewter buckle with a swinging drop-shaped ornament* set with a turquoise. German (?), ca. 1900. Showing affinities with Colonna's pendant (Catalogue number 122) in outline and pattern elements, one must assume either a direct link

between the two or a common starting point in Van de Velde. The tamer symmetry of the buckle, as well as its slower curves make it seem commonplace by comparison. Although nothing except symmetry seems to relate it to buckle number 126, both share traits of a brooch (Appendix, Figure 168) by Patriz Huber. (Figure 68)

129. *Silver buckle, partly gilt;* the outline is formed by the curves of an angel's head and wings. French, 1900. This buckle is illustrated in a catalogue of the manufacturer L. Baudet (Library of the Syndicat des Bijoutiers, Paris), otherwise it might pardonably be mistaken for an English work in the Pre-Raphaelite vein. The infinite care and unstinting labor that must go into the finishing of a piece such as this, even though it ranks only as a series product, may hold the more practical answer to the decline of Art Nouveau: it could not, in this form, compete with the products such as Number 126 above, which—for all their touches of luxury such as the stones and the enamel—could be made quickly and cheaply with a minimum of handwork. (Figure 68)

## XVII. *HAMBURG MUSEUM FÜR KUNST UND GEWERBE*

The interest in contemporary decorative arts during the 1890's was nowhere stronger than in Germany, where journals devoted to "Jugendstil" multiplied and prospered. The Kunstgewerbemuseum in Berlin had sent no less a personage than Wilhelm Bode, director of the Kaiser Friedrichmuseum, to scout the Columbian Exposition in Chicago, 1893; and in 1900 the Hamburg Museum für Kunst und Gewerbe, under the directorship of Justus Brinkmann, joined the Berlin museum in purchasing dozens upon dozens of articles in the new style, among them eight pieces of furniture from S. Bing's "Maison de l'Art Nouveau," from which the term for the whole period style derives its name. Bing was a native of Hamburg, and six of the pieces are by E. Colonna, his American designer, (see also nos. 122, 143, 144, 145 in this catalogue) thus creating a fortuitous "Hamburg—America line" at the same time when the shipping company of that name was in its heyday. The four exhibits listed next were part of the original purchase made by Brinkmann at the Paris Exposition of eighteen pieces of jewelry. Beautiful in themselves, they are also invaluable as documents because the dating and authorship are authenticated, and even the prices recorded.

130. *Pendant with a winter woodland landscape* in shades of blue to blue-

white enamel on gold; oval sapphire drop gold chain. Purchase price, 1620 francs. Signed, *Lalique;* France, after 1896. (Length (including sapphire drop) 3 3/4) The pear-shaped outline, closed on the right by a bough with sparse and withered leaves, on the left by the silhouette of the snow-laden fir tree, contains a minute landscape of amazing depth and variety, all produced by contrasting flat tones of enamel. Although Lalique's exhibit may have contained many more spectacular pieces, this is outstanding in its refinement of color composition and its lyricism.

This piece was probably done slightly after a larger version of a winter scene—a stomacher in glass and enamel—commissioned by a Russian (Vever, III, p. 714). (Plate 10)

131. *Gold Pendant and chain* with pearl drop, representing a water nymph whose head and shoulders rise out of the blue-enamelled ripples. The face, around which falls golden hair, is carved out of pale pink stone; pond lilies and reeds serve as background and frame. Purchase price, 1785 francs. Engraved signature on the back, *L. Zorra.* France, 1900. (l. 3 1/2 ins.)

A pendant with a similar cameo face was purchased from the same maker at the 1900 Exposition by the Kunstgewerbemuseum, Berlin (see *Werke um 1900,* catalogue of an exhibition, Berlin, 1966, fig. 8) which lists the cameo as being made of shell rather than stone. A further discrepancy of information about this otherwise little known master derives from Brinkmann's handwritten accessions entry: whereas all of the other purchases are designated as "Aus der Weltausstellung, Paris," this one is listed as "Aus dem Salon, Paris 1900"—a slip of the pen perhaps, but one that may turn out to be a clue to other works by this elusive master whose pieces are usually unsigned (see no. 61 this catalogue; and no. 183). (Figure 69)

132. *Tortoiseshell comb;* the top carved in an elaborate scrollwork design of studied elegance is intertwined with a bifurcating twig of mistletoe made out of gold with green enamelled leaves and pearl berries. The two elements support one-another in such a way that only a single stud on the back is needed to hold them together. Purchase price, 1900 francs. Signed, *Vever.* France, 1900. (l. 6 5/8) An almost identical comb was purchased at the same time by the Musée des Arts Décoratifs in Paris; consequently it is sometimes difficult to tell which of the two it is when they are reproduced as illustrations without the source listed. This one appears in *The Studio,* London, XXIII, p. 176; R. Barilli, *Art Nouveau,* London, N.Y., etc., 1969, Pl. 19; K. Dingelstedt, *Le Modern Style,* Paris, 1959, *L'Art Déco-*

*ratif,* Jan. 1901, ill. p. 141; *Dekorative Kunst,* XI, 1903, ill. p. 176; Kurt Dingelstedt, *Jugendstil in der angewandten Kunst,* Braunschweig, 1959, Dustjacket. (Plate 12)

133. *Horn comb* decorated with a free-form finial representing three gold water nymphs whose floating hair is executed in pale green-blue transparent enamel. The finial is detachable from the comb and has sockets on the back for attaching a bar pin (missing) so that it may be worn as a brooch. Price of purchase, 1900 francs. Signed, *Lalique.* France, before 1900. (l. 6 1/4)

Lalique worked at fever pitch for four years in order to furnish the rich display of his works assembled at the 1900 Exposition, many of them financed by private patrons. Not all of them, therefore, were made in 1900. The comb is more in accord with his 1898 style (see H. Vever, *Les Bijoux au Salon de 1898,* Librairie Centrale des Beaux Arts, Paris, 1898) in its carefree spirit; as the pressure of work increased, his subjects have a tendency to become more macabre. This comb appears in *Ankäufe,* 1900, p. 24; *Les Modes,* 6, 1901, ill. p. 12; Roger Marx, *La Décoration et les Industries d'Art de l'Exposition Universelle de Paris 1900,* Paris, 1902, plate opp. p. 79; *Deutsche Kunst u. Dekoration,* Oct. 1903, ill. p. 158; Scholz-Rogues, *Schmuck aus 5 Jahrtausenden,* Hamburg, 1960, ill. III; H. Seling, *Jugendstil,* ill. 317; Wallis, Mieczyslaw, Secesja, Warsaw, 1967, ill. 52 (Figure 70)

## XVIII. *FRENCH ART NOUVEAU*

Although England in the late XIX century was the pioneer in the decorative arts, there can be no doubt that French taste brought them to their pinnacle of perfection. Looking at the jewels around 1900 by Lalique, Gaillard, Vever and Fouquet can leave no doubt that theirs is one of the great moments in the history of jewelry. Enamelling, especially the transparent *plique à jour,* is the key to its breath-taking color schemes; yet a glance at the preceding plate showing English work of the same period with its brighter hues, makes one realize that the French impact is made in a more muted register through harmonies so subtle that they give the impression of a far wider color range than that actually employed. The refinements of French goldsmithery which sometimes, in mid-century, tended to obscure the designs, are still present; but the goldsmith's approach—essentially that of a sculptor of the miniature—is now modified, to its own great benefit, by two linear modes: the one from Japan, the other from England already touched by this wind from the east. Japanese subject matter and Japanese techniques were close enough to European ideals to make them readily acceptable in the west; their charm, however, lay in the perfection of execution, whether broad and seemingly spontaneous, or of unimaginably fine detail. After 1900 Gaillard (as Tiffany before him, around 1878) imported Japanese craftsmen and for a time the two streams of East and West become so intermingled that it is difficult to tell the works of Europeans under oriental influence from that of Japanese working for the western jewelry market.

134. *Wisteria brooch in gold,* with fresh water pearls and leaves of transparent enamel, ca. 1896–8. (3 x 5 3/16) The wisteria, along with other sinuous plants such as the water lily, became a sudden favorite at this moment; a relative newcomer to European gardens, its blossoms were also a favorite in Japanese painting and decoration. The desire for new kinds of lightness and mobility in jewelry (see also Figure 219) led several of the French jewelry designers to different versions of the swinging blossoms. Although this example has no master's mark or signature, it is similar to the comb and the brooch shown in the Appendix, Figure 174. (Figure 71)

135. *Silver mirror pendant,* Vve. Savard & Cie, before 1900. (1 7/8 x 2 1/4) This company received a prize at the 1900 Exposition for excellence in series production. A picture catalogue of their products, including this little piece, is preserved in the library of the Syndicat des Bijoutiers in Paris. Like the brooch above, it belongs to the early "soft-curve" phase of Art Nouveau design; this had its origin in Rococo ornament of the early XVIII century. The identification of women with flowers is nothing new, of course; but the portrayal of a female head actively engaged with the flowers in the composition makes their relationship more intimate than in earlier jewelry design "La femme-fleur" was a theme that pervaded all of the arts of the period: there were flower ballets; flower heroines in novels (one thinks of Fleur in *The Forsyte Saga,* or the title of one of Proust's novels, *À l'Ombre des jeunes filles en fleur*), and the famous beauties of the day (Liane de Pougy or Lily Langtry come to mind) chose flower pseudonyms. Even Picasso who was soon to shatter the human image with the hammer blow of Cubism was a child of that period and from time to time in later life he has produced a "femme-fleur" long after it had ceased to be a popular concept (see Françoise Gilot, *Life with Picasso,* 1964, p. 37). (Figure 71)

136. *Mistletoe brooch pendant.* Gold partially faced with platinum, set with diamonds and pearls, entwined by green transparent enamel leaves; after 1900. (2 x 1 7/8) The mistletoe, a symbol of good luck, was commonly presented as a New Year's gift (see also Catalogue number 196), and with its curling leaves and

waxy berries it lends itself naturally to Art Nouveau treatment (see also number 132). In this example, the soft curves of the early style have taken to sudden changes of direction resulting in a taut whiplash curve which is the most decisive feature of high Art Nouveau. Beginning as early as the XVIII century jewellers had begun to put facings of the "white" metals (silver, platinum, even aluminum) on the gold mountings for diamonds, since they present no contrast that might take away from the brilliance of the stones. It was not, however, until the early 1900's that they learned how to manipulate platinum as easily as silver, the favorite until then. From then on, platinum with its non-tarnishing properties replaced silver for such purposes, *La Revue des Arts Décoratifs,* XIII, pl. opp. p. 172, shows a brooch by Vever similar to this, but without the enamelled leaves. (Figure 71)

137. *Dragonfly bracelet,* green gold with opaque and transparent enamels, set with carved opals and zircons. Lalique, ca. 1902. (l. 8 1/2 x 1 5/8) The metal back of the bracelet is lightly worked in the same flower pod motifs as the enamels on the front, a refinement typical of Lalique's three-dimensional sculptor's approach to jewelry, even when—as in this case—the inspiration was probably as two-dimensional as a band of Japanese or Chinese embroidery. Although this elaborate bracelet continues an earlier predilection (see Catalogue number 130) for working entire panoramas into a space so small, one can sense here his groping for a new stylistic idiom to replace the vein of naturalism and, later, surrealism (the term, of course, had not yet been invented) of the great Exposition pieces (Appendix, Figures 160, 161, 165). As other works of the post-Exposition period indicate (see number 170), he experimented with abstract forms as well as with unusual subjects (number 138), without ever again achieving the single-minded vision of the works of 1900 (see Introduction). The dating of this piece is based on its similarity to the dog collar, Appendix, Figure 153, from *Deutsche Kunst u. Dekoration,* XIII, p. 157. (Figure 71)

138. *Wasp pendant/brooch;* gold, opaque enamel, multicolored stones and a kidney-shaped opal matrix. Lalique, ca. 1900. (2 1/2 x 1 7/8) A similar hat pin showing five wasps clambering over a fruit was part of Lalique's display in 1900. (see Vever, *La Bijouterie française au XIX siècle,* III, p. 727). It spawned what one might literally call a whole hive of stinging insects (see number 177) never before extensively found in the jeweler's repertory. Yet there is at least one strikingly similar ancestor for this brooch: a gold pendant dating from the Minoan

period of Crete, ca. 1700 B.C. (see Appendix 169) now in the museum at Heraklion, Crete. The French Archeological Institute in Athens had been active in Crete during the latter half the XIX century, though its major finds were made in the 1920's at the Mallia site, from which this piece comes. I have been unable to discover when this pendant was dug up, but it would be an almost incredible coincidence should Lalique have reinvented this curious subject without being aware of its ancient predecessor. In 1897 the Archeological Institute had a fiftieth anniversary celebration, and perhaps at that time there were illustrated articles about its finds, in which Lalique might have seen the pendant.

The back of the brooch, while not as elaborately worked as that of the preceding entry (see above), takes advantage of the counter-enamelling to bring out its resemblance to a fantastic mask. (Figure 71)

139. *Index finger ring,* 14 kt. gold set with opals and small diamonds, American, after 1905. Probably from a design by E. Colonna. (d. 7/8 x 2 1/8) This ring was included in the plate devoted to French Art Nouveau jewelry before I had seen the original design sheets left to the Newark, N. J. Public Library, among which (see Appendix, Figure 153) appears a clasp of similar, if more elegant design, by Colonna. One of the foremost designers employed by "La Maison de l'Art Nouveau" in Paris, Colonna was actually an American (see M. P. Eidelberg, "E. Colonna: an American in Paris," *The Connoisseur,* Dec., 1967, p. 261). When the Paris business closed in 1905, he apparently returned to the U.S.A. and settled in Newark which was a center of silver and jewelry manufacture. The ring, which is meant to be worn on the second joint of the index finger, is similar in detail to his other works (see numbers 122, 143, 144, 145); however it suffers from a curious stiffness which, along with the 14 kt. mark (which is standard in American gold jewelry) points to its post-Parisian place in his work.

Illustration in *Status,* March, 1966, p. 43. (Figure 71)

140. *Butterfly ring;* gold, vari-color enamel, and a pearl. French, ca. 1910. (d. 3/4 x 1 3/16) The insects confronted over a jewel (see above, no. 138) have reached the end of their naturalistic phase in this late example. Although the enamelling of the wings is still of the transparent technique used to such good effect in number 134 of this Figure, the exercise is in this instance a mere mechanical repetition, devoid of purpose: the colors appearing on the front are all applied to a couch of dark blue enamel which effectively blocks the light from shining through.

Like the late Colonna ring, above, this too seems to be a kind of dried up Art Nouveau. (Figure 71)

141. *Platinum pendant and chain,* set with diamonds, over a black enamel plaque. French or Swiss, ca. 1910. (11/16 x 1 1/4) Well before the outbreak of the First World War, which is usually cited as the blow that killed Art Nouveau, a reaction against its colorfulness and its curvaceous exuberance had begun. In the two rings discussed above, the petrification of the style has already started, and almost simultaneously this pendant shows the emergence of a "colorless" color scheme, and the increasing geometrization of forms presaged by Lalique's necklace, number 170, and the Viennese dog-collar, number 202. (Figure 71)

142. *"Egyptian" necklace* frontal in gold and platinum set with diamonds, emeralds, opal; with two confronted sphinxes carved in the round of opal, between them a chrysoprase scarab, *habillé* with diamond demarkations and an inset gold cartouche; an opal scarab, also mounted with diamonds, serves as drop. Wings of sphinxes in green and blue opaque enamel. Stamped twice with faun's head (import mark for platinum); the fitted box is stamped with the name of Auger, Paris, in the lid. French, ca. 1905–10. (3 x 3 1/2) A late but still well made piece in the art nouveau manner, it is far from certain that the retailer whose name is stamped in the lid of the box was the designer, let alone the maker.*

The import stamp (an owl in the case of all-gold jewelry) was employed by the French assay office for pieces coming into the country from countries which did not adhere to the same international standards of metal content (Germany, China, Russia, the United States). Since they appear quite frequently on "French" jewelry of the turn of the century, one comes to the conclusion that a great many French firms farmed their designs out for execution across the border in German workshops. (Figure 72)

143. *Floral pendant and chain;* a symmetrical fantasy flower amid strap-like foliage executed in red and green translucent enamel on gold; flower stamen, a pearl; two pearls in tandem, the lower one set in a matching enamelled "claw," form the drop. Elaborate chain of gold, the links interspersed at intervals with peacock feather design plaquettes with green or red enamel eye. S $\begin{smallmatrix} A \\ B \\ N \end{smallmatrix}$ hall mark, standing

---

* The firm, whose hallmark was a star within a square, is registered under the name of Alphonse Auger in 1889. On May 29, 1900, this entry is cancelled and a new one, using the same device on the mark, but with a change of initials, is entered for Georges Auger.

for "S. Bing, Art Nouveau." Design by E. Colonna; French, 1900. (2 x 4 3/8) As remarked under Catalogue number 139, it is difficult to know whether to designate Colonna as French, or American, when his style also shows the influence of Belgium and England. However execution must also be counted, and considering his success while he was in France, and his decline after he left one must give the anonymous Parisian craftsmen responsible for the perfect translation of his sketches into jewelry some of the credit as well. The design, in this case (the flower has more resemblance to a shell than to any botanical species), also has French Rococo antecedents.

Colonna's jewelry at the Paris Exposition, 1900 won favorable notice as being more "wearable" in daily life than some of the dazzling displays that outshone his at the moment. This was one of the pieces included in that group (illustrated in *Art et Décoration,* Sept., 1900). A sheet of his designs, including one for this piece, is reproduced in color in *L'Art Décoratif,* 1898–99, p. 183. (Figure 73)

144. *Insect composed of fresh-water pearls,* set against a formalized scroll motif of green enamel on gold; pearl drop. Stamped, Colonna; French, 1900. (1 7/8 x 2 9/16) A similar pendant, with an orchid instead of an insect, was in his display at the Paris Exposition, 1900 (see G. Meusnier, *La Joaillerie française en 1900,* Paris, n.d., Pl. XIX). Flowers made of these long splinter pearls, centered with a diamond, were common among the minor jewelry of the period; however it took a leap of the imagination to use them in this way. (Figure 74)

145. *A gold pendant of irregular contour;* the design, of curling leaves in relief against a background enamelled green, enfold a blister pearl; pearl drop. Colonna, French, ca. 1900. (1 1/8 x 2 7/16) Unmarked, but unmistakably of the same design series as the formalized peacock feather (Catalogue number 122), and of similar craftsmanship. The photograph of another pendant, half way between this and the peacock feather, is in the Colonna archive of the Newark, N.J., Public Library (Appendix, Figure 151). (Figure 75)

146. *Nude bust of a woman* with flowing hair surrounded by a garland of sparsely-leaved branches; executed in toned gold; the hair, having an orange glaze, is ornamented with small diamonds; the garland studded with pearls and two small diamonds. No hall mark; Falguières; French, 1900. (2 1/8 x 3 3/8) This brooch, with the title of "Fécondité," was exhibited in the Paris Exposition, 1900 (see G. Meusnier, Pl. IX, no. 4).

A master of uneven performance and strong imitative tendencies, Falguières'
display had at least two pieces that remain impressive, of which this is one (the
other illustrated in G. Meusnier, Pl. X, no. 2: "La Vague"). The bust is of careful
workmanship, though somewhat at variance in its rounded heaviness with the design
of the garland, which is inferior to it.

The reviewer for *La Revue de la Bijouterie, la Joaillerie, et l'Orfèvrerie,* II,
p. 75 ff., speaks of Falguières' entries in the Salon of 1901 as "disappointing"; therefore one may assume that the best of his works in 1900 represent a pinnacle that he
did not attain again. (Plate 8)


147. *Bracelet of four identical shield-shaped gold plaquettes;* the vertical axis
of each is marked by an attenuated oval opal from the top of which sprouts a cluster
of blue enamelled antennae; a small diamond accentuates the central peak of each
"shield"; the pierced interstices of the design are filled with light gray *plique à jour*
enamel. In its own fitted box, marked "E. Feuillâtre, Paris"; engraved *Feuillâtre,
15 Août 1918* in script. French, 1907. (l. 7 3/8 x 1 3/8)

The last line, above, serves as a needed warning to take a circumspect view
of internal documentation provided by signatures and dates appearing on pieces of
jewelry: pieces were not always signed or stamped at the time when they were
made, but only at the time of sale—in this case eleven years after the manufacture—
and when contrary documentation, or style, point unmistakably (see, e.g., under
number 157) to a different date, they must be heeded.

The bracelet is one of three by Feuillâtre illustrated in Vever (III, p. 763);
although the caption does not contain a date, it occurs in a series of text illustrations
all of the year 1907. It might be slightly earlier; cannot be later as the book was
published in 1908, and indeed, the design of the cover features a motif very much
akin to the bracelet's; both are ultimately traceable to the bronze and glass grille
(a succession of winged women whose outline assumes this pointed shield shape)
used by Lalique in his booth in the 1900 Paris Exposition.

Feuillâtre was Lalique's preferred enameller and executed most of the latter's
ambitious designs in that medium. He was Belgian by origin, and had worked independently and experimentally with enamels before moving to Paris (*Le Bijout
1900,* Brussels, 1965; p. 20). (Figure 76)


148. *Landscape pendant and chain* of gold with vari-colored *plique à jour*
enamel; pearl drop. Engraved, *Gges. Fouquet;* French, before 1900. (1 15/16 x
3 3/16) Second only to Lalique among French Art Nouveau jewellers, Fouquet's

fame rose sharply after 1901 when he had Alphonse Mucha, the noted designer of Sarah Bernhardt's billboard posters, create a complete shop for him, interior, exterior, and down to the last detail. The forms that his signature took follow the same course as Lalique's: before his fame was assured he used the form indicated above ("Gges.," being the abbreviation of "Georges"); afterward the pieces are marked simply "Fouquet." The signatures usually are engraved, either in script (early) or Art Nouveau lettering (late).

This landscape of twin trees whose roots and tops intertwine, breaking the smooth outline of the oval frame, is similar to another illustrated in "Modern Jewelry and Fans" (Special winter number of *The Studio,* London, 1901–2, Pl. II, Fig. B). In comparison to number 130 (Lalique) neither is especially distinguished in design, although this presumably earlier one is of a pleasing simplicity. (Figure 77)

149. *"Sarah Bernhardt" brooch;* a miniature painted on parchment of a woman—presumed to be the actress—is framed in a gold crescent incised with two concentric patterned bands of champlevé enamel which tilt away from the ridge where they meet so that the inner one forms a "shadow box" for the little picture. The rim is closely studded with beads of precious stones in a spectrum of red-blue-yellow in fanciful claw settings. The circle is "pierced" through its horizontal diameter by a dagger whose handle and point protrude at either side. From this fine chains are hung (two from the handle and two from the blade), each bearing a seemingly random assortment of semi-precious "pebbles," some plain and others encased in gold "cages" of varied designs. The design is by Alphonse Mucha, the execution by Fouquet. Engraved on back, *G. Fouquet,* in Art Nouveau lettering; French, 1900. (4 x 5 7/8)

This splendid "barbaric" brooch is almost, but not quite identical with the one that Fouquet had in the Paris Exposition, 1900 (see illustration in Vever, III, p. 625). Whereas this lady holds a quill in one of her hands resting on a tablet, the one in the Exposition piece holds a flower. The motif of a woman pausing momentarily in her writing was fairly standard at the time; it was used by Grasset in his "Encre L. Marquet" poster, 1892 (advertising ink); and by Mucha in his poster for "The West End Review," 1898. Evidently the act of writing (or the pause for inspiration) was, in those days considered to be a form of "communication." The style of draftsmanship is different also, this example being softer. There are other minuscule discrepancies between the two settings (most noticeable in the dagger handles); Jiri Mucha, son of the artist, reproduces our version (J. Mucha, *Alphonse Mucha,* Prague, 1966, p. 177), expressing no doubt as to its authenticity.

In my opinion the one here exhibited is the original since it is finer in details such as the dagger blade (here set with rose diamonds, but left plain in the other) as well as in the painting, which in its counterpart seems routine at best, and where the hand holding the flower is concerned, grossly misunderstood. The probability is that the owner—possibly the diva herself—did not want to part with it for the duration of the exhibition (Lalique's booth was a veritable "retrospective" of his work with many of the pieces borrowed back from their owners); therefore Fouquet made a duplicate of what was surely one of his most important pieces. (Plate 11)

150. *Lyre-shaped brooch* of gold, ivory, diamonds with a *plique à jour* enamel in red and green; emerald (?) bead and pearl in tandem form the drop. Engraved, G. Fouquet, in art nouveau lettering; French, 1900? The swan-necked lyre shape superimposed upon the enamelled rose-window harks back to the more forceful formulation of this same motif in Lalique's work (see number 160); and the ivory face with the flowing hair that continues, somewhat awkwardly, under the chin puts one in mind of number 157, though Lalique repeated it in more refined style in a large cameo-faced brooch which was also exhibited in 1898. I would guess that the brooch proper was executed in the course of 1899, with the two hanging beads (the one encircled with gold as are the pebble drops of no. 149) added just before the opening of the Paris Exposition in 1900. A pendant of mystifying similarity was included in Falguière's 1900 display. (Figure 78)

151. *Beetle ring* consisting of an oval turquoise cabochon set in "cage" of gold, enamelled green, which defines the insect shape. Stamped, *G. Fouquet;* French, after 1904. (d. 7/8 x 1 1/4) In 1904 Mucha (see under number 149) departed to work for Tiffany in New York. After that Charles Desrosiers, who was already designing for Fouquet by 1900 (Vever, III, p. 629; the bumble bee brooch, now in the Victoria & Albert Museum, is also illustrated in M. Amaya, *Art Nouveau,* paperback, London & New York, 1966, p. 113, bottom) under strong Mucha influence, developed a taut-lined, pointed style which is intimated in the early work; a fruit-shaped pendant, very similar to this ring in design (Musée des Arts Décoratifs, Paris), is dated 1910 (G. Hughes, *Modern Jewelry,* New York, 1968, Pl. 175, upper left). There seems to me a possibility that the choice of this stone with its black markings suggesting those of the insect's wings, may show the influence of Tiffany, whose pronounced liking for irregular or oddly marked stones had been evident since 1889 (see Introduction), and who often employed such turquoises himself (see R. Koch, *Artistic America, Art Nouveau, and Tiffany Glass,* Cam-

bridge, Mass., 1970, p. 165, Pl. 68). Another "Egyptian revival" in French jewelry at this time was attributed to influence coming from America, and Tiffany's scarabs may well have been the instigation. (Plate 14)

152. *Orchid brooch* consisting of a network of gold cloisons simulating the veins, filled with green and purple *plique à jour* enamel, studded with rose diamonds and centered with stamens and pistils of oriental and fresh-water pearls; the lower cupped petal is faced with an elaborately scrolled "cage" of green-enamelled gold, behind which is caught a large iridescent baroque pearl. Engraved. *G. Fouquet,* in Art Nouveau lettering; its fitted box bears the legend, "G. Fouquet, 6 Rue Royale, Paris." French, 1897-8. (3 3/8 x 4 1/4) Compared to other orchids of the period (see no. 184, Appendix, Figure 166. Wolfers also exhibited one in 1902, now in the Victoria & Albert Museum: G. Hughes, p. 105, fig. 177) this example—probably by Fouquet's designer G. Desrosiers—is surprisingly abstract and imaginative. The treatment of the "caged" pearl is almost a signature of this firm; however the use of the pearl slivers and the liberties taken with natural forms betray a certain familiarity with the work of E. Colonna. This brooch was exhibited in the Paris Salon of 1898 (*Revue des Arts Décoratifs,* 1898, XVIII; second unnumbered plate following p. 170). (Plate 16)

153. *Thistle necklet* consisting of two rigid semicircles with a spring-hinge at center back; the thistle-like composition is executed in gray-green opaque and *plique à jour* enamels for the leaves, and light translucent brown for the stems. Three clusters of buds are of closely set opals, and the edges of the leaves are picked out in brilliants. Engraved, *L. Gaillard;* French, ca. 1903-4. (d. 4 1/2, 3 x 3 1/2) Lucien Gaillard (b. 1861), who was a year younger than Lalique, had won acclaim as a silversmith at the Paris Exposition of 1889 (see number 98). He stuck to his last until after 1900, in which year he moved his workshop to larger quarters with more modern equipment at 107 Rue de la Boëtie (the fitted box of the necklet bears this address in the lid). It was at this time, too, that he imported Japanese artisans to satisfy the ambition which he had nursed since his youth of perfecting his Japanese techniques (see under number 58).

It was Lalique who persuaded this perfect craftsman to change over from silver work to jewelry; he won the first prize at the Salon, 1904, from which this handsome piece probably dates. The same reviewer who chided Lalique in that year (see under number 171) remarks that Gaillard has increasingly come to fill the place that Lalique seemed to be abdicating. Not unexpectedly the design, with its boldly veined leaves, some with curled edges (see Appendix, Figure 163) owes a great deal to Lalique's 1902 style. However, Gaillard had a special elegance not unlike that of Boucheron whose diamond necklet with pendant sycamore cluster of the mid '80's (Vever, III, p. 425) has a great deal in common with this piece. (Plate 13)

154. *Pendant opal* of roughly trapezoidal shape set in a gold frame embellished with clusters of gold blossoms and three leaves in green *plique à jour* enamel; pearl drop. Signed, *L. Gaillard,* in Art Nouveau lettering; French, ca. 1905–10. It is difficult to assign exact dates to Gaillard's work; his late start in the art of jewelry coupled with his discreet borrowing from older as well as contemporary colleagues often make his works seem slightly earlier than they in fact are; here the focusing of the design around a large flat opal, the very discreet touches of enamel, even the little blossom clusters, are akin to a pendant that Vever showed in 1901 (Vever, III, p. 684), while the general outlines of the piece are reminiscent of even earlier pendants (ca. 1898). Yet one wonders whether such a perfectionist as he would have allowed the slight irregularity of the stone to remain if a fashionable acceptance of nature's vagaries had not already taken place. The baroque pearl (see Numbers 92, 93) had been accepted for some time already; but it was Fouquet, I believe, with his "pebbles" (Number 149) and clever use of other irregular stones (number 151) who broadened their acceptance. A similar opal pendant of symmetrically shaped stone, by the firm of Louis Aucoe is illustrated *La Revue de la Bijouterie, etc.,* Oct., 1900. (Figure 79)

155. *Pendant showing an "Egyptian" head* in profile wearing a fanciful headdress of emeralds and diamonds with a serpent on the brow; her tresses, of green *plique à jour* enamel with heart-shaped opals, resemble peacock plumes. Attached by two chains to a slide of similar motif; diamond and pearl drop. Engraved, *L. Gautrait;* French, ca. 1900. (2 1/16 x 4 9/16) This minor master who, however, rarely missed an opportunity to sign anything that he made, apparently worked for various different firms. He is not listed as an independent manufacturer in the Paris Assay office registry, but worked as modeller and finisher for the firm of Gariod.

Another Egyptian profile, less elaborate than this, appears as a work of Gariod in Vever, *La Bijouterie française au XIX siècle* (III, P. 617); a brooch of identical design is in the Hessisches Landesmuseum's collection (see *Kunsthandwerk um 1900,* Darmstadt, 1965; jewelry section, no. 120). Vever (III, P. 618) admired his talent.

The Egyptian motif was, apparently, inspired by Sarah Bernhardt's "Cleopatra." (Figure 80)

156. *Dormouse pendant* of carved and tinted bone. Signed on the back, *Lachenal* and underneath that, *Selomko.* It is unclear which of them designed and which carved the piece. Nothing is known about Selomko. French, ca. 1905. (1 3/8 x 1 3/4) Edmond Lachenal is famous as a potter from 1880 until well into the XX century. His son, Raoul first exhibited his own works in 1904 (Catalogue, *Dr. Gerhard P. Woeckel, Jugendstilsammlung,* Munich, 1968; no. 123), and it is probably he, rather than his senior, who is responsible for this delightful pendant. Neither father nor son is listed in the registers of the Paris assay office, and so it may be assumed that small personal ornaments such as this were only incidental in their oeuvre. (Figure 81)

157. *Brooch with smiling woman's face* of gold embellished with touches of blue, green and pink enamel plus colorless glass *à jour,* and set with rose diamonds and small ruby cabochons. Engraved, *Lalique;* ca. 1894(?) (2 3/8 x 2 5/8) The signature in engraved letters accords with that of the other early piece (see next entry) in Lalique's oeuvre, and the other evidence also points overwhelmingly to a date around 1890.

By his own account he did not develop his passion for enamelling until after the move to his larger quarters on the Rue Thérèse, 1890. Before that his major source of income was the execution of diamond-set pieces for better known firms. "Between times (Vever, III, p. 708) his taste for color would lead him to try his hand at enamelling. He made some flowers and some butterflies charming in shape and color . . ." This piece with its symmetry, its pretty but far from exciting color scheme, and the butterfly motif is in tune with that description. But above all, the smiling woman's face with its wealth of curly golden hair is an ideal of feminine beauty which Sarah Bernhardt (and the artists who made her theater posters, costumes, and personal adornments—Lalique and Mucha among them) had rendered obsolete by 1895. (For another example of this type see Catalogue number 98.) The pert, laughing face which was the ideal of the early '90's was inspired by the posters of an older artist, Jules Cheret. (Figure 82)

158. *Gold enamelled necklace* made up of plaquettes in two designs alternating; enamelled on both sides in sage green and shaded yellow, and set with small brilliants. Engraved, *R. Lalique;* French, ca. 1892. (l. 39 1/2 x 1 3/8) The long

necklace with its Gothic quatrefoils and green-yellow tonality puts one in mind of the Aesthetic Movement's romantic medievalism (or at least Gilbert and Sullivan's lampoon, *Patience,* of the Movement with its "greenery-yallery, Grosvenor Gallery, foot-in-the-grave young man") in England during the 1870's and '80's. There is a certain perversity in expending so much patience and time on transforming the look of gold to that of old silver, and one may be allowed to speculate upon the possibility that some recollection left over from Lalique's sojourn in England (see Introduction) prompted it. Not that more immediate French inspiration should be discounted: a sheet of designs, published in 1891, as one of the prize winners in a competition of students of the School of Design maintained by L'Union Centrale des Arts Décoratifs (Appendix, Figure 183, upper left corner), also shows a spikey flower alternating with a Gothic trefoil, as well as other motifs that we shall encounter in Lalique's work.

He himself won a second prize in addition to an honorable mention in a cup design competition of the Union, in 1893 (both illustrated in *La Revue des Arts Décoratifs,* XIV, p. 167), and his relationship with the school at that time seems to have been close. The prize winner is a chalice composed of thistles and their foliage—a motif whose popularity may be attributed to Gallé, who used it often; the honorable mention, a cup with handle, is in a totally different mode, seemingly derived from Flemish ornament of the XVII century;* both styles are present in his early jewelry (Vever, III, p. 700 right side, and p. 701 upper, the latter related to our necklace).

Thus, right from the start, Lalique had a "tense" style and a "relaxed" style, the former more in evidence during the early years ca. 1893–98, the latter predominating after 1900. During the period between, when the intensive preparation for his Exposition pieces was going on, the two coalesced.

The engraved signature, *R. Lalique,* indicates the modesty of a beginner. (The same succession occurs when he began his career as a glass maker after 1904.) Evidently the piece was made before his self-assurance presumed that "Lalique" would convey instant recognition. An interim stage (numbers 157, 158) has the signature engraved, but already in the block letters used in the stamped signatures which follow. (The Q's in the engraved version seem to have two tails instead of the one tail common in his stamped signature.)

The muted charm of this necklace is still far from possessing the appeal, or the power to amaze, of his later work. The fact that it found its client and is today

* See *L'Argenterie des Pays Bas, XVII-XVIII Siècles,* Paris, Institut Néerlandais, 1962: pp. 28, 30, 31, all made in Utrecht in the second quarter of the XVII century.

in the Metropolitan Museum is due to the appreciation of another jeweller, Edward C. Moore, for many years chief designer of Tiffany & Co., and later director of its Paris branch; his son gave it to the museum in 1924. (Figure 83)

159. *Rooster brooch* of gold with black, white, and green opaque enamelling. Stamped, *Lalique*. France, ca. 1893-4. (3 x 2 1/4) The reader will recognize this pecking rooster with the flourishing tail as another of the designs on the sheet of Appendix Figure 183 (left side, second from the bottom). This, along with the unspectacular enamelling, serve to date the piece in the early '90's. The freedom of the modelling, however, and the abandoning of the closed outline of the kind found in the two pieces already discussed, gives ample promise of his coming style. (Figure 84)

160. *Brooch of woman's face in profile,* gold with dark blue enamel and rose diamonds. Stamped, *Lalique;* French, ca. 1895-6. (1 3/4 x 1 7/8) This design bears an inverse relationship to one that was exhibited in the Salon of 1898 (Illustration, Vever, III, p. 712), which turns the outline formed by face and hair (minus the daisy halo) upside down, and within the arbitrary shape thus obtained, inscribes a different profile. Less stylized than the 1898 version, this one would therefore be slightly earlier.

The "Swooning Woman" (see Introduction, under Cameos) of pre-Raphaelite ancestry (Appendix, Figure 144) here makes her Art Nouveau debut; the model for this tiny portrait was one of Lalique's circle (Appendix, Figure 158). (Figure 85)

161. *Gold pendant and chain of tall pyramidal shape,* depicting a floating swan enamelled in opaque blue-white, on a rippled pond showing the swan's reflection (also white); the water shades from opaque ultramarine to transparent grey-blue at the top of the pendant, and is dotted with gold lily pads. The hanger at the top is in the shape of another swan's head. Stamped, *Lalique;* French, 1897. (1 11/16 x 2 3/8) A similar shield-shaped pendant containing two swans, with two swans' heads at the top was exhibited in 1898; the partial return to a stricter delineation of the edges of his designs is accompanied in the year or two before 1898 by the full mastery of the enamelling techniques which had preoccupied him for more than five years. Although Lalique seldom labored for ultimate refinement and finish, as did the professional enamellers such as Tourrette (who worked for the Vever firm), he had developed a superior sense for contrasts of color and surface which often

makes his work in the medium more striking than theirs. In Appendix, Figure 183, lower right, we already find the floating swan motif presented in Art Nouveau terms; Appendix, Figure 145 shows that both swans and the woman with flowing hair were current in the artistic vocabulary by 1893; Appendix, Figure 143 demonstrates the latter's source. Although Lalique's version is more solid, and the water more static, we encounter in this piece for the first time his bird's head (see also Appendix, Figure 162), a phantasmagoria, which was to play so effective a part in the jewels that he designed for the Paris Exposition of 1900. The imagination that could transform a routine drawing from nature (Appendix, Figure 159) into a surrealistic fantasy (Appendix, Figure 162) may, without exaggeration, be called genius. (Figure 86)

162. *Ivory brooch* consisting of a lozenge-shaped carved ivory plaquette depicting the upper part of a nude with blowing hair. The gold frame, enamelled in various shades of brown, simulates the twigs of the oak; at the four corners sprout clusters of oak leaves and acorns. Stamped, *Lalique;* French, ca. 1899. (3 3/4 x 2 3/4) After 1898 Lalique's outlines of frames tend to loosen up again—indeed, to become rather fussy in small pieces such as this,—and his colors which had had a tendency to remain on the cool side, now become warmer, the contrasts more delicate.

The plaquette, which seems to be hand carved with stunning subtlety, is an example of a process that he originated. His first exhibit at the Palais de l'Industrie in 1894 caused a sensation among other jewellers because of it. Since the XVIII century various refinements of the pantograph had led to machines which could enlarge or reduce any design fed into them; beginning with silhouettes and ending with sculpture (the Parian ware figurines illustrating our Introduction were copied from the full scale statues by this method). In the XIX century every central mint had such a reduction tower for making coins and medals. Nobody had thought of applying the process to other materials as well, until Lalique was successful with these small ivory reliefs. Once the secret was out, every other jeweller rushed to the single workshop in Paris that owned a reduction tower: they were booked for months ahead. (Vever, III, p. 718–19). Once Lalique, who was a competent sculptor himself and who married into a family of sculptors who sometimes assisted him (Appendix, Figure 157), had made the model he would have several copies of it "reduced" at the same time; thus one sometimes finds two or three examples of the same composition still extant, although they usually received different settings. This was as close as Lalique came to the mass production of jewelry until he turned to the manufacture of glass after 1904. (Figure 87)

163. *Purse with frame of gold* depicting a hunt scene in low relief. Engraved, *Lalique;* French, ca. 1895(?). (7 x 9) The upper line of the frame with its bowed center ending in upturned corners was popular not only for purse mountings (to which the shape is well adapted) in the last years of the XIX century; Lalique also used it for a tortoiseshell comb of Japanese effect exhibited in 1898 (Vever, III, p. 713). The relief is the product of the same process described in the preceding entry; the reverse sides are also nicely finished. That sporting jewelry and accessories changed probably less than adornment of any other category during the second half of the XIX century may be verified by comparing this hunting scene with the watch chain of about 1850 to which it is still related. (Figure 88)

164. *Pendant of keyhole shape,* in gold with opaque and translucent enamels in grey, black, and orange. Stamped, *Lalique;* French, ca. 1900. The fitted box in which it came, covered with leather that match the orange tones in the enamel, and stamped with sycamore leaves such as appear in the pendant. (1 1/8 x 3 15/16) Another example of the same piece in the Kunstgewerbemuseum, Berlin, was acquired in 1901 (catalogue, *Werke um 1900,* Berlin, 1966). Whether it originated the year before or the year after the Exposition, it certainly represents Lalique's "Exposition style." Glancing back to the ivory brooch of a year or two earlier (number 162) one finds that its almost saccharine sweetness has here turned into something far more challenging—the head of the woman, heavy-featured, assertive, and somewhat unkempt, is what would in French be called *une jolie laide.*

This paradoxical combination of attraction and repulsion is the quintessence of Lalique's greatest show pieces (see Appendix, Figures 156, 160, 161, 162 and catalogue number 165) and this small piece catches an echo of their fascination. (Plate 15 and Figure 89)

165. *Gold necklace* of nine plaquettes alternating with nine large round cabochon opals; each of the identically designed plaquettes represents a standing female nude, whose legs metamorphose below the knee into insect's legs merging with the scarab-like base which is centered with an oval amethyst cabochon. A crescent on top of her head is enamelled black and fuses with the black locks of hair which curl out symmetrically on either side, forming apertures through which the links connecting the plaquettes to the gold opal mountings pass. The arms of the figure turn imperceptibly into the outlines of wings which, in their sudden outcurving toward the base, shelter a pair of confronted swans, executed in black enamel, which also give the effect of wing markings. The interstices of the design are filled

with blue-grey *plique à jour* enamel. The luxuriant fronds of the opals' gold frames are gathered at the top to a rhomboidal element, which holds the links connecting with the neighboring two figured plaquettes; each is set with an amethyst cabochon having a rectangular base. Stamped, *Lalique;* French, 1900.

This huge necklace is one of the bravura pieces that Lalique made especially for his display at the Paris Exposition, 1900. It may be discerned as one of the two necklaces on stands, toward the left side of the photograph of Lalique's booth reproduced by Vever (III, p. 735), where the large round opals and the black splotches made by the swans form an immediately recognizable pattern.

The precursor of the plaquette figures is his spectacular dragonfly woman corsage ornament (Appendix 160) which is far more realistic in detail. An intermediate stage of abstraction in this series of insect-winged figures is represented by a bracelet of four linked plaquettes similar to those of this necklace, but without the swans (*Art et Décoration,* V, 1899, p. 13 ff.). Earlier than any of these, presented along with his legendary bracelet of horn and silver, were two combs topped with winged female figures (one a butterfly with wings enamelled blue and brown; the other a dragonfly with *plique à jour* wings). These were both in the Salon of 1896 (descriptions in the review appearing in *Art et Décoration,* I, 1897, p. 68 ff.). Eventually the trail leads us back to number 157 in this exhibition, and by that we can measure just how far Lalique had developed in a few years, both as artist and as artisan. (Plate 20)

166. *Gold ring* consisting of a tiny relief of aquatic figures which continues around the entire circle. Stamped, (?) *Lalique;* France, 1900. (d. 1 x 1) Amid all of the polychrome marvels of his 1900 exhibit, Lalique included some pieces made out of plain gold (see Vever, III, p. 726 for a pendant); these allow an undistracted appreciation of his ability as a sculptor.

That he thought of them—even on this tiny scale—as sculpture rather than jewelry in the conventional sense, is made clear by their lack of the usual finishing techniques employed by goldsmiths. The forms and composition are not so much suited to wearing as to the pleasure of the eye; they could be enlarged many times over without seeming incongruous. Lalique's ambition (see Introduction) to have his jewelry accepted as art and not mere ornament is nowhere made so clear as in the group of sculptures in gold. (Figure 90)

167. *Gold watch case* enamelled in matte colors of tawny orange, grey, and pale green. Lalique; French, 1900–01. (2 3/16 x 3) The recurvature of the carnation

petals left in plain gold is in appropriate contrast to the tawny shade of the flower. In 1901–2 (see "Modern Design in Jewellery and Fans," special winter number of *The Studio,* London, 1902, Pl. 5, 6.) Lalique exhibited a group of carved combs ornamented with wilting flowers or foliage, whose curled edges present them in unfamiliar shapes. The watch cover carnation may be placed at the beginning of this series. (Figure 91)

168. *Opal ring* of scrolled bands terminating at the front in two serpents' heads confronted; between their open jaws an opal is supported. Gold with dark blue opaque enamel; translucent light blue and yellow enamel. Stamped, *Lalique;* French, 1900. (d. 15/16 x 1 7/16) A miniature variation on the theme of the great nine-headed knot of snakes which was the centerpiece of Lalique's vitrine at the Paris Exposition, 1900. Since it does not seem to have been reproduced in any of the illustrated journals of the period, one must infer that it was on public display from the existence of a similar, though very crude ring (wrongly labelled "U.S.A.(?), ca. 1890") in the Hessisches Landesmuseum, Darmstadt (catalogue, *Kunsthandwerk um 1900,* Darmstadt, 1965; no. 195 in jewelry section). It is reputed to have belonged to the French designer, Louis Majorelle. (Plate 17)

169. *Pendant of a nude framed in willow boughs;* frosted and ivory toned shield shaped plaquette of glass, depicting a standing nude holding on to two willow boughs. The pendant is completed by a framework of four gold willow boughs, enamelled blue-green, two of which pass behind the plaquette, the other two in front. Opal drop. Engraved, *Lalique;* France, ca. 1902. (1 7/8 x 2 3/4) The "fussy" style (see number 162) which probably served both as a relief from the large works undertaken for the 1900 Exposition, as well as finding favor with such clients as were not ready to accept his more bizarre designs, had a sequel in the post-Exposition period (cf. an ivory nude within a trailing wistaria frame; Vever, III, p. 739).

Although Lalique was accustomed to using glass for cups, vases, fitted bowls, in conjunction with metal and enamelled mountings throughout the 1890's, it was only after 1902 that glass came increasingly into use in his jewelry. The simulation of ivory, as well as the garland enclosure place this pendant very early in the glass jewelry sequence. (Figure 92)

170. *Necklace consisting of eleven identical geometric motifs* connected by links. The complex, interpenetrating, spikey rhomboids are of gold, enamelled sage green, each set with a light and a dark facetted topaz (the larger, oval; the smaller,

round). The edges were, in part, originally set with rose diamonds (missing). Stamped, *Lalique;* French, early 1900's(?) (l. 19 1/2 x 1 5/8) This baffling piece has much in common with necklace no. 158. The rather mournful green-yellow color scheme, with tiny diamonds serving to lift it out of drabness; the "perversity" of covering the bright gold so completely; and the stiffness of the shapes would seem to point to a date in the early 1890's. However, the facetted stones are of the same kind used in the bracelet, number 137; and the forms owe nothing to any previous historic style, but are of a new, purely geometric and abstract kind hitherto absent from Lalique's work. For the latter reasons I believe it to be a work roughly similar in date to the "crozier" comb finial, number 137, which also exhibits some of the same recapitulations of his early style, but with telltale modifications. (Figure 93)

171. *Double-faced brooch;* the front, a carnation of pinkish opaline moulded glass, framed by its own greenery of gold enamelled pale green bracketing two oval opals (see number 167). It is attached to a background which, when the piece is turned over (as apparently it was never meant to be when worn), is fully as elaborate: a hydrangea blossom of bluish opaline glass, in the *plique à jour* technique, atop of two matching gold leaves which are glazed on the reverse to harmonize with the carnation's coloration. Stamped, *Lalique;* French, ca. 1903-4. (2 9/16 x 2 1/4) This insanely complicated piece of work represents but one aspect of Lalique's total dedication, in this period of transition from jewelry to glass, to the exploration of glass as a jeweller's material (see numbers 169, 172, 56). The reviewer for *La Revue de la Bijouterie, la Joallerie, et l'Orfèvrerie* (V, 1904) says of Lalique's display in the Salon, "In his small display M. Lalique seems to be about to conquer woman all over again—by bludgeoning her into submission." Doubts concerning the wearability of Lalique's jewelry had been freely expressed already in 1900, centered about the over-sized display pieces which he had made, as such, for the Exposition. By now there is a certain justice in such criticism; astounding in its technical virtuosity, and beautiful from any point of view, this brooch is nevertheless poorly designed for wearability; the slightly convex surface of the hydrangea interferes with the pin, while the massive carnation on the front would tip the brooch forward when worn. At first one wonders whether it could have been intended for the stopper of a perfume flacon, only altered for wear at some later time. However it is not exactly suited to such a purpose either, and one can only conclude that its maker was primarily interested in the making, not in the practical purpose. (Figures 94, 95)

172. *Lilac pendant and chain;* a triangular glass plaquette with outcurving

edges set into a twig-like frame of gold enamelled pale blue-green, embellished with baguette diamonds at the three corners and a pear-shaped diamond drop. Matching enamelled chain. Stamped, *Lalique;* French, ca. 1905. (2 13/16 x 2 13/16) Lalique's impassioned experiments (see under number 171) in glass for use in jewelry yielded one form which proved to be wearable, adaptable, and so successful that it continued in moulded versions of various shapes long after Lalique had shifted the emphasis of his business to mass-produced glassware. This was the intaglio on glass (see also, number 174, a later, simplified example). In this pendant he has come to an entirely successful solution of the problem that preoccupied him in number 171: how to make both sides of the piece equally interesting. The exquisite lilac blossom is partly carved into the back of the plaquette and completed in raised opaline glass on the front (for a slightly earlier, heavier stage in this evolution see Vever, III, p. 740). Always delighting in the juxtaposition of unexpected materials, one may deduce his satisfaction with this plaquette (which, after all, is only a piece of glass), from the fact that he saw fit to accent it with the finest of diamonds.

As to the source of the "inflated triangle" which, along with the crystal heart, he was to use over and over again, I would like to suggest that both may have stuck in his memory (unconsciously attuned, perhaps, to things made of glass) after a perusal of Rossetti's paintings (see also under number 57). Two early watercolors, "Fra Pace" (Appendix, Figure 139) and the first version of "Dante's Dream" contain little stained glass windows of this shape. Rossetti himself must have owned a carved crystal heart, for it, along with a swirl-shaped brooch, appears in several of his pictures. A crystal pendant carved with a Cupid appears suspended from the trellis background in the later version of "Regina Cordium" (Appendix, Figure 140). (Plate 18)

173. *Pendant of purple glass thistles* held against a copper back by a setting of green-enamelled gold. Stamped, *Lalique;* ca. 1905-10. (3 3/4 x 1 3/8) Final stage of the moulded glass plaquette before it dispenses entirely with its jeweller's setting (see number 112). Though already geared to a minimum of hand work, the glimmer of the polished metal back through the glass of varying thickness lends the composition great visual interest. It exploits the same refractive principle first used by L. C. Tiffany in his stained glass windows, much praised by critics in Europe during the 1890's. Instead of shading by the gradation of pigments, Tiffany accidentally discovered that a more subtle effect could be achieved by varying the thickness of glass of a uniform tint. (Figure 96)

174. *Brooch of carved glass,* triangular in shape, set in a green-enamelled frame simulating a ribbon with bowknots at the corners; large pendant pearl. Signed, *Lalique*; ca. 1906. Half way between the complexities of the "Lilac" pendant (number 172) and the first successfully mass produced moulded pendants (number 175, number 112), the little figures in this one are still carved by hand; but as the desire to experiment with innovations in glass (still strong in numbers 169, 171, and 172) decreased, Lalique's feeling for the purity of the crystalline material sets him at odds with their mountings. He experiments with frames of ever-diminishing complexity, and with gems of ever-rising value (Vever, III, p. 760), as the only suitable companions for the etherial substance. (Figure 97)

175. *Elongated heart-shaped pendant* of glass with a flying figure moulded into the under side, and beading around the rim. *R. Lalique,* in block letters, is engraved with a pointed tool on the top right-hand edge. French, ca. 1908. (Modern cord and tassel). According to Gustave Geffroy ("René Lalique," in series *L'Art Décoratif Moderne,* Paris, 1922, p. 39), "An entire section of Lalique's work as a glass maker, and at its inception the most important part, consists of transparent surfaces whose blank purity is hollowed by light modelling." This design, along with a Cupid in a more conventional heart shape, is illustrated to demonstrate the technique.

It is interesting to note that the beading of the gold, 1860's setting of Appendix, Figure 182 is echoed here still in the beaded edging of the glass. (Figure 98)

176. *Flower ring,* consisting of a fresh water pearl growing out of a scrolled and looped gold shank set with brilliants, simulating the stem; flanked with leaves of green *plique à jour* enamel. Owl hallmark, but otherwise unmarked. Le Turcq; French; 1900. (d. 3/4 x 1 3/8) The attribution is certified by the inclusion of this ring among five by this jeweller in Vever (III, p. 647). However, it should be noted that another ring, closely related to the one reproduced at the extreme left of the same plate, was acquired in 1901 from a source listed as "Beaudouin," Paris; it is in the Schmuckmuseum, Pforzheim (*Goldschmiedekunst des Jugendstils,* Pforzheim, 1963; Pl. IV, no. 5). (Figure 99)

177. *Bee Brooch* of gold, pearls and opaque and translucent enamels. Two confronted bees alighting on a wistaria frond. Signed, *Liénard;* French, 1905 or later. (3 5/8 x 4 5/8) A brooch of similar design with flowers in place of the bees, exhibited in 1908: Vever, III, p. 771.

A Fortuné Liénard, 23 Blvd. Beaumarchais, registered in the Paris assay office in 1901. However, this brooch is by Paul Liénard, who only registered in 1905, 7 Rue Joubert. His hallmark shows a maple leaf with the initials PL. Vever illustrates an earlier brooch, dated 1903. It was not at all unusual for jewellers to defer registration at the assay office (cf. under number 183) until reminded that it was required. Nevertheless, Paul Liénard does not seem to have been active under his own name until after the Paris Exposition, 1900. The cascade of spherical baroque pearls (as against the long fresh-water pearls preferred until 1900 for massed effects such as no. 134) is probably inspired by the pendants coming out of the snakes' mouths in Lalique's great stomacher in the Exposition. (Plate 21)

178. *Circular pendant* of gold showing a woman in profile wearing a fantastic diamond-studded tiara from which a trailing peacock feather sweeps backward. Background a gold grille set with small diamonds at every intersection, and backed by dark blue *plique à jour* enamel, which is also the medium in which the gray-green and blue peacock feather is executed. Stamped (letters in relief), *Masriera H⁸-;* Barcelona, ca. 1900. (1 3/8 x 3 3/16) Son of a painter-goldsmith, Luis Masriera and his brother inherited the family jewelry concern which had made traditional Spanish ornaments. After seeing the display at the Paris Exposition in 1900, so the story goes, Luis came home, closed the store, melted down the entire stock, and after six months reopened the business with his own Art Nouveau designs: he was sold out within a week! (A. Cirici Pellicer, *El Arte Modernista Catalan,* Barcelona, 1951, p. 293 ff.).

This pendant with its allusions to things that Masriera must have seen in Paris (see similarity, e.g., to number 160 and number 155) nevertheless has a pleasing severity about it which differentiates it from French Art Nouveau jewelry, although the workmanship—including the enamelling which he is said to have learned by himself through trial and error—is in the finest tradition. (Figure 100)

179. *Gold brooch with a pearl;* within a circle, enamelled black, sits a gold fairy, shown in profile, holding a pearl. Her wings and the border of her dress are enamelled in various shades of blue to gray in the *plique à jour* technique, although some of the cells are filled with opaque enamel where the wing markings make it appropriate. Unmarked, but from a design of ca. 1900 by Luis Masriera. Spanish. (1 9/16 x 2 3/4) The Masriera firm was in business until quite recently, but continued to use Luis' Art Nouveau designs. The later pieces, such as this, are less carefully made than number 178 (a comparison of the reverses also shows an economizing of gold), but a comparison of the fairy to two similar creatures in a design

sheet by Masriera (A. Cirici Pellicer, Color plate opposite p. 296) testifies to the faithfulness with which his designs were propagated. (Figure 101)

180. *Grotesque winged mask of gold,* with diamond eyes, holding a ruby (?) in its mouth. The wings are of green-gray *plique à jour* enamel. Diamond and pear-shaped ruby (?) drop in tandem. Hallmark with a sitting cat; Plissen & Hartz; Paris, ca. 1900. (2 x 2 1/16) A traditional design except for the style of the enamel work. Such masks—animal and quasi-human—have a history going gack to antiquity. Alone, or as part of a larger composition, they flourished throughout the XIX century, and adapted themselves well to Art Nouveau.

The great pendant by Froment-Meurice (Appendix, Figure 181), which was part of a retrospective exhibit of French goldsmith work at the 1900 Exposition, was a sort of design compendium from which lesser jewellers "minded" motifs. It too contains a grotesque mask. (Figure 102)

181. *Dragonfly pendant.* Silver, gold, and enamel pendant in the shape of a trilium leaf with a dragonfly perched on it. Monogrammed on the counter-enamel; *Fernand Thesmar,* French ca. 1900. (2 1/8 x 3 3/8) Along with Tourrette and Feuillâtre (see number 151), Thesmar was one of the great enamellers of the end of the century, beginning ca. 1880 to produce small bowls of the most exquisite *plique à jour* enamel. (Appendix, Figure 154) It is therefore surprising that in the occasional pieces of jewelry that he designed himself, he avoided the technique which he had pioneered for other jewellers, and preferred somber colors such as these. The pendant is not without its technical curiosities, however, being made on a silver base with gold cloisons; enamelling on silver presents some difficulties which gold and copper do not, having to do with the greater expansion of the metal during the firing, and consequent tendency of the enamels to crack when cooling. Feuillâtre (number 147) also experimented in this medium. (Figure 103)

182. *Gold peacock pendant,* set with diamonds, emeralds and opals, and enamelled in green and gray *plique à jour;* pearl drop. Has its own fitted box with a dedication to another jeweller's firm printed in the lid: "A$^{we}$ M$^{on}$. Marret & Baugrand, Vever, 19 Rue de la Paix, Paris. Grand Prix, Exp$^{on}$ Univ$^{le}$, Paris 1889." The piece is stamped with the eagle's head, and engraved, *Vever,* with the serial number 28. French, ca. 1900. (2 5/8 x 2 3/4) The date on the lid is an allusion to the Exposition in which the Vever firm established its prominence and has nothing to do with the date of the pendant.

It is not one of the firm's masterpieces, and it exists in a line-for-line simulacrum, signed on the front *L. Gautrait* now in the Pforzheim Schmuckmuseum (see *Goldschmiedekunst des Jugendstils* etc., Pforzheim, 1963; Pl. XIII, left), which, however, acquired the piece from the firm of Vever in 1900—whether by purchase or by gift it does not tell. Possibly Vever had a whole series of these made by Gautrait (see under number 155) for souvenir presentations in 1900. (Figure 104)

183. *Gold pendant with pearl drop,* representing a water nymph whose head and shoulders rise out of a pond with blue enamelled ripples and a green lily pad. L. Zorra; Paris, 1900. (2 3/8 x 4) The greatest reward that the organizer of an exhibition can have is to identify additional works by a relatively unknown master. There is no mention, as far as I know, of L. Zorra in the literature on the jewelry of Paris ca. 1900. Yet the director of the Museum f. Kunst u. Gewerbe in Hamburg, as well as the Berlin Kunstgewerbemuseum purchased pieces from him, either at the Exposition (though no mention is made of him as an exhibitor in the roster), or as J. Brinkmann implies in accession notes (number 131), at the Salon.

By extension this piece, which is identical with the Hamburg nymph except for the face, finely wrought in gold instead of carved stone (or shell), may unhesitatingly be attributed to Zorra, although it lacks any identifying marks.

In addition, the comb, number 61, bears such marked resemblance in facial type as well as finish to this pendant that an attribution to Zorra may be ventured.

He did not register in the Paris assay office until 1901, i.e., after the German purchases had been made, and after the close of the Exposition. At that time his address was 30 Rue Volta, then as now a street of small jewelry manufacturers. His hallmark, as described in the registry, was "A Roman eagle surrounded by a wreath" with the initials L.Z. (the L. stands for Louis). The hallmark insignia sometimes give clues to the identity or the specialty of the master, and though it is risky, one may cautiously accept the clue given by the Roman eagle in combination with the un-French name as pointing to his possibly Italian origin. (Figure 105)

184. *Orchid brooch* with three petals of lavender-mottled white enamel on gold, the other three and the stem of silver-faced gold, paved with diamonds interspersed with an occasional amethyst (?). French, ca. 1890. (1 7/8 x 2 3/8) The rise of the orchid as a jewelry motif in the '90's is remarked by Joan Evans ("Jewels of the Renaissance," *Notice of the Proceedings etc. of The Royal Institution of Great Britain,* XXIV, 1923–25, p. 178) and already documented in the report by P. Bourde on the jewelry display at the Paris Exposition of 1889 (*L'Exposition de Paris,*

2 vols. of the weekly newspaper of the exposition; I, p. 214 ff.), who moreover points out the displacement of "bijouterie" by the rise in favor of the smaller sort of "joaillerie" in consequence of the drop in diamond prices, a trend which he says had already been lamented in Martial Bernard's report on the Exposition of 1878 in Paris. He also takes cognizance of the influence of Japanese art on the crafts in France, opining that it had already crested and was on the decline (a wrong guess, as the study of Figures 60 and 61 in this catalogue proves).

Although a little stiffer, and minus the fanciful labradorite mask which appears in the center of a fine enamelled orchid, ca. 1900, by the Paris firm of Vever (reproduced in color in *Le Bijou 1900,* Brussels, 1965, p. 52, Pl. 9, cat. no. 82), the basic design, as well as the exquisite quality of the enamelling, make it likely that both were designed and executed by the same hand, though our piece has no hallmarks or other signature to bear out the conjecture. It may be, therefore, that the brooch was made by the firm of Vever shortly before 1889, for it was only in the Exposition of that year that the house, having won the grand prize for jewelry, became prominent. Another possibility is that both orchids were made by one of the enamellers who worked for the various large firms, the earlier example having been done independently of Vever for a private client. One would like to hazard an attribution to Tourrette, the favorite enameller of the Vever firm (see *Revue de la Bijouterie, la Joaillerie, et l'Orfèvrerie,* I, p. 141 ff.) who also maintained his own workshop; the examples of his work that I have seen have a greater depth of luminosity, which is no proof that Tourette was incapable of working in the manner that the two orchids have in common. (Figure 106)

185. *Dragonfly of horn,* gold, two rubies, four emeralds, small diamonds, and many-colored enamels: opaque, *plique à jour,* and in a technique for which there is no special name whereby the enamel is built up to resemble a cabochon jewel. No marks; French, ca. 1900. (5 1/8 x 2 5/8) The dragonfly with its shimmering wings, along with the butterfly, has been a challenge to jewellers as far back as the XVII century (see E. Steingräber, *Antique Jewellery,* London, 1957, p. 118, fig. 194). In the late 1860's insects became a craze (M. Flower, p. 33-34), and they continued as subjects for the small diamond-set pieces so popular in the late '70's and '80's. The development of the *plique à jour* enamel in light colors during the '90's gave jewellers, for the first time, a medium that could hope to rival the gossamer of wings. Then, after Lalique had exhibited his horn bracelet in 1896 (see under number 166) another shimmering substance was available, though color had to be added to it in one way or another. Later, opals joined the parade of materials.

The maker of this exquisite dragonfly (and probably of the similar butterfly illustrated in M. Flower, p. 233, fig. 111a) is unknown; however I should like to hazard a guess.

In *La Bijouterie française au XIXᵉ siècle* (III, p. 636 ff.) Vever describes Lucien Gaillard's passionate research into Japanese metal and lacquer techniques, which led him—still dissatisfied with his own experiments—to import Japanese artisans after 1900. We know little about the jewelry that he made before 1902 (see under number 153), but a grasshopper done in the Japanese "chakudo" technique, which had the look of real opal, "made of horn, gold, and enamelled in opalescent enamels in several layers" (*Revue de la Bijouterie, la Joaillerie, et l'Orfèvrerie*, IV, 1903, pp. 36-8) sounds very much like the glorious offspring of our dragonfly. (Plate 19)

186. *Siren brooch,* a large baroque pearl of roughly triangular shaped is "set" in the foliage of a gold iris; the flower appears at the top, and next to it the upper part of a tiny gold siren (completed on the back of the brooch); a pearl drop, set in a collet of platinum with small diamonds depends. No identifying marks; French, 1900. (1 3/8 x 2 1/2) The configuration of the lifted arm and the modelling of the figure are related to the works of a Paris firm, Haas Neveux & Cie. (G. Meusnier, Pl. XXIV). (Figure 107)

187. *Gold pendant* representing a woman with hands raised toward a water lily blossom; she has the wings of a dragonfly folded at her sides, and stands upon two lily pads. She is surrounded by the twining stems of the lilies and bullrushes. Translucent enamels in shaded greens and browns; opaque white and pink enamel for the blooms. Amethyst drop mounted in a gold "cage," No marks; French, ca. 1900. (1 7/16 x 3 5/16) The figure is vaguely related to similar winged creatures by Lalique, but is of less fine design and workmanship. It also differs from Lalique's habitual design for such standing nudes in that it has arms as well as wings; one of Lalique's first exhibits, a corsage ornament, 1895, provoked a small scandal because it featured a nude, lifelike except that the arms were broken off in the manner of an ancient statue. To measure the prudery of the end of the century one has only to realize that in 1854 F. D. Froment-Meurice (Vever, II, p. 125) exhibited a huge pendant in the Renaissance revival style, topped by an enamelled Venus standing amid rushes, without evoking any but favorable comment (Appendix, Figure 181). (Figure 108)

188. *Gold pendant shaped over a wooden core,* showing a woman's profile in relief; suspended by a chain from a slide, and finished with two pendant motifs of the same sort, all three set with pearls. No identifying marks; French, ca. 1900. (pendant: 1 7/16 x 4 1/8, core: 1 5/16 x 1 3/8) The piece is interesting because the matrix over which it was shaped accompanies it; a very old technique for making gold reliefs with a minimum of precious metal. (Figure 109)

189. *"Four o'clock" brooch,* gold with pale green translucid enamel background set with many small brilliants; diamond and opal drop; opal navet, center top. Engraved *PF* under the enamel (center bottom); French, ca. 1898. (2 x 2 1/8) The gold profile of a girl with pursed lips blows the seeds off a "four o'clock" (dandelion gone to seed) which she holds in one hand. Each seed is pinpointed with a brilliant. The signature *P F*—if that is the purpose of the two letters—is also the sound that she makes as she blows, resulting in a kind of audio-visual pun.

The outline of the plaquette is very much like one by Lalique, exhibited in 1898 (see under number 160), but it is less arbitrarily bizarre and closer to the shape of a tulip; the delicate frame of two dandelion leaves completes the composition.

Exceptionally fine in every respect, this brooch has tentatively been ascribed to Paul Follot on the basis of the inscribed PF. Follot was the author of a book of jewelry designs, which, however, must have been published ca. 1905–10 to judge by the late Art Nouveau style (the publication bears no date). Little is known about his pre-1900 work.* (Plate 22)

190. *Circular brooch* consisting of a gold iris enamelled in natural colors, set against a gold plaquette showing the rising sun enamelled orange to yellow. French? ca. 1900. (d. 3.2 cm) No identifying hallmarks are given for this piece, a trait which it has in common with another of similar design (Sataloff collection; not in exhibition) also showing a floral motif against a rising sun. This unusual background occurs in a brooch by G. Gurschner illustrated in J. Hoffmann, Pl. 47. (Figure 110)

## XIX. *BELGIAN ART NOUVEAU*

191. *Gold ring,* the shank formed by two water nymphs who meet at center front and "hold" a spherical opal. Ring unmarked, but in its original box with

---

* However he won a prize for a programme cover in 1897 (*Art et Décoration,* 1897; II, p. 136), and the left-hand margin of this design is decorated with a motif of two fading dandelions (thistles?) in a shower of stars, very similar in concept to the charming floral fantasy of this brooch.

"Knein Goutelle, Joailler-Orfèvre, 5 Montagne de la Cour, Bruxelles," in Art Nouveau lettering printed in the lid. (d. 7/8 x 1 3/8)

Since Belgian jewelry is only rarely hallmarked (see under number 195), it is useful to publish whatever documentation is available. Considering the dimensions, these tiny figures have a notable sculptural quality which may help identify other pieces by the same maker. (Figure 111)

192. *Bat brooch,* gold with silver facing makes a symmetrical brooch centered with a gold bat, whose spread wings have two dragonflies (which the bat grasps, one in either front paw) outlined against them, their wings cresting above the bat's wings; set with diamonds, rubies, and emeralds. Stamped indistinctly on the back, *Feys, Jacques;* Bruxelles. Belgian, ca. 1900? (3 1/4 x 1 3/4)

The workmanship and design, are more reminiscent of the late 1880's than of the Art Nouveau period; yet the amalgamation of the dragonflies with the bat's wings suggest the kind of metamorphoses that Lalique was doing in the late '90's. This Belgian was either well ahead of his time as a designer, or he was a retardataire craftsman who had picked up some new ideas. (Figure 112)

193. *Brooch in the form of a moth* with outspread wings; gold set with rubies and diamonds and enamelled in translucent green and opaque black, as well as *plique à jour* shading from gray to rose (into which paillons have been set for added fire) to green. Raised monogram *PW* with underneath it a curved band bearing the lettering *Ex. Unique* (exemplaire unique). Philippe Wolfers, Belgian, 1902. (4 3/4 x 3)

Wolfers' first signed pieces of jewelry were exhibited in 1895, and he ceased his activity to devote himself to sculpture after 1905. During those ten years he designed some of the most splendid of Art Nouveau jewels. This piece shares with an orchid brooch, 1902, (G. Hughes, *Modern Jewelry,* New York, 1968; Pl. 177, top center) the fine network of gold reticulation imbedded in the transparent enamel, as well as its rich and luminous colors. Unless the enamelled and lacquered grasshopper by Gaillard (see under number 186) should come to light, it would be impossible to say whether any jeweller or enameller surpassed Wolfers in the iridescent effects exemplified by this work, which rival the opal. (Plate 23)

194. *Eve and serpent pendant,* with a sculptured rose quartz figure of Eve, entwined by a gold serpent, framed by a triangular niche featuring two rather abstract cobras executed in gold, opals and green enamel, with a finial of outcurved

gold strands flanking an emerald-centered oval of green enamel, its upper edge trun-
cated by the row of square-cut diamonds that tops off the composition. A gold chain
at top center leads to a pearl which marks the bifurcation of the chain, each end
terminating in a gold, enamel and diamond motif echoing that of the pendant. A
simple black silk cord makes the necklace. At the bottom of the pendant a yellow
diamond facetted tear drop hangs from the square cut diamond that serves as
plinth for the tiny statue. Signature: *Philippe Wolfers;* Belgian, ca. 1905. (3 1/8
x 5 3/8) Eve and the Serpent was a symbol that appeared all too often in the
period of popular misogyny at the turn of the century, especially in the works
of Germanic artists, such as Franz von Stuck and Arnold Böcklin. Wolfers made
more than one on this scale (*Modern Design in Jewellery and Fans,* London, 1902,
Belgian chapter, Pl. 4; another in *The Studio,* XVIII, 1900; p. 197 a third, 1899,
in catalogue of the exhibition *EUROPA 1900,* Brussels, 1967, fig. 55) and at least
one, exhibited at Ostende in 1965, as full-scale sculpture. A winged figure pendant
(G. Hughes, Pl. 175) of 1898–9 is an earlier variant.

Although the necklace frontal (as this should be called, since the two attach-
ments leading to the cord are an integral part of the design), begins in Wolfers'
work as early as 1898, the elements of abstraction—including the predilection for
square and baguette-shaped stones so pronounced in our piece—does not start until
1901. An illustration of this piece, showing that it originally had a gold chain instead
of the black silk cord, is in J. Hoffmann, *Auswahl von Motiven aus dem Modernen
Stil,* Stuttgart, n.d. (after 1905); Pl. 73, no. 3. (Figure 113)

195. *Mistletoe necklace,* the leaves and stem segments (which form the chain)
of gold; the berries of pearls. Unmarked; probably Belgian, ca. 1903. (1.20 x 1 1/2)
Submission of jewelry for the assay office stamp was voluntary in Belgium until
1913, and some of the best makers, such as Wolfers never did so. In England and
France, where it was required by law, it took a certain amount of defiance, once a
jeweller was registered, to fail to submit pieces for the stamp. The provenance of
this necklace is Belgian, and Wolfers had previously made an elaborate necklace
frontal of this popular motif ("Modern Design in Jewellery and Fans," special
winter number of *The Studio,* London, 1902; Belgian section, Pl. 6). (Figure 114)

196. *Silver necklace of ginko leaves.* Designer unknown. Stamped, Arnould.
Paris, ca. 1903. (l. 18 x 2) Another piece executed by the same firm, but probably
not by the designer of this necklace, was in the Citroën collection, now in the Hessisches Landesmuseum, Darmstadt (see catalogue, *Goldschmiedekunst des Jugend-*

*stils; Schmuck u. Gerät um 1900,* Pforzheim, 1963, Pl. XXIV lower center) A page of Arnould's jewelry, each piece by a different (named) designer, is to be found in J. Hoffmann, Pl. 89. (see Bibliography) (Figure 114)

## XX. *AUSTRIAN ART NOUVEAU*

197. *Oval silver box* with foliage design in repoussé on the lid. Stamped with the monograms of the Wiener Werkstätte and Josef Hoffmann; Austrian, ca. 1910 (4 1/16 x 2 5/16) The dating of Wiener Werkstätte designs sometimes is difficult because their products continued popular after the end of World War I, often with little change, although a certain cross-fertilization of styles occurred between the masters who taught in the school.

Hoffmann was one of its founders, in 1903, and remained its artistic director until 1931. The style of this box is related to other works of the pre-World War I period in his work (see exhibition catalogue, *Die Wiener Werkstätte, Oesterreichisches Museum f. Angewandte Kunst,* Vienna, 1967; Pl. 17, cat. no. 97). (Figure 115)

198. *Silver figure of an oriental dancer;* silver repoussé done in two halves which are joined at the sides and top; set with various semi-precious stones, and with silver chains (all but one now lost) interspersed with pearls or other "pebbles." No marks. (h. 11 3/4) This curious, attenuated figure is one of a series (for another see Catalogue, *Wiener Werkstätte,* Galérie St. Étienne, N.Y., 1966; no. 5) by Dagobert Peche, presumably ca. 1910–15.

At that time cults derived from Indian mysticism were popular, not only in Austria but in the United States, propagated by two famous women, Mme. Blavatsky and Annie Besant. It has recently been made clear that the movement had a great deal to do with the inception of abstract art (S. Ringbom, *The Sounding Cosmos,* Åbo Academy, Helsingfors, 1970) especially in Austria, Russia, and Germany. The ghostly quality of the little dancer, along with its oriental allusion, reflects a trend which was to be further explored in the major arts, and which today seems to be undergoing a revival. (Plate 24)

199. *Square silver box* with a cutout abstract plant design silhouetted against a shagreen panel set into the lid. Stamped with Wiener Werkstätte and Josef Hoffmann monograms; Austrian, ca. 1920. (2 3/4 x 2 3/4) The success of the Wiener Werkstätte as an artists' brotherhood in the English tradition of the previous century

(see under number 114) was considerable; not only did it endure longer than any other similar venture (1903–32), its members had a tendency to take on each others' artistic styles. Dagobert Peche only joined the group as a designer in 1917, yet this piece resembles his style more than it does Hoffmann's own earlier work (number 198). (Figure 116)

200. *Maple leaf brooch,* gold faced with platinum; a maple leaf and seed cluster enamelled a pale, translucent green shading to orange. The forms are completed with outlining of brilliants; two round diamonds are botanically incorrect "fruits"; and the whole is encircled by a diamond-studded crescent moon. Wheat-ear hallmark of the Czechoslovakian government pawn shop; probably Austrian, ca. 1905. (1 5/8 x 1 3/4) The design is adapted from one of Alphonse Mucha's published in his *Documents Décoratifs* in 1901 (included in the illustration of this Catalogue entry, Figure 117). So closely was Mucha associated with Paris (see under numbers 148, 149) and so closely is Vienna associated with a far different development coming out of Art Nouveau (numbers 202, 203, 197, 198, 199) that a piece of jewelry as thoroughly in the French style and taste as this might pardonably be presumed French. Yet Mucha's native land (there was not yet a Czechoslovakia before 1917, and although he was a strong Pan-Slavic nationalist, the Austrians would have considered him a native son) was proud of his success, and it is natural that his book of designs should have been used there.

The misfortunes of war have decimated much of Austrian jewelry. Although there may have been many jewellers working in Vienna in the style of Mucha, I have only been able to find one firm, Roset & Fischmeister (see "Modern Design in Jewellery and Fans," *The Studio* London, 1902, Austrian section Pl. 2) with pictorial documentation sufficiently decisive to prove that the connection existed. The detail of the round diamonds hanging down from rigid stems, which has in neither case anything to do with Mucha, speaks in favor of the attribution of this brooch to the same firm. (Figure 117)

201. *Brooch of gold,* chrysoprase and diamonds. No marks; Austrian (?), ca. 1900–05. (1 3/16 x 1 3/8) The carved chrysoprase was used by Lalique, not only in the great dragonfly corsage ornament (Appendix, Figure 160), but in more modest form as well (for color illustrations of both see *Le Bijou 1900,* Brussels, 1965; Pls. VI, VII.); he also seems to have been the one to first introduce this turban-like coif (for another adaptation of Lalique's piece by Marcel Bing for "La Maison de l'Art Nouveau," see G. Meusnier, Pl. XXVII, no. 2).

The crescent used as a frame, however, points in the direction of Mucha's designs (e.g. no. 153), as does its presence in the previous entry (no. 200), to which this piece is related not only stylistically but by its lack of hallmarks. (Figure 118)

In 1902 another world's fair took place in Turin. Exhausted from the great effort of 1900, the French exhibit was comparatively modest, and suddenly the center of interest in the decorative arts shifted to the Glasgow school, principally the architect-decorator Charles Rennie Mackintosh and his wife. Although only one piece of jewelry of his is known (see G. Hughes, *Modern Jewelry,* p. 106, no. 181) there can be no doubt that their leaded windows and decorative panels (Appendix, Figure 175), pervaded by a kind of lyrical geometry, have been the inspiration of much of the design that succeeded Art Nouveau, right down to the present.

First to make the new style their own were a group of painters and designers in Vienna, where Mackintosh executed a commission in 1902 to decorate a music room in a private home.

202. *"Dog-collar" necklace;* silver, set with lapis lazuli and gold; ca. 1905. (l. 11 7/8 x 1 3/4) The revulsion against the polychrome, curvilinear jewels of 1900 is manifest in this early example of Viennese work in the new style (the "dog-collar" necklace, along with its counterpart the whale-boned dress collar, had an understandably brief vogue, from ca. 1885–1905). Here, the tendency toward a monotone color scheme, discussed at the end of the French series (above), is well under way, and the effect of the jewel is mainly achieved through a nice spacing of the strict forms in repetition. Although such a design could (and very soon would) be carried out by machines, they were as carefully hand crafted in the beginning as the more dazzling works of the Paris school.

Exhibited at the Busch-Reisinger Museum, Cambridge, Mass., 1970. (Figure 119).

203. *Cover for a dance program,* 1909; gilt copper; Marked *Wiener Werkstätte* inside, lower margin. (4 9/16 x 5 5/8) Very typical of the Viennese style as it settled to the popular level, where the products of the Wiener Werkstätte enjoyed continuing success throughout the next two decades, this pretty trifle shows the rather prim marriage that has taken place between Art Nouveau motifs (vine, flower, feather) and abstract linear interpretation. Groups of small tight design elements make a network over the entire surface, a formula that easily palls if repeated ad infinitum, but which expresses the new, anti-naturalistic theory hammered out by

the Symbolist painters (Gauguin, Maurice Denis, etc.) at the end of the XIX century: in brief, that a surface is only a surface, not a "window onto the world," as art theory ever since the Renaissance had assumed.

Exhibited at the Busch-Reisinger Museum, Cambridge, Mass., 1970. (Figure 119)

204. *Brooch; painted miniature* set in a gold frame, ca. 1910. (2 1/2 x 1 3/8) This echoes the style of the painter, Gustav Klimt, a Viennese who created an attractive amalgam out of the conflicting trends mentioned in the preceding entry. Without abandoning realism in the faces that he portrayed (see Appendix, Figure 134) he kept the figures flat, and contrast with the background minimal in order to avoid any illusion of depth. Wherever they occur in clothes, background, etc., he allows flattened and formalized patterns to take over the picture; the same combination of naturalistic face against flowers rendered in a deliberately childlike "shorthand" can be seen in the brooch. (Figure 119)

## XXI. *GERMAN ART NOUVEAU*

205. *Gold brooch;* the frame, a modified shield shape surrounds a cameo-profile carved of pinkish stone (or shell?) completed with a flowing coiffure whose locks fall to the base of the triangle, enfolding a diamond, from which hangs a pearl drop. Three smaller diamonds embellish the upper edge of the frame. Serial number scratched on back, but otherwise no marks. German, ca. 1900. (1 3/8 x 1 9/16) This brooch has a distinctive "soft" style not only in the design, but also in the way it uses polished gold (not popular in French work of the turn of the century). It may be the work of Georg Kleemann, or one of his pupils; he taught at the Staatliche Fachschule für Edelmetall in Pforzheim, the German center of jewelry manufacture.

A cameo brooch by him, showing similar features in the design of the frame with its discreet jewelled touches, and a profile related to this one (including the knot of hair, which is better integrated in this coiffure than in our brooch) is illustrated in the catalogue *Jugendstil: Sammlung K. A. Citroën, Amsterdam,* Darmstadt, 1962; p. 35, fig. 83. (Figure 120)

206. *Silver clasp* of symmetrical floral design. German, ca. 1900. (8.2 cm. x 5.1 cm.) A number of firms produced designs which satisfied the desire for something in the art nouveau manner without startling the customer of essentially conserva-

tive taste. For a clasp of related shape and floral design see G. Bott, *Kunsthandwerk um 1900* Catalogue of the Hessisches Landesmuseum, Darmstadt, 1965, no. 166. (Figure 121)

## XXII. *RUSSIAN ART NOUVEAU*

The various subjects for which Fabergé enjoys continuing fame can only be hinted at in this exhibition. More conservative in his conception of the jewelled arts than any of the other designers of the late XIX century, his inspiration was chiefly taken from either traditional Russian or French XVIII century pieces, which his greatest works rivalled or even outdid in intricacy and in delicacy of enamelling. The Richmond, Virginia, Museum of Art contains a splendid collection of his works, to name the one most easily accessible in this vicinity. Lacking any example of his famous Easter eggs, made for members of the Russian court, our selection must modestly seek to show his popular vein: the flower subjects, much beloved of the English royal family, continue to be imitated to the very present.

207. *Mallow plant*; gold stem bearing two translucent quartz flowers, each centered with a blue pearl surrounded by gold stamens; nephrite leaves and buds "planted" in an octagonal nephrite pot (height 6 3/4). These flower subjects were inspired by a group of XVIII pieces in the Hermitage Museum, Leningrad (see K. Snowman, *The Art of Carl Fabergé,* Boston, n.d., fig. 291). (Figure 122)

208. *Cornflowers and stalks of oats:* gold stems bearing on one side three flowers enamelled dark blue with diamond-tipped stamens, and on the other the oat seeds stalks, with free-swinging seeds (height 8), the whole rising from a glass of "water" (also glass). (For similar plants see Snowman, Pl. LXII; and H.C. Bainbridge, *Peter Carl Fabergé,* London, 1966, Pl. 37) (Figure 122)

209. *Strawberry plant:* gold stems bearing nephrite leaves, a chalcedony flower with a rose diamond center and gold stamens, and four purpurine berries, set in a white jade bowl, with silver foot bearing stamp (height 6 5/8). (Figure 122)

210. *"Shooting star" plant;* a single gold stem rising between two nephrite leaves bears a burst of six blossoms of rhodonite tipped with white chalcedony, and three buds of rhodonite and nephrite. Implanted in a gilt bronze pot ornamented with six panels of bloodstone (height 4), Stamped on base. (Figure 122)

211. *Cigarette box of lapis lazuli* with hinges and clasp of silver niello and gold set with small diamonds. (3 x 2 1/2 x 5/8) Some doubt always exists about the authenticity of Fabergé's carved stone pieces unless of known provenance, for they have no hallmarks or signatures, even when they are unquestionably his. For a box of similar shape see, H. C. Bainbridge, Pl. 112 (lower). For Greek key pattern used in the sale in Geneva, Nov. 19, 1970, no. 122 (ill.). (Figure 122)

212. *Miniature hippopotamus* of smoky quartz with diamond eyes. (2 1/4 x 1 1/4) The same reservations apply to this piece as to number 211, above. Fabergé employed more than one stone carver, each with his own style. K. Snowman, Pl. 37 (lower left) shows a similar hippo; another appears in the catalogue of Christie's sale in Geneva, Nov. 19, 1970, no. 122 (ill.) (Figure 122)

213. *Floral pendant* of gold enamelled green shading to pink, set with a peridot, a ruby, small diamonds; peridot drop. Stamped *K F* (in Cyrilic letters), the monogram used for small works by Fabergé; Russian, ca. 1902–3? (15/16 x 2 15/16) Officially the court jeweller of Russia, and unofficially to every other royal house of Europe, Fabergé's style tended toward the conservative. Although Art Nouveau touches are discernible here in the curved elements, as well as in the ombré enamel, the general effect is rococo of the Louis XV period. Fabergé would occasionally design excellently in the art nouveau manner, but (as in earlier times, see number 66) aristocracy inclined more toward traditional styles, and he had no need to cater to a bourgeois clientele. (Figure 123)

214. *Gold mirror locket* with top enamelled in opalescent white over a guilloché sunburst pattern; over this, and framing it, is a tracery of mistletoe twigs and leaves, the berries being diamonds and rubies; the center of the sunburst is covered with an oval cabochon sapphire. An oval hallmark with Cyrillic G (or E ?) H; and another hallmark, both very indistinct. Russian, ca. 1905. (2 1/4 x 2 7/8) The exquisite color and sheen of the enamel work give some idea of this outstanding Russian technique, perfected by Karl Fabergé. The ornamental tracery is in the art nouveau manner (for a Fabergé pendant in that style, also using the mistletoe motif, see G. Huges, p. 91, fig. 145). (Figure 124)

## XXIII. *AMERICAN ART NOUVEAU*

215. *Gold pendant* (convertible to brooch) with matching chain, set with opals and diamonds. Stamped, *Marcus & Co.;* American, ca. 1910. (chain: l. 14 1/2,

pendant: 1 15/16 x 2 3/4) The brooch has many reminiscences of French Art Nouveau design of the 1900 period, and the vertical axis could well have been invented by Colonna (number 139), yet the total effect shows the influence of Tiffany's "marine" compositions (Appendix, Figure 150). The chain with its interlace links, on the other hand, is more in the English taste for Celtic revival (cf. number 81). Reliance upon fine stones rather than enamelled embellishment, however, is in the American tradition already remarked by Bode at the Paris Exposition of 1889 (see Introduction). (Figure 125)

216. *Silver inkwell* embellished with blue and green enamel and five opals. Stamped, *Marcus & Co.;* American, ca. 1910. (7 1/8 x 4) A cross-breeding of design similar in its elements to the necklace by the same maker (no. 215) can be observed here, and with much the same result. Resembling whirlpools left in the sand, the general outline of the stand is like those of Lalique's pendant designs of ca. 1898. However the working of the metal is in the line of English craftsmanship which uses the repoussé technique for moulding the metal, while the French are more apt to use casting. (Figure 126)

217. *Brooch of copper and silver and belt of silver plaquettes* linked by silver chains. Neither piece is marked, but both are probably by Unger Bros.; American, ca. 1915. It is ironic that America, while providing the initial impetus that turned the XIX century historical revival styles and the English reform styles into Art Nouveau, was late to adopt the latter. Even Tiffany could not find broad patronage for the jewelry that is his most original (compare number 94 with number 120, his "popular" vein of Art Nouveau jewelry).

The most successful adaptations of French-inspired Art Nouveau jewelry in this country were produced in quantity by Unger Bros., Newark, N.J. The individual plaquettes or reliefs are stamped, but carefully finished; and the combination of copper and silver (brooch) is both original and attractive. (Figure 127)

## XXIV. *ENGLISH ART NOUVEAU*

The prodigious development and dissemination of the English illustrated book from about 1870 on was, perhaps more than any other single factor, responsible for the sudden change which enlivened all of the decorative arts, including jewelry, in both Europe and America beginning about 1890. The major arts were at a moment of indecision, older forms having lost their energy and new ones not yet having gained the amount of recognition which is needed for new impetus. It is moments such as this that offer the minor arts a chance to fill the void; and filled it was with the burst of creative energy best known under the title of "Art Nouveau" which served as farewell to the old century and herald of the new during the brief (ca. 25 years) of its ascendancy.

218. *Flower pendant* or brooch, rose-red enamel on pure silver, amethyst center. C. R. Ashbee ca. 1890. (1 1/2 x 2 1/6) Under the influence of William Morris, Ashbee founded The Guild of Handicraft in 1888, acting as its director and chief designer during the 19 years of its existence. His philosophy of design (see his book, *Silver and Jewellery,* London, 1912) does not sound essentially different from Morris', or other craftsmen-artists, of the '90's. Fortunately, for us, his style is unmistakable, once the eye has picked it out, for he explains that the jewelry produced by the Guild was never hallmarked during the first ten years of its existence. His effects are achieved, especially during the early period, by a combination of pure line and color areas of deliberate simplicity; the elaborate detail and the massed effect common from the middle of the XIX century on, begin to break down in the '80's, but no immediate inspiration came as to what to put in their place. By concentrating upon the elements which had been lacking before in Victorian jewelry—smooth surfaces and abstract shapes—Ashbee's early designs leapfrogged over half a generation (including his own later work), making him the first recognizable creator of "modern" jewelry in our sense of the word. (Figure 128)

219. *Gold, enamel, and garnet necklace* with pearl shell pendants. C. R. Ashbee, ca. 1895. The refinements of this necklace lie entirely in the subtle engineering of the design rather than in its rather ordinary materials. The only unusual thing about the latter are the enamel "wings" flanking the three cabochon garnets. These are not applied to the metal, as is usually the case with enamel, but are shaped masses of red enamel veined with smoke blue (to suggest the veining of insect or bat wings perhaps) which have been set in the manner of stones (for similar design elements, Appendix 179). The astonishing novelty of the necklace is entirely due to the way the elements are connected by the chains: when worn, each movement of the wearer slightly alters the composition of the tripartite "insects"; thus, Ashbee has given them a life-like quality which is quite different from the detailed surface imitation of natural forms, so familiar in previous XIX century jewelry. This infusion of the spirit of life into geometric shapes, which are at best vaguely suggestive

of a creature, does not come about again until Alexander Calder creates the "mobile" in the 1920's. (Figure 128)

220. *Gold and turquoise necklace,* with pearls. Liberty & Co., ca. 1900. (l. 4 x 2 7/8) Ashbee's influence can be seen in the gold jewelry produced by this famous firm at the turn of the century; however the refinement of thought which qualifies Ashbee's seemingly similar necklace (above) as a work of art, rather than craft, is 176). (Figure 128)

221. *Gold and enamel pendant* in the form of a stylized peacock feather with a fresh-water pearl. Liberty and Co., ca. 1900. (1 3/8 x 4) Liberty's employed several designers of jewelry, none of whom were identified. It is only recently that a collection of the firm's designs, now in the Victoria & Albert Museum, has been studied, along with the pieces themselves, in the hope of sorting out the various hands. The designer who displays the greatest assurance is responsible for this piece—probably Archibald Knox; although English Art Nouveau jewelry in general has the "feel" of drawing as its source (rather than modelling, as is the case of French Art Nouveau, Figure 71), the illustrations of Aubrey Beardsley can be pointed to as the source of this particular designer's controlled yet fluid line (see Appendix, Figure 176). (Figure 128)

222. *Silver brooch* set with an enamel on copper plaque depicting "The Guardian Angel," after 1900. (3 x 4 9/16) The impressive size of this piece suggests that the maker was aware of the over-size jewels in Lalique's display at the 1900 Paris Exposition. Comparison with the enamelled box top (number 112) signed by Alexander Fisher, the best English enameller of the period, points either to him or one of his many pupils as the author. Although not a copy, subject, style and color point to a source for the composition in Pre-Raphaelite painting. A similar "Guardian Angel" by Fisher is in J. Hoffmann, *Auswahl von Motiven aus dem Modernen Stil,* Stuttgart, n.d., Pl. 50, no. 2; Pl. 2, fig. 5. (Figure 128)

223. *Necklace,* green enamel on silver with pearls and amethysts. Stamped under the enamel *Child & Child,* after 1900. (l. 5 1/2, pendants: 7/8 x 7/8) This cheaply, semi-mass produced necklace frontal shows what an attractive design combined with attractive colors (the same piece has also come to my attention in pale yellow and in red enamel) can do in the mass market. Although William Morris preached the amelioration of industrial design in order to "improve" the lives of ordi-

nary people, neither he nor his followers ever produced jewelry on such a scale. It was left to lesser firms, such as this one, to carry out his precepts. The wing motif was common by the time this was made, but probably originated in the work of the illustrator, Walter Crane. (Appendix, Figure 177) (Figure 128)

224. *Pendant,* gold set with an enamel on copper plaque. Phoebe Traquair. (1 13/16 x 2 13/16) One of a number of English and Scotch women who worked in enamel at this time. The composition reminiscent of Crane's illustrations (see previous entry) is nevertheless Pre-Raphaelite only in the sense that it goes back to XV century Italian painting. The frame, a Gothic quatrefoil, shows that the Medieval revival of mid-century, survives—indeed takes on new life for a brief time— around 1900 in England. (Figure 128)

225. *Necklace with swivel pendant;* enamel on silver and gold with ornaments of gold, moonstones, garnets, and amethysts. Perhaps Harold Stabler, ca. 1910. (pendant: 1 1/4 x 3 15/16) The attribution is based on a chalice by this silversmith in the Victoria & Albert Museum (see G. Hughes, *Modern Silver,* N.Y., 1967, p. 148, no. 253) which not only has figures of running girls that are similar, but in general contains the same forms and elements in different arrangement. The great English literary tradition has a way of creeping into even the most minuscule of the arts: the center of the pendant not only swivels independently within the frame, it also can be opened to reveal an enamelled quotation from *The Rubaiyat!* Seeing this in combination with the green and white chevrons, vaguely reminiscent of Medieval blazonry; the vine and leaf motif harking back to mid XIX century; and the rather demure bacchantes, one is inclined to be grateful that this endearing but somewhat foolish object sounds "finis" to the XIX century revival styles. (Figure 128)

226. *Gold brooch in the shape of a peacock* with partially spread tail; the breast is set with a navet-shaped opal, the crest with brilliants; the plumage is studded with pearls and turquoises; enamelling in opaque blue, yellow, red, green, white, and black. The bird stands on a pear-shaped pearl from which depends a short chain with three turquoises and pearl drop. No marks; C. R. Ashbee design ca. 1900; probably executed by Gebhardt of the Guild of Handicraft.

Peacock feathers, rather than the whole bird, are more typical of art nouveau jewelry; and this, along with Vever's peacock (number 182), is of rather old-fashioned design. The 1880's were especially fond of the fantailed variety in everything from diamond jewelry to bedsteads (a headboard with three peacocks was exhibited in 1888 in Munich; it was commissioned for Ludwig II of Bavaria; of similar size were the bronze peacocks designed by Mucha for Fouquet's shop in 1901).

It must have been one of Ashbee's most popular designs, to judge by the number of examples which have survived. Another, almost identical with this, is illustrated in M. Flower, p. 232, fig. 110d; it is executed in silver and gold (no enamel) with pearls and diamonds. For variations on the theme see also, M. Amaya, *Art Nouveau,* London and New York, 1966, p. 43, and R. Schmutzler, *Art Nouveau,* New York, 1962, p. 176, fig. 181 (Figure 129)

227. *Mermaid overwhelmed by an octopus.* Multicolor enamel on copper tondo. Signed on the back, *Ernestine Mills* and initialled *EM* on the front. English, ca. 1910. (d. 7)

Mrs. Mills (catalogue cover), a pupil of Alexander Fisher (number 222 this catalogue), was a gifted enameller who won many prizes (*The Studio, Yearbook of Decorative Design,* 1909, p. 149).

"Siren *n.* (sī' ren; -rin. L., fr. Gk *seiren;* cf. F. sirène) 1. *Gr. Relig.* One of *a* group of minor divinities or deities associated with death, and sometimes represented as carrying off souls, or as mourning for the dead. They are represented with the heads, and sometimes the busts and arms, of women, but otherwise with the forms of birds . . . Odysseus escaped (their song) by filling his sailor's ears with wax. 2. Hence a) A mermaid b) a woman who sings sweetly c) something insidious or deceptive; esp. a woman of such character; an enticing, dangerous woman." Webster's *New International Dictionary.*

The reader, who will find the rest of this catalogue organized loosely according to chronological sequence, will perhaps forgive a reversal so that "the last shall be first" on the cover. Although the siren, in all of the dictionary's definitions, appears in the art of the turn of the century (for a medley, see the catalogue of the exhibition *Symbolists,* Spencer A. Samuels & Co., 18 E. 76th St., New York, 1970) the most frequently represented was the mermaid. How it came about that Victorian woman was cast in the role and how, in the end, she was trapped in it, to the discomfiture of men and women alike is discussed in our Introduction. The amount of mutually inflicted agony can only be imagined with difficulty, for its visual formulations often verge on the ludicrous.* However, there can be no doubt that by the beginning of

---

* For XIX century man's "adjustment" to the "belle dame sans merci" whom he had re-created out of romantic yearnings toward the Middle Ages and the new, stern enforcement of sexual morality which seemed the only way to cope with the heterogeneous populations in the mushrooming cities, see

the present century women, as in this instance, were in a mood to cry: "Have done with the Siren." (Cover)

228. *Dog-collar* which comes apart in two pieces (one shortened?) so that it can be worn as two bracelets. Red gold set with oriental and fresh-water pearls, cabochon garnets. No marks; probably English ca. 1900. (first part: l. 7 5/8 x 1 7/8, second part: l. 7 1/4 x 15/16) The combination of gems (see also number 219) is one especially beloved in England; and the imaginative use of the chains, each row different, is all too typically English. However the maker had certainly seen Colonna's designs for Bing's "La Maison de l'Art Nouveau" in Paris. The orchid motif (see number 139; also Appendix, Figure 156) was tantamount to Colonna's personal trademark. It appeared not only in his jewelry designs, but in fabrics as well. (Figure 130)

---

our Introduction. At its most extreme it turns into masochism, a perversion whereby self-punishment is the only pleasure, though a woman in furs seems to have taken the place of the penitent's own hair shirt (Sacher-Masoch, "Venus in Furs"). That this moral psychomachia had pervasive effect, reaching as far as the blithe art of jewelry, may seem far-fetched; yet F. J. Partridge (*The Studio;* 1905, XXXV, p. 127 ff.) confirms it in a review of Lalique's exhibition at the Agnew Gallery. Writing for his English audience accustomed to the tenets of William Morris, he says, "Many people might be prone to underrate the genius (of Lalique), for are we not rather in the habit of measuring achievement in art not alone by the beauty of the results, but by outside reasons? We rather like an artist to have a moral pose . . ."

The works of Lalique (see Appendix, Figures 156, 182) and others in the French jewelry section of the Paris Exposition, 1900, demonstrate that he too was affected by end-of-the century melancholy; but by 1905 he had passed to a less gloomy phase.

## NOTES

1. In the 1780's Lady Templetown and Diana Beauclerc designed for Wedgwood, side by side with a number of men, including the painter-engraver John Flaxman. (See *Early Wedgwood Pottery: Exhibited at 34 Wigmore St., London W.1*, London, 1951.) Madame de Pompadour, and later Queen Victoria took lessons in the art of cameo carving and, although we do not have any examples of their work, their participation established the cameo as a province of the fine crafts not only produced for women, but one in which they might properly take an active hand.

2. The visual prototype for the maiden becalmed in a state of voluptuous trance must be traced back to the Pre-Raphaelites, in particular the paintings and illustrations of Dante Gabriel Rossetti (Appendix, Figure 144). Although he never took part in public art exhibitions, after one early and disastrous showing, his illustrations were in circulation during his lifetime, and after his death in 1883 a posthumous exhibition of his paintings set off a spate of books and illustrated articles on his work. His most famous painting, "Beata Beatrix" of 1863, a recollection of his recently deceased wife (for whose death he felt a certain guilt) not only has the pose, but also other attributes of many similar subjects transformed at the end of the century in Art Nouveau terms. (viz. Appendix, Figure 156, adorned with the poppy, ancient Greek symbol of eternal sleep, hence death).

3. H. W. Janson has suggested to me that this ubiquitous figurine, which in its miniature version shares some of the charm of incongruity discussed in connection with cameos, above, may be the inspiration of Lear's famous limerick about the "Young lady of Niger, who smiled as she rode on a tiger. They came back from the ride with the lady inside, and the smile on the face of the tiger." This example dates from 1848.

4. The following quotations are taken from Diana Holman-Hunt's fascinating reconstruction of her grandfather's life, *My Grandfather, His Wives and Loves,* New York, 1969.

5. The rousing success of the revival of Shaw's *Pygmalion* as the musical comedy *My Fair Lady* makes one wonder whether the message finds an echo in the revised feminist movement of the present day.

6. The confusion may stem from the fact that many English books were issued in the United States under the imprint of the collaborating American publisher.

7. To indicate the view of the opposition, the following extract from Henry Havard, eminent French critic of the period and compiler of a splendid encyclopedia of the decorative arts, deplored the deterioration of Tiffany, "whose exhibits in the (Paris) exposition of 1878 made such a great impression on French goldsmithing. . . . This year his entries are of a depressing heaviness and inelegance. His vases (are) loaded down with thick ornamentation and bloated reliefs; reminiscent of Friesian goldsmith work of the XVIII century, they outdo even these in their gross excesses which leave the eye no room to come to rest." *L'Exposition de Paris, 1889* (2 bound volumes of the weekly "newspaper" of the exposition), v. 2. p. 250.

8. H. Bouilhet in *Revue des Arts Décoratifs*, XIV, 1893-94, p. 88 ff.

9. Under his aegis several pieces were bought by the Kunstgewerbe Museum in Berlin, cf. *Werke Um 1900,* Kunstgewerbe Museum, Berlin, 1966, nos. 26 and 27, both illustrated in the Appendix.

10. See H. Bouilhet, above. He persuades Henri Vever, who is doing the same kind of scouting at the Chicago Fair for *L'Union des Arts Décoratifs* as Bode for the German museums, to buy such a piece ("Mais quel prix!"), although he notes with regret that the Kunstgewerbe Museum in Berlin has been there ahead of them and bought the best one.

11. This is a mysterious phase in his career. According to his account, he spent the years studying design at "le collège de Sydenham." While no roster of English schools of the period shows any educational institution of that name, a desultory attempt had been made in 1859 to found an art school—"strictly limited to female education,"—in the Crystal Palace which, after the Great Exhibition of 1851, was transferred and rebuilt in Sydenham. One can see from the annual school reports of *The Art Journal,* that it was never a flourishing institution and by 1880 it had vanished from the roster. Whether it accepted male students in its final year is not revealed.

On the other hand, Sydenham seems to have had a large colony of artist and artisan refugees (Zola lived there during his exile) after the Franco-Prussian war and the Commune uprising and perhaps Lalique was quartered in such a refugee household. While we have no evidence that he distinguished himself in art school while in Sydenham—if indeed he attended one—there is a strong indication that he picked up something of the reforming ideas of William Morris who, at just about that time, began to give more thought to social reform than to his business. A young foreigner, unversed in English, would not have been likely to gain access to the Morris circle: but he might have been in contact with Bazin, the French weaver whom Morris had brought from Lyons in 1877 to instruct him in the techniques of the Jacquard loom. Whatever the case, Lalique's attitude toward being a successful jeweller changed, after 1900, very much along Morrisan lines: he did not limit himself to a small, monied clientele that could afford his jewelry, says a retrospective article by Gabriel Mouray in the *Chicago Tribune,* 1922, "for his ideals were both higher and broader." By turning to the manufacture of glass, which he began in 1902, he thought to bring his art within the reach of all.

12. The practice of making and selling design sheets goes back to the early days of the printing press: Dürer and Holbein, as well as many lesser artists of the Renaissance, made a solid income from such ventures. The last great design books were those of Alphonse Mucha, published in 1901 and 1904. Since then the gradual, regrettable diminishing of small entrepreneurs in crafts and decorative arts, who were always the best customers of such compendia of new designs, has extinguished this particular form of publishing.

13. Actually, it was the exhibit of the Nancy glass maker, Emil Gallé, at the 1889 Exposition that prompted more than one jeweller to begin experimenting with new enamelling processes and materials. The display was housed in a tent purporting to reproduce the abode of a Druid, or a Gallic chieftain: the side hangings were held up by pikes tipped with wild boars' heads in bronze, each with a torque made of glass in its mouth. The decorative ensemble was completed by Gallic roosters. Inside this patriotic pergola was a dazzling assortment of the master's incomparable glass. "M. Gallé uses in the preparation of these polychrome pieces over 100 different preparations; by combining them in various ways he is able to produce an infinite variety of deliberate "accidents" and hitherto unknown shades." *Revue des Arts Décoratifs,* X, 1889-90, p. 177, "Gallé also invented a whole new range of translucent enamels for low temperature firing on metal, which let the gleam of the metal shine through. These run easily, and so it takes a good deal of experience to handle them." (p. 182)

14. These masterpieces, along with many others of more wearable dimensions, were acquired by Callouste Gulbenkian and may now be seen in the museum bearing his name in Lisbon, Portugal. For a representation of some of the finest objects, see Graham Hughes, *Modern Jewelry: an International Survey, 1890-1964,* London, 1964.

15. That he was cordially disliked by other jewellers less gifted and magnanimous than his biographer, Henri Vever (see Vever, *La Bijouterie française au XIXᵉ siècle,* Paris, 1908, III, pp. 690-747, from which I have abstracted the biographical information) is revealed in an unpublished account of the jewelry exhibit in 1900. The author, J.

Marest, secretary of the Chambre Syndicale des Bijoutiers at that time, was annoyed because he was not allowed to inspect the exhibits of Lalique in private, nor make any notes while viewing the cases, but was in fact treated like any other tourist, barely able to elbow his way to the front for a quick look. He berates the master for everything from his prices to his manners. "Though he was acknowledged by the other jewellers, who named him to the council of the Syndicate in 1896, he has always been standoffish. He never attended a meeting, and resigned his post in January, 1897. Many of us can say that we don't even know what he looks like." He accuses Lalique of publicity-seeking, saying that many of the pieces on display were not really new, but were already the property of some eminent personnages who had lent them for the duration of the Exposition, and whose names were "part of the show." Another explanation might have taken the more charitable view that Lalique could hardly have afforded the investment in materials needed for so many pieces if they had not been subsidized by prior sales. Marest was particularly irritated by the critic Leonce Bénédite, who proclaimed that Lalique's works, being art rather than jewelry, would be preserved for the ages, rather than melted down when the styles changed, as has often been the fate of some great and most minor examples of the jeweller's art throughout history.

Alas for the battle of spleen against genius: Bénédite, fortunately for us, turned out to be right!

## BIBLIOGRAPHY

Mario A m a y a, *Art Nouveau,* London and New York, 1966

*A n k ä u f e,* 1900, p. 24

a n o n., "René Lalique," *L'Art Décoratif Moderne,* Paris, 1922

*A r c h i t e c t u r a l Record,* XII, 1902, p. 68

*L' A r t Décoratif,* Jan. 1901, ill. p. 141

*A r t et Décoration,* Paris

      (a) I, 1897

      (b) V, 1899

      (c) VIII, Sept. 1900

Charles Robert A s h b e e, *Silver and Jewellery,* London, 1912

H. C. B a i n b r i d g e, *Peter Carl Fabergé,* London, 1966

R. B a r i l l i, *Art Nouveau,* London, New York, etc., 1969

Adam B a r t s c h, *Le Peintre Graveur,* XIV and XV, Vienna, 1813

M. B a t t e r s b y, *Art Nouveau,* Feltham, England, 1969

[L. B a u d e t] *Catalogue of the Manufacturer L. Baudet,* Paris, ca. 1900

B e r l i n, 1939, Staatliche Museen zu Berlin and Leipzig, 1939. *Katalog der Ornament-
    stichsammlung der Staatlichen Kunstbibliothek Berlin*

B e r l i n, 1966, Kunstgewerbe Museum. *Werke um 1900*

Rudolf B e r l i n e r, *Ornamentale Vorlage-Blätter des 15. bis 18. Jahrhunderts,* Leipzig,
    text vol., 1926

Ludwig B i e l e r, *Ireland, Harbinger of the Middle Ages,* [first English edition] London,
    New York, 1963

Georges B i z e t, *Carmen,* 1875

Wilhelm B o d e, *Kunst und Kunstgewerbe am Ende des XIX. Jahrhunderts,* Berlin, 1901

Rudolf B o s s e l t    see: *D e u t s c h e Kunst und Dekoration*

Gerhard B o t t    see: D a r m s t a d t, 1965

H. B o u i l h e t    see: *R e v u e des Arts Décoratifs*

B r u s s e l s, 1965. *Le Bijou 1900, Modern Style—Juwelen*

B r u s s e l s, 1967. *Europa 1900*

S. B u r y, "An Arts and Crafts Experiment: the Silverwork of C. R. Ashbee," *The Victoria
    and Albert Museum Bulletin,* Jan. 1967, pp. 12-25

Alessandro C a s t e l l a n i, *Antique Jewelry and Its Revival,* Philadelphia, n.d.

C h r i s t i e, Manson, and Woods, Ltd., London. *Catalogue of Sale in Geneva,* no. 19,
    1970

Alejandro C i r i c i Pellicer, *El Arte Modernista Catalan,* Barcelona, 1951

C l e v e l a n d, 1967, Cleveland Museum of Art. *Fabergé and his Contemporaries*

C o l l e c t i o n Connaissance des Arts    see: F a n i e l and S p a r

D a r m s t a d t, 1962. *Jugendstil: Sammlung K. A. Citroën, Amsterdam*

D a r m s t a d t, 1965, Hessisches Landesmuseum (Gerhard Bott). *Kunsthandwerk um 1900. Jugendstil, Art Nouveau, Modern Style, Nieuwekunst*

Cyril D a v e n p o r t, *Jewellery*, London, 1905

Charles D e K a y, *The Art Work of Louis Comfort Tiffany*, Garden City, 1914

*D e k o r a t i v e Kunst*
 (a) VI, 1900, p. 423
 (b) XI, 1903, ill. p. 176

*D e u t s c h e Kunst und Dekoration*, Darmstadt
 (a) Rudolf Bosselt, VII, 1900-01, p. 131
 (b) Oct. 1903, ill. p. 158
 (c) XIII, 1903-04, p. 157

Kurt D i n g e l s t e d t
 (a) *Jugendstil in der angewandten Kunst*, Brunswick, 1959
 (b) *Le Modern Style*, Paris, 1959

M. P. E i d e l b e r g, "E. Colonna: an American in Paris," *The Connoisseur*, Dec. 1967, p. 26

Joan E v a n s, "Jewels of the Renaissance," *Notice of the Proceedings . . . of the Royal Institution of Great Britain*, XXIV, 1923-25, p. 178

Stéfan F a n i e l, ed. *Le Dix-neuvième siècle français* (Collection Connaissance des Arts, II) Paris, 1957

Margaret F l o w e r, *Victorian Jewelry*, New York, 1967

Claude F r é g n a c, *Jewelry*, New York, 1965

John G a l s w o r t h y, *The Forsyte Saga*, London, 1906ff.

J. H o f f m a n, *Auswahl von Motiven aus dem Modernen Stil*, Stuttgart, n.d.

Françoise G i l o t and Carlton Lake, *Life with Picasso*, New York, 1964

Jean G i r a u d o u x, *Ondine*, 1939

Félix H e r b e t, "Les Graveurs de l'école de Fontainebleau," *Annales de la société historique et archéologique du Gatinais*, Fontainebleau, IV, 1900

R. H i g g i n s, *Jewelry from Classical Lands* (British Museum publication) London, 1969

Gustave G e f f r o y, "René Lalique," *L'Art Décoratif Moderne*, Paris, 1922

Diana H o l m a n - Hunt, *My Grandfather, His Wives and Loves*, New York, 1969

Graham H u g h e s
 (a) *Modern Jewelry, an International Survey, 1890-1963*, London and New York, 1963 (several eds.)
 (b) *Modern Silver*, New York, 1967

H. W. J a n s o n, *Apes and Ape Lore in the Middle Ages and the Renaissance* (Studies of the Warburg Institute, XX) London, 1952

Peter J e s s e n, *Meister des Ornamentstichs, Das Barock*, II, Berlin, 1923

R. K o c h, *Artistic America, Art Nouveau, and Tiffany Glass*, Cambridge, Mass., 1970

Ernst K r i s, *Goldschmiedearbeiten des Mittelalters, der Renaissance und des Barock,*
      Vienna, 1932

Carlton L a k e    see: Françoise G i l o t

[Gilles L é g a r é], *Liure des Ouurages d'Orfèurerie fait par Gilles Légaré . . . ,* 1663

L e i p z i g, 1939    see: B e r l i n, 1939

L o n d o n, 1903-04. *Catalogue of the Goldsmiths and Silversmiths Co. Ltd.*

L o n d o n, 1951. *Early Wedgwood Pottery: Exhibited at 34 Wigmore Street, London W. 1*

H. C. M a r i l l i e r, *Dante Gabriel Rossetti: an Illustrated Memorial of his Art and Life,*
      London, 1899

Roger M a r x, *La Décoration et les industries d'art de l'Exposition Universelle de Paris
      1900,* Paris, 1902

Giuseppe M a z z a r i o l, *Mobili Italiani del Seicento e del Settecento,* Milan, 1964

G. M e u s n i e r, *La Joaillerie française en 1900,* Paris, n.d.

Giacomo M e y e r b e e r, *Robert le Diable,* 1831

M i e c z y s l a w    see: Helmut S e l i n g

*Les M o d e s,* VI, 1901, ill. p. 12

Alphonse M u c h a, *Documents décoratifs,* 1900

J. M u c h a, *Alphonse Mucha,* Prague, 1966

M u n i c h, *Schatzkammer der Residenz München* (Hans Thoma), 1958

M u n i c h, 1968    see: G. P. W o e c k e l

N e w York, 1955, Cooper Union Museum, *Nineteenth Century Jewelry from the First
      Empire to the First World War*

N e w York, 1966, Galérie St. Étienne. *Wiener Werkstätte*

N e w York, 1970, Spencer A. Samuels and Co., 18 East 76th Street. *Symbolists*

Helmut N i c k e l, "The Battle of the Crescent," *The Metropolitan Museum of Art Bul-
      letin,* XXIV, no. 3, Nov. 1965, p. 110

Pierra N u m a, drawing, *Metropolitan Museum of Art Bulletin,* XXVI, no. 3, November,
      1967, p. 145

O m a r Khayyam, *The Rubaiyat*

M. L. d'O t r a n g e, "The Exquisite Art of Carlo Giuliano," *Apollo,* LIX, June 1954,
      pp. 145ff.

P a r i s, 1889. *L'Exposition de Paris,* 1889, 2 vols.

P e l l i c e r    see: Alejandro C i r i c i Pellicer

Mary P e t e r, "Italian Influence on Victorian Jewelry," *Auction,* III, no. 1, Sept. 1969

P f o r z h e i m, 1963. *Goldschmiedekunst des Jugendstils; Schmuck und Gerät um 1900*

Marcel P r o u s t, *À l'Ombre des jeunes filles en fleurs*

*La R e v u e de la Bijouterie, la Joaillerie, et l'Orfèvrerie*
      (a) I, 1900, p. 141ff.
      (b) II, 1901
      (c) V, 1904

*R e v u e des Arts Décoratifs*
  (a) X, 1889-90, p. 177 and 182
  (b) H. Bouilhet, XIV, 1893-94, p. 88f.
  (c) XVIII, 1898
M. R h e i m s, *L'Object 1900,* Paris, 1964
S. R i n g b o m, *The Sounding Cosmos* (Åbo Academy), Helsingfors, 1970
J. C. R o c h e, "The History, Development and Organisation of the Birmingham Jewellery," *The Dial* (supplement), Birmingham, n.d., pp. 27f.
Robert S c h m u t z l e r, *Art Nouveau* (trans. Edouard Roditi), New York, c. 1962
S c h o l z-Rogues, *Schmuck aus 5 Jahrtausenden,* Hamburg, 1960
Sir Walter S c o t t, *Waverly* novels, 1814ff.
S e c e s j a   see: Helmut S e l i n g
Helmut S e l i n g, ed., Wallis, Mieczyslaw, and Secesja (intro. Kurt Bauch), *Jugendstil; der Weg ins 20. Jahrhundert . . . ,* eds. Heidelberg/Munich, 1959 and Warsaw, 1967
Rodolfo S i v i e r o, *Jewelry and Amber of Italy. A Collection in the National Museum of Naples,* New York, 1959
Harold Clifford S m i t h, *Jewellery,* London, (1908)
K. S n o w m a n, *The Art of Carl Fabergé,* Boston, n.d.
Francis S p a r, ed. *Le Style anglais* (Collection Connaissance des Arts, IV), Paris, 1959
*S t a t u s,* March 1966, p. 43
Erich S t e i n g r ä b e r,
  (a) *Antique Jewellery,* London, 1957
  (b) ed., *Royal Treasures* (trans. Stefan de Haan), London and New York, 1968
*The S t u d i o,* London
  (a) XVIII, 1900, p. 197
  (b) XXIII, June 1901, p. 176
  (c) "Modern Design in Jewellery and Fans," special winter number, 1901-02
  (d) XXIV, 1902, p. 245ff.
  (e) XXV, 1902, p. 141
  (f) XXVII, 1903, p. 207
  (g) M. J. Partridge, XXXV, 1905, p. 127 f.
Hans T h o m a   see: M u n i c h, *Schatzkammer . . .*
Henri V e v e r
  (a) *La Bijouterie française au XIXe siècle,* 3 vols., Paris, 1908
  (b) *Les Bijoux au Salon de 1898,* Paris 1898
  (c) "Les Bijoux au Salon de 1898," *Revue des Arts Décoratifs,* Paris, 1899
V i e n n a, 1967, Oesterreichisches Museum für Angewandte Kunst. *Die Wiener Werkstätte*

Wallis    see: Helmut Seling

H. B. Walters, *Catalogue of the Engraved Gems and Cameos, Greek, Etruscan and Roman in the British Museum,* London, 1926

R. Watkinson, *Pre-Raphaelite Art and Design,* London, 1970

[G. P. Woeckel], *Dr. Gerhard P. Woeckel, Jugendstilsammlung,* Munich, 1968

*Zeitschrift für Bijouterie,* Weimar

     (a) II, no. 4, 1848, fig. 44-51

     (b) III, 1851

     (c) IV, no. 2

Henri Zerner, *The School of Fontainebleau, Etchings and Engravings,* New York, 1969

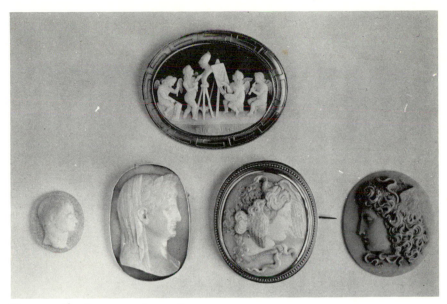

Figure 1. Catalogue number 1

Figure 2. Catalogue numbers 2-6

Figure 3. Catalogue numbers 7-11

Figure 4. Catalogue number 12

Figure 5. *Ariadne Riding on the Panther*

Figure 6. *The Greek Slave*

Figure 7. Statue by E. A. Carrier-Belleuse

Figure 8. Statue by E. A. Carrier-Belleuse

Figure 9. Catalogue numbers 13-27

Figure 10. Catalogue numbers 28-33

Figure 11. Catalogue numbers 34-35

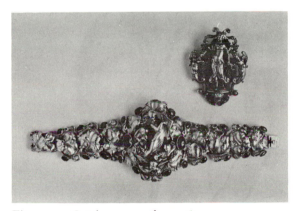

Figure 12. Catalogue numbers 36-37

Figure 13. Catalogue numbers 38-41

Figure 14. Catalogue numbers 42-44 · Figure 15. Catalogue number 45

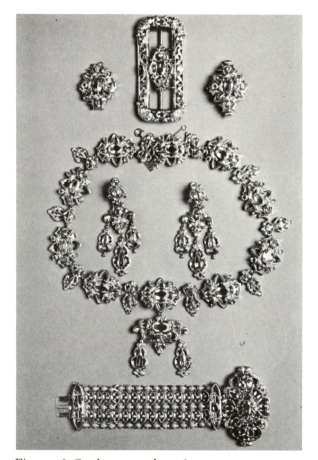

Figure 17. Catalogue number 47

Figure 16. Catalogue number 46 · Figure 18. Catalogue number 48

Figure 19. Catalogue number 49

Figure 20. Catalogue number 51

Figure 21. Catalogue number 52

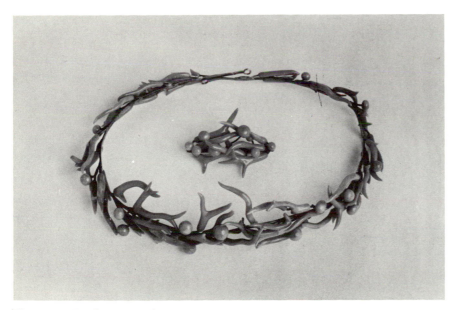

Figure 22. Catalogue number 53

Figure 23. Catalogue number 54

Figure 24. Catalogue number 55

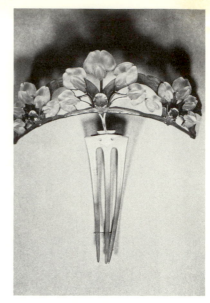

Figure 25. Catalogue number 57

Figure 26. Catalogue number 58

Figure 28. Catalogue number 60

Figure 27. Catalogue number 59

Figure 29. Catalogue number 61

Figure 30. Catalogue number 62

Figure 31. Catalogue number 63

Figure 32. Catalogue number 65

Figure 33. Catalogue number 66

Figure 34. Catalogue number 67

Figure 35. Catalogue number 68

Figure 36. Catalogue number 70

Figure 37. Catalogue number 73

Figure 38. Catalogue number 75

Figure 40. Catalogue number 76

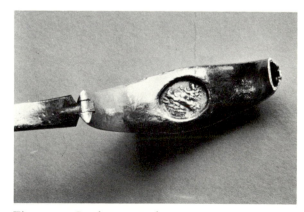

Figure 39. Catalogue number 75

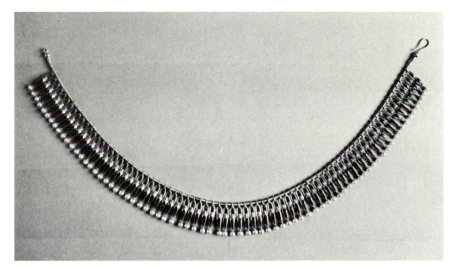

Figure 41. Catalogue number 77

Figure 42. Catalogue number 78

Figure 43. Catalogue number 79

Figure 44. Catalogue number 80

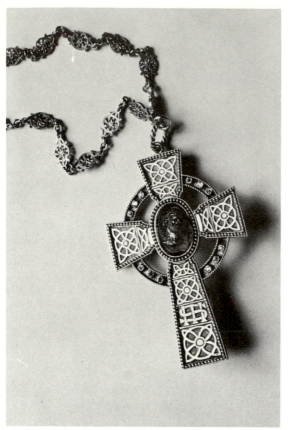

Figure 46. Catalogue number 81

Figure 47. Catalogue number 83

Figure 48. Catalogue number 84

Figure 49. Catalogue number 85

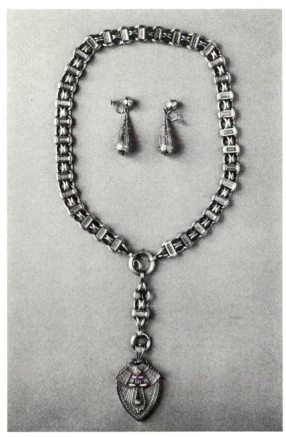

Figure 50. Catalogue number 86

Figure 51. Catalogue number 87

Figure 53. Catalogue number 89

Figure 52. Catalogue number 88

Figure 54. Catalogue number 90

Figure 55. Catalogue number 91

Figure 57. Catalogue number 94

Figure 56. Catalogue number 92

Figure 58. Catalogue number 95

Figure 60. Catalogue numbers 101-104

Figure 61. Catalogue numbers 105-113

Figure 59. Catalogue numbers 96-100

Figure 62. Catalogue number 114

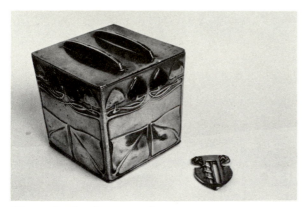

Figure 63. Catalogue number 115

Figure 64. Catalogue number 116

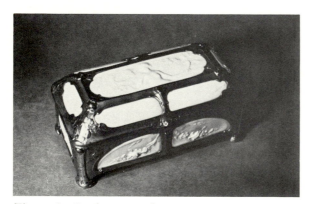

Figure 65. Catalogue number 117

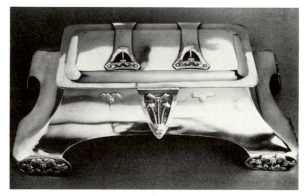

Figure 66. Catalogue number 118

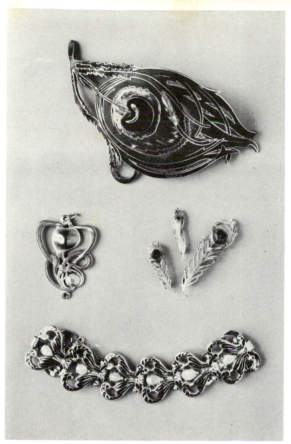

Figure 67. Catalogue numbers 119-122

Figure 69. Catalogue number 131

Figure 70. Catalogue number 133

Figure 68. Catalogue numbers 123-129

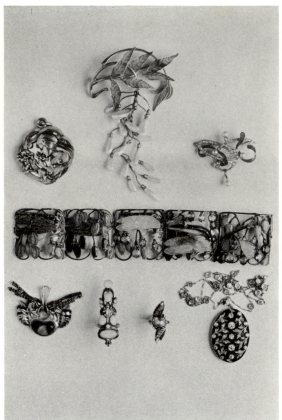

Figure 72. Catalogue number 142

Figure 71. Catalogue numbers 134-141

Figure 73. Catalogue number 143     Figure 74. Catalogue number 144     Figure 75. Catalogue number 145

Plate 2. Catalogue number 56

Plate 1. Catalogue number 50

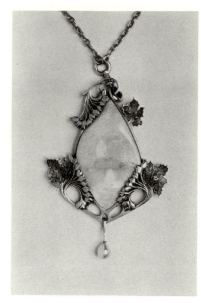

Figure 76. Catalogue number 148     Figure 77. Catalogue number 150     Figure 78. Catalogue number 154

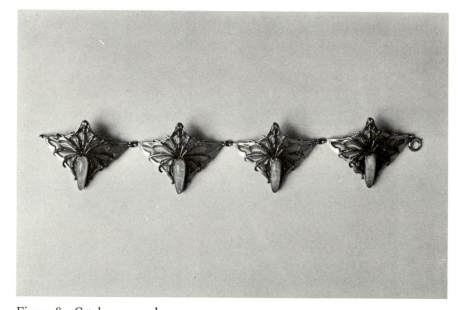

Figure 79. Catalogue number 155     Figure 80. Catalogue number 147

Figure 81. Catalogue number 156

Figure 82. Catalogue number 157

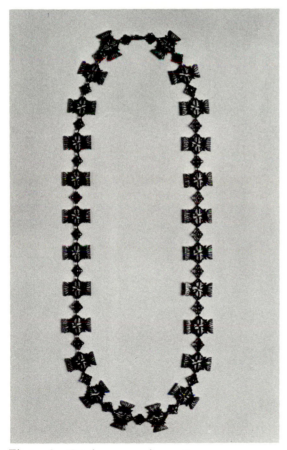

Figure 83. Catalogue number 158

Figure 84. Catalogue number 159

Figure 85. Catalogue number 160

Plate 5. Catalogue number 71

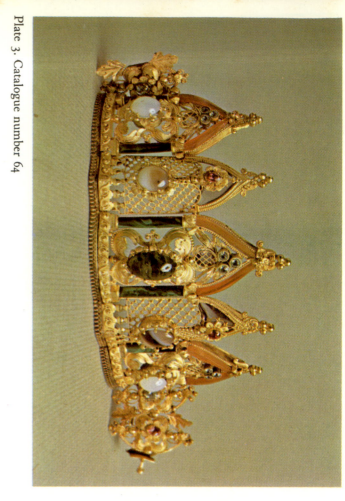

Plate 3. Catalogue number 64

Plate 6. Catalogue number 74

Plate 4. Catalogue number 69

Plate 7. Catalogue number 72      Plate 8. Catalogue number 146      Plate 9. Catalogue number 93

Plate 10. Catalogue number 130

Plate 11. Catalogue number 149

Figure 87. Catalogue number 162

Figure 86. Catalogue number 161

Figure 88. Catalogue number 163

Figure 89. Catalogue number 164     Figure 90. Catalogue number 166     Figure 91. Catalogue number 167

Figure 92. Catalogue number 169

Figure 93. Catalogue number 170

Figure 94. Catalogue number 171

Figure 95. Catalogue number 171

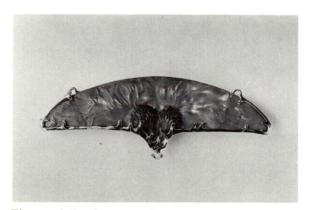

Figure 96. Catalogue number 173

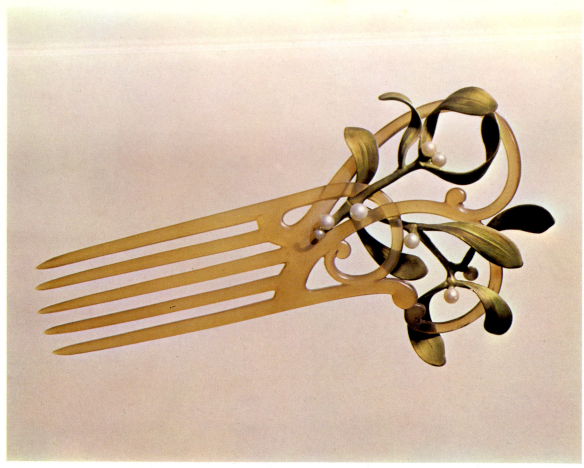

Plate 12. Catalogue number 132

Plate 13. Catalogue number 153

Plate 14. Catalogue number 151

Plate 15. Catalogue number 164

Plate 17. Catalogue number 168

Plate 16. Catalogue number 152

Plate 18. Catalogue number 172

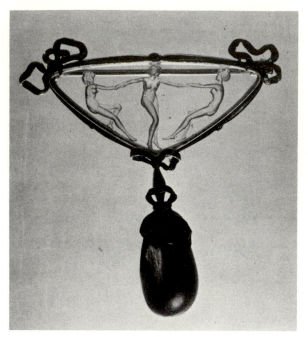

Figure 97. Catalogue number 174

Figure 98. Catalogue number 175

Figure 99. Catalogue number 176

Figure 100. Catalogue number 178

Figure 101. Catalogue number 179

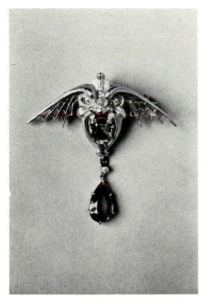

Figure 102. Catalogue number 180

Figure 103. Catalogue number 181

Figure 104. Catalogue number 183

Figure 105. Catalogue number 182

Figure 106. Catalogue number 184

Plate 19. Catalogue number 165

Plate 20. Catalogue number 185

Plate 21. Catalogue number 177

Plate 23. Catalogue number 193

Plate 24. Catalogue number 198

Plate 22. Catalogue number 189

Figure 107. Catalogue number 186

Figure 108. Catalogue number 187

Figure 109. Catalogue number 188

Figure 110. Catalogue number 190

Figure 111. Catalogue number 191

Figure 112. Catalogue number 192

Figure 113. Catalogue number 197

Figure 114. Catalogue numbers 195-196

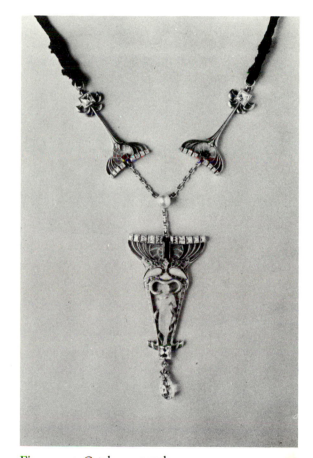

Figure 115. Catalogue number 194

Plate 25. Catalogue numbers 218-225

Figure 116. Catalogue number 199

Figure 117. Catalogue number 200

Figure 118. Catalogue number 201

Figure 119. Catalogue numbers 202-204

Figure 120. Catalogue number 205

Figure 122. Catalogue numbers 207-212

Figure 123. Catalogue number 213

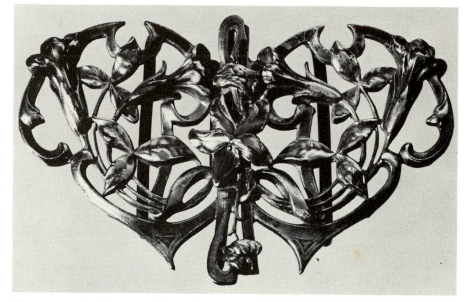

Figure 124. Catalogue number 214

Figure 121. Catalogue number 206

Figure 125. Catalogue number 215

Figure 129. Catalogue number 228

Figure 126. Catalogue number 216

Figure 128. Catalogue number 226

Figure 127. Catalogue number 217

Figure 130. *Le Parnasse Satirique,* by Félicien Rops

Figure 131. *Mors Syphilitica,* by Félicien Rops

Figure 132. Portrait of Sarah Bernhardt, by Georges Clairin, 1876

Figure 133. *Peace in the Home,* by Jean Dampt, ca. 1900

Figure 134. Gustav Klimt, Portrait, 1906

Figure 135. Burgundian brooch, 15th century

Figure 136. *Ariel*, by Joseph Severn, 1828

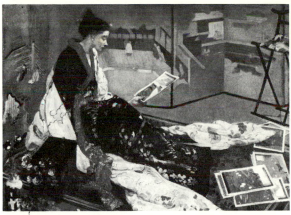

Figure 137. *Caprice in Purple and Gold*: No. 2, by James A. McN. Whistler, 1864

Figure 138. Enamelling demonstration kit, by Alexis Falize (Victoria and Albert Museum)

Figure 139. *Fra Pace*, by Dante Gabriel Rossetti

Figure 140. *Regina Cordium* (detail) by Dante Gabriel Rossetti

Figure 141. *The Loving Cup*, by Dante Gabriel Rossetti

Figure 142. *The Bride*, by Dante Gabriel Rossetti

Figure 143. *Desdemona's Death Song*, by Dante Gabriel Rossetti (1878)

Figure 144. Study for *Dante's Dream*, by Dante Gabriel Rossetti

Figure 145. *Swan Princess*, print by Jan Toorop, 1893

Figure 146. Tiffany & Co., sugar bowl, 1893

Figure 147. Tiffany & Co., coffee service, ca. 1893 (Hartman Galleries)

Figure 148. Tiffany & Co., box, ca. 1893

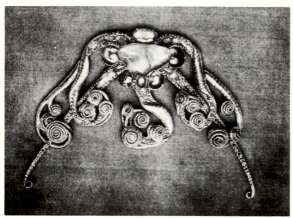

Figure 150. Louis C. Tiffany, Octopus necklace, ca. 1906

Figure 149. Tiffany & Co., silver vase with baroque pearls, ca. 1893

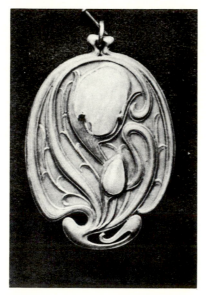

Figure 151. Edward Colonna, pendant, ca. 1898

Figure 152. Edward Colonna, pendant, ca. 1898

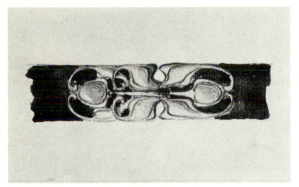

Figure 153. Edward Colonna, design for a dog-collar plaque (Newark, N. J., Public Library)

Figure 154. Bowl of plique á jour enamel, Thesmar, ca. 1900

Figure 155. Bowl of plique á jour enamel, Thesmar, ca. 1900

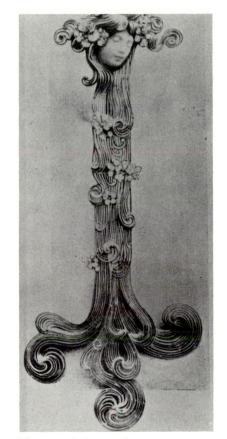

Figure 156. Cameo face corsage ornament, René Lalique

Figure 157. Horseman (plaster model), by René Lalique

Figure 158. Pastel portrait of a woman, by René Lalique

Figure 160. Dragonfly-woman corsage ornament, by René Lalique ca. 1895

Figure 159. Study of a cock's head, by René Laliquè

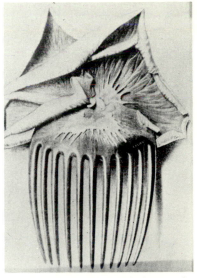

Figure 161. Serpent corsage ornament, by René Lalique, 1900

Figure 162. Cock's head comb, by René Lalique, 1900

Figure 163. Flower comb, by René Lalique, 1902

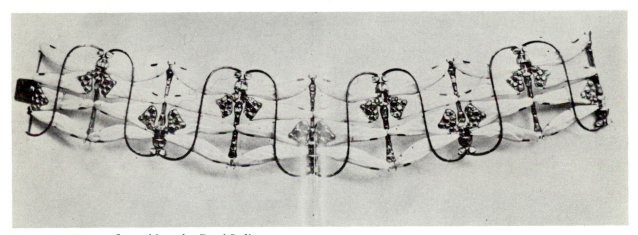

Figure 164. Dragonfly necklace, by René Lalique, 1902

Figure 165. Cameo Pendant, by René Lalique, 1900

Figure 166. Orchid brooch, by Vever Fres., ca. 1900

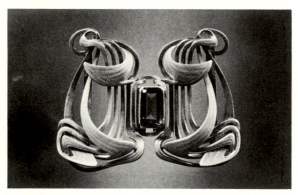

Figure 167. Buckle by Henri Van de Velde, ca. 1900

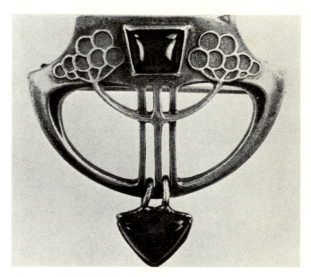

Figure 168. Buckle by Patriz Huber for Th. Fahrner & Co. ca. 1900

Figure 169. Pendant from Mallia (Crete) ca. 1700 B.C.

Figure 170. Shield (theater design) by A. J. Shirley, 1899

Figure 171. Japanese lacquer box, 17th century

Figure 173. Moulded bricks, Savannah, Georgia Cotton Exchange, late 1880's

Figure 172. The Eiffel Tower, 1889

Figure 174. Wistaria comb, by René Lalique, ca. 1900

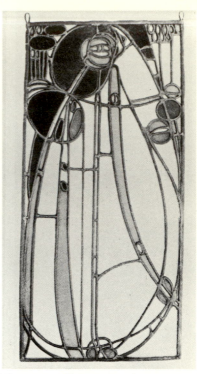

Figure 175. Decorative glass panel, by C. R. Mackintosh

Figure 176. Drawing for *Salome*, by Aubrey Beardsley

Figure 177. Drawing by Walter Crane

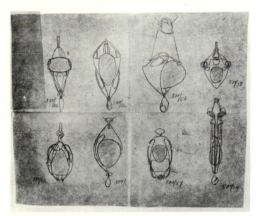

Figure 178. Jewelry designs for Liberty & Co.

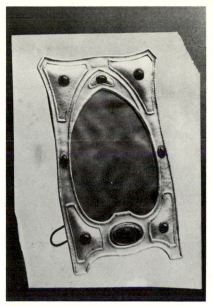

Figure 179. Picture frame, C. R. Ashbee design

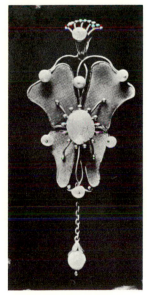

Figure 180. Pendant, C. R. Ashbee design

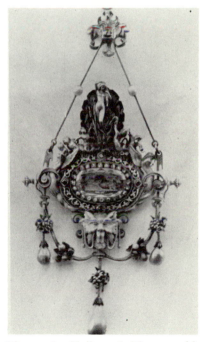

Figure 181. *Toilette de Venus* necklace by Froment-Meurice

Figure 182. Silver and cameo clasp, by René Lalique, ca. 1900

Figure 183. Competition designs, 1891, Union Centrale des Arts Decoratifs.

# Math in Focus®
## Singapore Math®
### by Marshall Cavendish

# Workbook

**Consultant and Author**
Dr. Fong Ho Kheong

**Authors**
Chelvi Ramakrishnan and Michelle Choo

**U.S. Consultants**
Dr. Richard Bisk, Andy Clark, and Patsy F. Kanter

**Marshall Cavendish**
Education

U.S. Distributor

Houghton
Mifflin
Harcourt

© 2015 Marshall Cavendish Education Pte Ltd

**Published by Marshall Cavendish Education**
*An imprint of Marshall Cavendish Education Pte Ltd*
Times Centre, 1 New Industrial Road, Singapore 536196
Customer Service Hotline: (65) 6213 9444
US Office Tel: (1-914) 332 8888  Fax: (1-914) 332 8882
E-mail: tmesales@mceducation.com
Website: www.mceducation.com

Distributed by
**Houghton Mifflin Harcourt**
222 Berkeley Street
Boston, MA 02116
Tel: 617-351-5000
Website: www.hmheducation.com/mathinfocus

First published 2015

*Math in Focus*® Workbook 2B
ISBN 978-0-544-19383-3

Printed in Singapore

11  12  13  14          1401    20  19  18
4500696653                      A B C D E

# Contents

# Fractions

# Customary Measurement of Length

# Time

# Multiplication Tables of 3 and 4

# Using Bar Models: Multiplication and Division

**CHAPTER 16**

# Graphs and Line Plots

**CHAPTER 17**

# CHAPTER 10 Mental Math and Estimation

## Practice 1   Meaning of Sum

**Find the sum of the numbers.**

---
**Example**

96 and 73

$$\begin{array}{r} 9\ 6 \\ +\ 7\ 3 \\ \hline \boxed{169} \end{array}$$

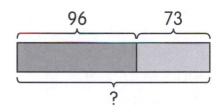

The sum of 96 and 73 is ___169___.

---

1.   700 and 200

$$\begin{array}{r} 7\ 0\ 0 \\ +\ 2\ 0\ 0 \\ \hline \boxed{\phantom{000}} \end{array}$$

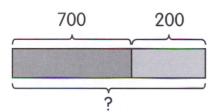

The sum of _____ and _____ is _____.

2.   215 and 507

$$\begin{array}{r} 2\ 1\ 5 \\ +\ 5\ 0\ 7 \\ \hline \boxed{\phantom{000}} \end{array}$$

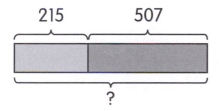

The sum of _____ and _____ is _____.

**Solve.**
**Use bar models to help you.**

3. Al spent $27 on a shirt and $120 on books.
   Find the sum of money Al spent.

   _____ + _____ = _____

   The sum of money Al spent is $_____.

4. Harry is 12 years old.
   His sister is 9 years younger.
   Find the sum of their ages.

   _____ − _____ = _____

   _____ + _____ = _____

   The sum of their ages is _____ years.

5. Greg has collected 32 green jumping beans.
   His mother gives him 15 red jumping beans more.
   Find the sum of jumping beans Greg has now.

   _____ + _____ = _____

   The sum of jumping beans Greg has now is _____.

**Name:** _____  **Date:** _____

# Practice 2   Mental Addition

**Climb each step by adding mentally.**

1.

93 + 6

63 + 4

72 + 7

96 + 2

54 + 3

45 + 4

73 + 3

29

21 + 8

**Find the missing numbers.**
**Add mentally.**

┌─ **Example** ─────────────┐

38 + 7 = ?

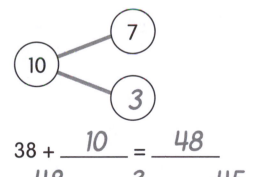

10 — 7
     — 3

38 + __10__ = __48__

__48__ – __3__ = __45__

So, 38 + 7 = __45__.

└──────────────────────────┘

2.   75 + 6 = ?

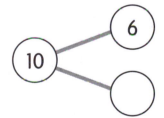

10 — 6
     — ○

75 + _____ = _____

_____ – _____ = _____

So, 75 + 6 = _____.

3.   69 + 5 = _____

4.   48 + 4 = _____

5.   29 + 9 = _____

6.   65 + 8 = _____

**Find the missing numbers.**
**Add mentally.**

---
**Example**

123 + 5 = ?

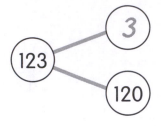

__3__ + 5 = __8__

__120__ + __8__ = __128__

So, 123 + 5 = __128__ .

---

**7.**   632 + 7 = _____

**8.**   712 + 3 = _____

**9.**   534 + 5 = _____

---
**Example**

409 + 7 = ?

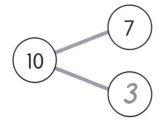

409 + __10__ = __419__

__419__ − __3__ = __416__

So, 409 + 7 = __416__ .

---

**10.**   375 + 6 = _____

**11.**   275 + 8 = _____

**12.**   629 + 9 = _____

**Find the missing numbers.**
**Add mentally.**

**Example**

$246 + 20 = ?$

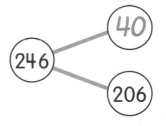

$\underline{\phantom{4}40\phantom{4}} + 20 = \underline{\phantom{4}60\phantom{4}}$

$\underline{206} + \underline{\phantom{4}60\phantom{4}} = \underline{266}$

So, $246 + 20 = \underline{266}$.

**Example**

$352 + 70 = ?$

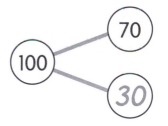

$352 + \underline{\phantom{4}100\phantom{4}} = \underline{452}$

$\underline{452} - \underline{\phantom{4}30\phantom{4}} = \underline{422}$

So, $352 + 70 = \underline{422}$.

**13.**  $348 + 50 = $ _____

**14.**  $741 + 30 = $ _____

**15.**  $653 + 10 = $ _____

**16.**  $427 + 80 = $ _____

**17.**  $535 + 90 = $ _____

**18.**  $164 + 60 = $ _____

**Find the missing numbers.**
**Add mentally.**

**Example**

315 + 200 = ?

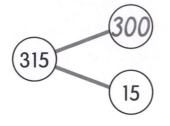

*300* + 200 = *500*

*15* + *500* = *515*

So, 315 + 200 = *515*.

**19.** 765 + 100 = ?

_____ + 100 = _____

_____ + _____ = _____

So, 765 + 100 = _____.

**Add mentally.**

**20.** 452 + 500 = _____

**21.** 264 + 300 = _____

**22.** 412 + 300 = _____

**23.** 178 + 300 = _____

**24.** 708 + 200 = _____

**25.** 320 + 600 = _____

# Practice 3   Meaning of Difference

**Find the difference between the numbers.**

---

**Example**

40 and 17

```
  4 0
– 1 7
```

___40___ – ___17___ = ___23___

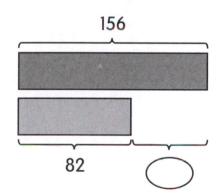

The difference between 40 and 17 is ___23___.

---

**1.**   156 and 82

```
  1 5 6
–   8 2
```

_____ – _____ = _____

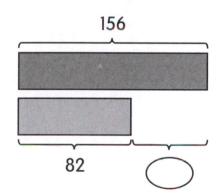

The difference between 156 and 82 is _____.

**2.**   800 and 785

```
  8 0 0
– 7 8 5
```

_____ – _____ = _____

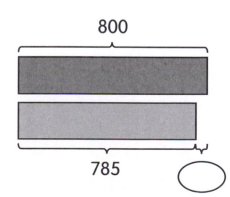

The difference between 800 and 785 is _____.

## Solve.
## Use bar models to help you.

**3.** Tonya collected 320 friendship bracelets and her sister collected 290.
Find the difference between the number of friendship bracelets.

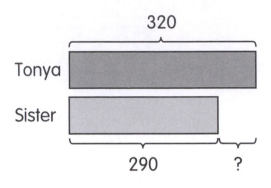

_____ – _____ = _____

The difference is _____ friendship bracelets.

**4.** Joe and Susan went for a run.
Joe ran 24 laps and Susan ran 15 laps.
Find the difference between the number of laps they ran.

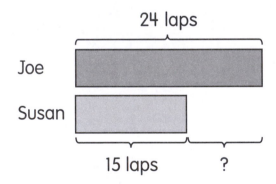

_____ – _____ = _____

The difference is _____ laps.

Name: _____     Date: _____

## Solve.
## Use bar models to help you.

**5.** Kiki baked 120 muffins on Monday.
She baked 219 muffins on Tuesday.
What is the difference between these two amounts?

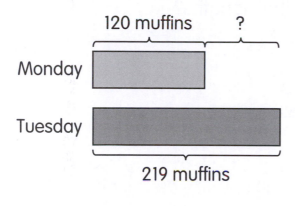

120 muffins     ?

Monday

Tuesday

219 muffins

_____ − _____ = _____

The difference is _____ muffins.

**6.** Mr. Wong wants to buy a camera that costs $401.
He saved $315.
What is the difference between the amounts of money?

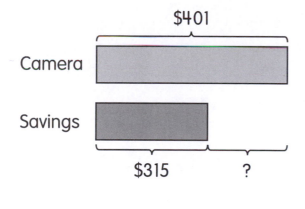

$401

Camera

Savings

$315     ?

The difference shows how much more money Mr. Wong needs to buy the camera.

_____ − _____ = _____

The difference is $ _____.

**Solve.**
**Use bar models to help you.**

**7.**     Elizabeth has a blue ribbon and a red ribbon.
The blue ribbon is 27 centimeters long.
The red ribbon is 18 centimeters long.
What is the difference between their lengths?

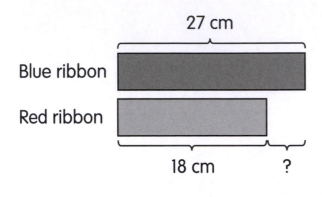

_____ − _____ = _____

The difference is _____ centimeters.

# Practice 4   Mental Subtraction

**Find the missing numbers.**
**Subtract mentally.**

**Example**

43 – 6 = ?

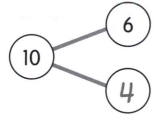

43 – _10_ = _33_

_33_ + _4_ = _37_

So, 43 – 6 = _37_.

**1.**    56 – 8 = ?

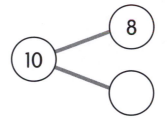

56 – _____ = _____

_____ + _____ = _____

So, 56 – 8 = _____.

**Subtract mentally.**

**2.**    84 – 7 = _____

**3.**    38 – 9 = _____

**4.**    62 – 8 = _____

**5.**    76 – 7 = _____

**Find the missing numbers.**
**Subtract mentally.**

**Example**

789 – 5 = ?

789 ── 9
     └─ 780

___9___ – 5 = ___4___

___780___ + ___4___ = ___784___

So, 789 – 5 = ___784___.

6. 398 – 4 = _____

7. 427 – 2 = _____

8. 358 – 6 = _____

**Find the missing numbers.**
**Subtract mentally.**

**Example**

364 – 6 = ?

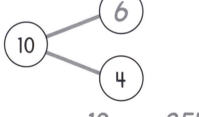

10 ── 6
   └─ 4

364 – ___10___ = ___354___

___354___ + ___4___ = ___358___

So, 364 – 6 = ___358___.

9. 472 – 3 = _____

10. 513 – 9 = _____

11. 394 – 7 = _____

**Find the missing numbers.**
**Subtract mentally.**

┌─── **Example** ─────────────────┐

348 − 20 = ?

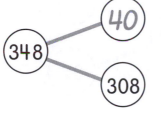

$\underline{40} − 20 = \underline{20}$

$\underline{308} + \underline{20} = \underline{328}$

So, 348 − 20 = $\underline{328}$.

└────────────────────────────────┘

**12.** 475 − 40 = _____

**13.** 466 − 30 = _____

**14.** 654 − 50 = _____

**Find the missing numbers.**
**Subtract mentally.**

┌─── **Example** ─────────────────┐

641 − 50 = ?

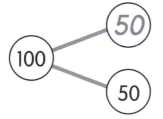

641 − $\underline{100}$ = $\underline{541}$

$\underline{541} + \underline{50} = \underline{591}$

So, 641 − 50 = $\underline{591}$.

└────────────────────────────────┘

**15.** 516 − 70 = _____

**16.** 228 − 30 = _____

**17.** 436 − 40 = _____

**Find the missing numbers.**
**Subtract mentally.**

$256 - 100 = ?$

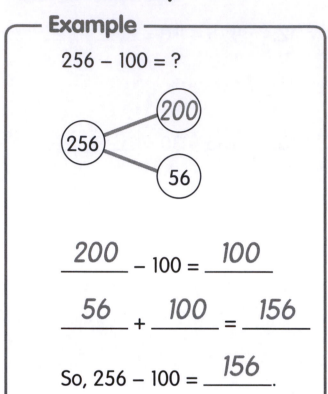

$\underline{\quad 200 \quad} - 100 = \underline{\quad 100 \quad}$

$\underline{\quad 56 \quad} + \underline{\quad 100 \quad} = \underline{\quad 156 \quad}$

So, $256 - 100 = \underline{\quad 156 \quad}$.

**18.**  $832 - 400 = ?$

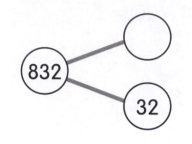

$\underline{\qquad} - 400 = \underline{\qquad}$

$\underline{\qquad} + \underline{\qquad} = \underline{\qquad}$

So, $832 - 400 = \underline{\qquad}$.

**Find the missing numbers.**
**Subtract mentally.**

**19.**  $348 - 300 = \underline{\qquad}$

**20.**  $548 - 300 = \underline{\qquad}$

**21.**  $615 - 400 = \underline{\qquad}$

**22.**  $465 - 200 = \underline{\qquad}$

Name: _____    Date: _____

# Practice 5   Rounding Numbers to Estimate

**Mark each number with an X on the number line.**

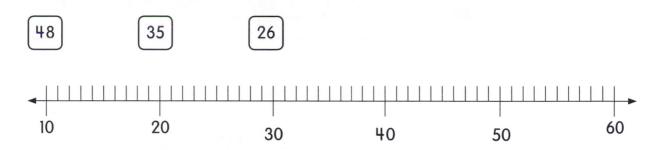

| 48 | | 35 | | 26 |

10    20    30    40    50    60

**Round each number to the nearest ten.**
**Circle it on the number line. Then fill in the blanks.**

┌─ **Example** ─────────────────────────────────────────────┐

12 is nearer to ___*10*___ than to ___*20*___.

10 ──X────────── 20

12 is about ___*10*___ when rounded to the nearest ten.

└───────────────────────────────────────────────────────────┘

1.    48 is nearer to _____ than to _____.

      48 is about _____ when rounded to the nearest ten.

2.    35 is about _____ when rounded to the nearest ten.

3.    26 is nearer to _____ than to _____.

      26 is about _____ when rounded to the nearest ten.

**Look at the digits in the tens place. Then fill in the blanks.**

─── **Example** ───

37 is between ___30___ and ___40___.

4.     86        86 is between _____ and _____.

5.     93        93 is between _____ and _____.

6.     286      286 is between _____ and _____.

7.     721      721 is between _____ and _____.

**Mark each number with an X on the number line.**
**Round each number to the nearest ten.**
**Circle the number on the number line.**
**Then fill in the last column of the table.**

| Number | Number line | Write using 'is about' |
|---|---|---|
| **Example** 315 | 310    315    (320)   (X above 315) | *315* is about *320*. |
| 8.   769 | 760       770 | |
| 9.   501 | 500       510 | |
| 10.   896 | 890       900 | |

Name: _____   Date: _____

**Complete the table.**

| | Number | Rounded to the nearest ten | Write using 'is about' |
|---|---|---|---|
| | Example 78 | 80 | 78 is about 80 |
| **11.** | 15 | | |
| **12.** | 34 | | |
| **13.** | 217 | | |
| **14.** | 697 | | |
| **15.** | 728 | | |

**The numbers in each problem are rounded to the nearest ten. Find the greatest and least number that is rounded. Use the number line to help you.**

**Example**

Mr. Johnson spent about $80 at a department store.

The greatest amount he could have spent is $____84____.

The least amount he could have spent is $____75____.

**16.** Charles drinks about 790 milliliters of fruit juice in one day.

The greatest amount he could have had is _____ milliliters.

The least amount he could have had is _____ milliliters.

**17.** Shateel ran about 750 meters.

The greatest distance she could have run is _____ meters.

The least distance she could have run is _____ meters.

**18.** The mass of a bag of potatoes is about 830 grams.

The greatest mass of the potatoes could be _____ grams.

The least mass of the potatoes could be _____ grams.

**Find the sum or difference.**
**Then round each number to the nearest ten.**
**Estimate the sum or difference to check that the answers**
**are reasonable.**

---

**Example**

763 + 36 = 799

763 is about _____760_____.

36 is about _____40_____.

760 + 40 = _____800_____.

So, 763 + 36 is about _____800_____.

Is the answer reasonable?

Explain. _____Yes, because 800 is close to 799._____

---

**19.**   238 + 98 = _____

238 is about _____.

98 is about _____.

_____ + _____ = _____.

So, 238 + 98 is about _____.

Is the answer reasonable? Explain. _____

**20.**   847 − 95 = _____

847 is about _____.

95 is about _____.

_____ − _____ = _____.

So, 846 − 95 is about _____.

Is the answer reasonable? Explain. _____

**21.** 781 + 49 = _____

Check: _____ + _____ = _____.

Is the answer reasonable? Explain. _____

_____

_____

**22.** 259 − 72 = _____

Check: _____ − _____ = _____.

Is the answer reasonable? Explain. _____

_____

**23.** The school principal has $900 to buy items for the school.
Round the cost of each item to the nearest ten.
Then estimate the total cost.

A set of 4 textbooks costs $96.

**a.** 96 is _____ when rounded to the nearest ten.

A printer costs $215.

**b.** 215 is _____ when rounded to the nearest ten.

A camera costs $147.

**c.** 147 is _____ when rounded to the nearest ten.

A computer costs $385.

**d.** 385 is _____ when rounded to the nearest ten.

The estimated total cost is $_____.

Does the principal have enough money to pay for all the items?

_____

# Chapter Review/Test

## Vocabulary

**Fill in the blanks with words from the box.**

| |
|---|
| sum |
| difference |
| nearest ten |
| reasonable |

1.    You can use an estimate to check that a sum

is _____.

2.    86 is 90 when rounded to the _____.

3.    Add to find the _____ of two or more numbers.

4.    Subtract to find the _____ between two or more numbers.

# Concepts and Skills

**Add mentally.**

5.    325 + 9 = _____

6.    436 + 20 = _____

7.    691 + 70 = _____

8.    635 + 300 = _____

**Subtract mentally.**

9.    541 – 5 = _____

10.    863 – 50 = _____

11.    238 – 70 = _____

12.    617 – 400 = _____

**Round each number to the nearest ten.**

13.    65 is about _____.

14.    132 is about _____.

15.    29 is about _____.

16.    396 is about _____.

**Find the sum or difference. Then round each number to the nearest ten to check that the answers are reasonable.**

**17.** 76 + 83 = _____

_____ + _____ = _____

**18.** 182 + 95 = _____

_____ + _____ = _____

**19.** 628 – 145 = _____

_____ – _____ = _____

**20.** 598 – 136 = _____

_____ – _____ = _____

## Problem Solving

**Solve. Then use estimation to check that the answers are reasonable.**

**21.** Mrs. Brown buys a set of books and a giant teddy bear.
The set of books costs $154.
The giant teddy bear costs $122.
Find the sum of the amount for both prices.

_____ + _____ = _____

Check: _____ + _____ = _____.

Is the answer reasonable? Explain. _____

_____

The two things cost about $_____.

**22.** Pete earns $103 a month delivering newspapers.
Shawn earns $175 a month delivering pizzas.
What is the difference in the amounts they earn?

_____ – _____ = _____

Check: _____ – _____ = _____.

Is the answer reasonable? Explain. _____

_____

The difference is about $_____.

Name: _____   Date: _____

# Money

## Practice 1   Coins and Bills

Circle the bills that make the given amount.

**Example**

=

1.

=

2.

=

## Circle the coins that make one dollar.

**3.**

 =

**4.**

 =

## Find the value of the coins.
## Then write *less than*, *equal to*, or *more than*.

— **Example** —

__more than__ $1.

**5.**

_____ $1.

**Name:** _____  **Date:** _____

**6.**

_____ $1.

**7.**

_____ $1.

## Write the amount of money.

**Example**

$10

**8.**

$ _____

**9.**

$_____

## Write the amount of money.

**Example**

Eighty-two dollars and seven cents

$ *82.07*

**10.**

Ninety-six cents

$_____

**11.**

Sixty-one dollars

$_____

**Name:** _____  **Date:** _____

## Write the amount of money.

**12.**

Fourteen dollars and ninety-nine cents

$_____

**13.**

Thirty dollars and fifty cents

$_____

**14.**

Fifteen dollars

$_____

**15.**

Seventy-eight dollars and twenty-five cents

$_____

## Fill in the blanks.

**Example**

$20.00 ..................... ____20____ dollars ____0____ cents

**16.**  $.03  .....................  _____ dollars _____ cents

**17.**  $40.20  .....................  _____ dollars _____ cents

**18.**  $27.15  .....................  _____ dollars _____ cents

**Match.**

**19.**

•                    •    $1.45

**20.**

•                    •    $.15

**21.**

•                    •    $8.00

**22.**

•                    •    $13.35

# Count the money.
# Then circle the correct amount.

**Example**

$ 2.06

$20.60

($26)

---

**23.**

$7.00

$7.07

$7.70

---

**24.**

$1.10

$11.00

$.11

---

**25.**

$50.15

$.65

$5.15

## Complete.

**Example**

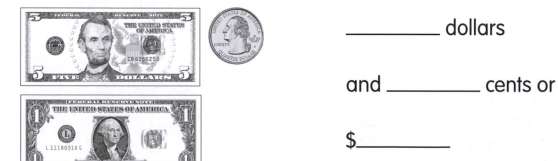

_____6_____ dollars

and _____10_____ cents or

$_____6.10_____

26.

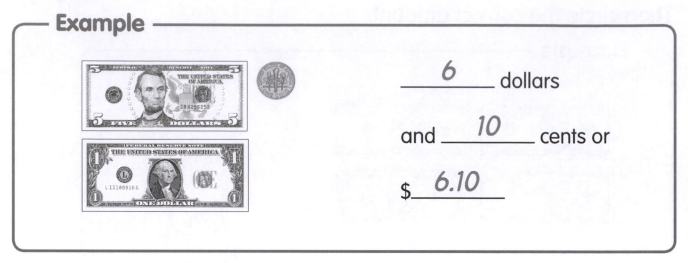

_____ dollars

and _____ cents or

$_____

27.

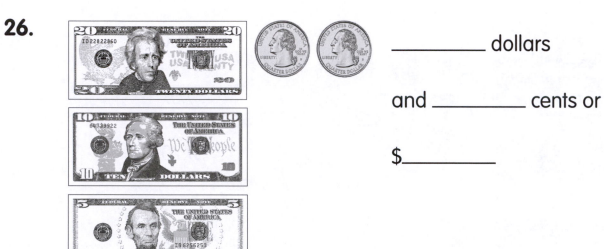

_____ dollars

and _____ cents or

$_____

**28.**

_____ dollars

and _____ cents or

$_____

**29.**

_____ dollar

and _____ cents or

$_____

**30.**

_____ dollar

and _____ cents or

$_____

# Write the amount of money in two ways.

**Example**

___65___ ¢ or $___.65___

**31.**

_____ ¢ or $_____

**32.**

$_____ or $_____

**33.**

$_____ or $_____

# Write the amount of money in two ways.

**Example**

$ _____2.20_____ or _____220_____ ¢

**34.**

$_____ or _____¢

**35.**

$_____ or _____¢

**36.**

$_____ or _____¢

## Write the cents in dollars and cents.

---
**Example**

| 20¢ | $.20 |
|-----|------|
---

**37.** 120¢ _____

**38.** 543¢ _____    **39.** 106¢ _____

**40.** 350¢ _____    **41.** 83¢ _____

**42.** 17¢ _____    **43.** 2¢ _____

## Write the dollars and cents in cents.

---
**Example**

| $4.80 | 480¢ |
|-------|------|
---

**44.** $3.51 _____

**45.** $6.95 _____    **46.** $1.05 _____

**47.** $.44 _____    **48.** $.69 _____

**49.** $8 _____    **50.** $7 _____

# Practice 2  Comparing Amounts of Money

**Compare the amounts.**
**Complete the tables and fill in the blanks.**

## Example

Joey
$14.20

| Dollars | Cents |
| --- | --- |
| 14 | 20 |

Carl
$15.00

| Dollars | Cents |
| --- | --- |
| 15 | 00 |

First, compare the dollars. 15 is greater than 14.

$ *15.00* is more than $ *14.20* .

$ *14.20* is less than $ *15.00* .

**1.**

Mae
$70.40

| Dollars | Cents |
| --- | --- |
|  |  |

Karen
$70.35

| Dollars | Cents |
| --- | --- |
|  |  |

$_____ > $_____

$_____ < $_____

**2.**

| Dollars | Cents |
|---------|-------|
|         |       |

$16.70

| Dollars | Cents |
|---------|-------|
|         |       |

$16.15

| Dollars | Cents |
|---------|-------|
|         |       |

$16.45

Are all of these amounts the same? _____

$_____ is the greatest amount.

$_____ is the least amount.

**3.**

| Dollars | Cents |
|---------|-------|
|         |       |

$45.30

| Dollars | Cents |
|---------|-------|
|         |       |

$42.95

| Dollars | Cents |
|---------|-------|
|         |       |

$45.75

Which is the greatest amount? _____

Which is the least amount? _____

# Write the amount in each set.
# Then check (✓) the set that has the greater value.

### Example

$50.00 _____

$51.00 _____     ✓

**4.**

_____

_____

**5.**

_____

_____

## Circle the amount that is less.

**6.**  $3.85          $4.10

**7.**  $62.40          $62.25

## Circle the amount that is more.

**8.**  $28.90          $27.95

**9.**  $71.09          $7.90

## Compare the amounts.

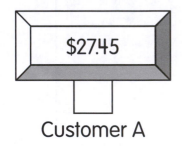

$27.45

Customer A

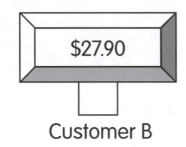

$27.90

Customer B

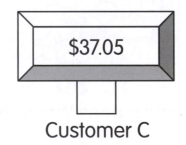

$37.05

Customer C

**10.**   Which customer paid the most?  Customer _____

**11.**   Which customer paid the least?  Customer _____

© Marshall Cavendish International (Singapore) Private Limited.

# Practice 3   Real-World Problems: Money

**Solve.**
**Draw bar models to help you.**

1.    Maddy buys a pencil for 25¢ and an eraser for 17¢.
      She gives the cashier 50¢.
      How much change does she get?

2.    The Lesters have $600.
      They spent $110 on food and $97 on electricity.
      How much do they have left?

3.    Walter buys a notebook for 50¢.
      He buys another notebook that costs 12¢ more.
      How much does Walter pay in all?

**Solve.**
**Write your answers using $ or ¢.**

95¢

80¢

65¢

$1

4. Tyler buys a book and a pen.
How much does he spend?

5. Rosie buys a teddy bear.
Pamela buys a pencil sharpener.
How much do they spend?

6. How much more is a pen than a pencil sharpener?

Name: _____ Date: _____

**7.** Jessie has a dollar bill and a quarter.
She wants to buy a teddy bear and a book.

    **a.** Does she have enough money?

    **b.** If not, how much more does she need?

**8.** Henry has a $10 bill.
He buys a teddy bear, a book, and a pen.
How much does he have left?

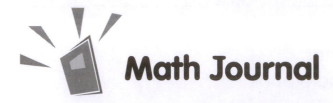

# Math Journal

Shawn made some mistakes in his homework.
Help him correct the mistakes.

**Example**

Shawn's mistake: 35¢ = _$3.50_

Correct answer: _35¢ = $.35_

1. Shawn's mistake: One dollar and sixty cents = $1.06

   Correct answer: _____

2. Shawn's mistake: 450¢ = $450

   Correct answer: _____

3. Shawn's mistake: $6 is $5 less than $10.

   Correct answer: _____

4. Shawn's mistake: $90 is $10 more than $100.

   Correct answer: _____

# Put On Your Thinking Cap!

 ## Challenging Practice

Draw the amount of money using  5¢ ,  10¢ ,  25¢ , $1 , and $5 .

**Example**

$5.70

 $5   25¢   25¢   10¢  10¢

**1.** $4.60

**2.** $9.40

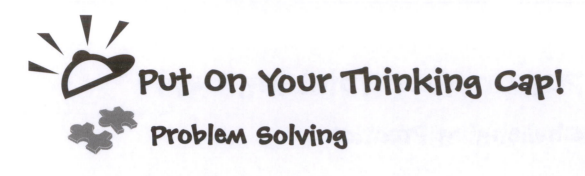

# Put On Your Thinking Cap!
## Problem Solving

Find different combinations of coins and bills that can make each amount.

**Example**

$8.50

|       | $20 | $10 | $5 | $1 | 25¢ | 10¢ |
|-------|-----|-----|----|----|-----|-----|
| Set A |     |     | 1  | 3  | 2   |     |
| Set B |     |     | 1  | 2  | 6   |     |
| Set C |     |     | 1  | 3  |     | 5   |

**1.** $60.30

|       | $20 | $10 | $5 | $1 | 25¢ | 10¢ |
|-------|-----|-----|----|----|-----|-----|
| Set A |     |     |    |    |     |     |
| Set B |     |     |    |    |     |     |
| Set C |     |     |    |    |     |     |

**2.** $25.00

|       | $20 | $10 | $5 | $1 | 25¢ | 10¢ |
|-------|-----|-----|----|----|-----|-----|
| Set A |     |     |    |    |     |     |
| Set B |     |     |    |    |     |     |
| Set C |     |     |    |    |     |     |

Which amount is the greatest? _____

Name: _____  Date: _____

# Chapter Review/Test

## Vocabulary

<table>
<tr><td>$</td><td>_____</td></tr>
<tr><td>¢</td><td>_____</td></tr>
<tr><td colspan="2">decimal point</td></tr>
</table>

**Fill in the blanks with words or symbols from the box.**

1.   A _____ separates the dollars from the cents.

2.   100¢ makes _____ 1.

3.   $.75 can also be written as 75 _____.

## Concepts and Skills

**Identify the value of each bill or coin.**

4.     5.     6.     7.

_____   _____   _____   _____

**Write the amount of money in words and numbers.**

8.

_____ or _____¢

9.

_____ or _____¢

**Write the amount in dollars or cents.**

10.   50¢ = $_____    11.   125¢ = $_____

12.   $16 = _____¢    13.   $7.02 = _____¢

**Compare.**

| $71.25 | $72.52 | $17.95 |

14.   Which is the least amount? _____

15.   Which is the greatest amount? _____

# Problem Solving

**Solve. Draw bar models to help you.**

16.   Jeffrey has two $1 bills.
      He buys an ice cream for 70¢.
      How much does he have left?



      He has _____ left.

17.   Anita has $150.
      She spends $53 on books and $35 on a pair of shoes.
      How much does she have left?



      She has $_____ left.

# CHAPTER 12 Fractions

## Practice 1   Understanding Fractions

Put an ✗ in the box if the shape is divided into equal parts.

**Example**

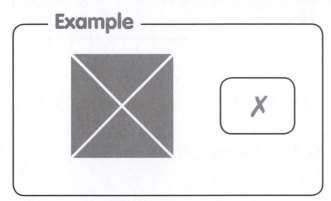

| ✗ |

1.

2.

3.

4.

5.

6.

7.

## Look at the pictures.
## Then fill in the blanks.

**Example**

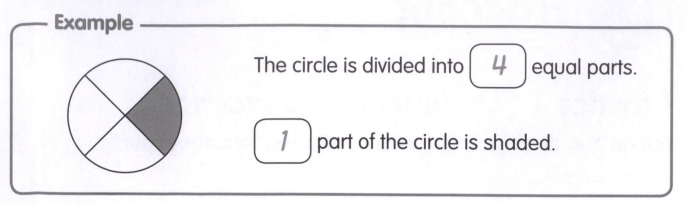

The circle is divided into 4 equal parts.

1 part of the circle is shaded.

**8.**

The rectangle is divided into _____ equal parts.

_____ part of the rectangle is shaded.

## Circle the fraction and words that match the picture.

**Example**

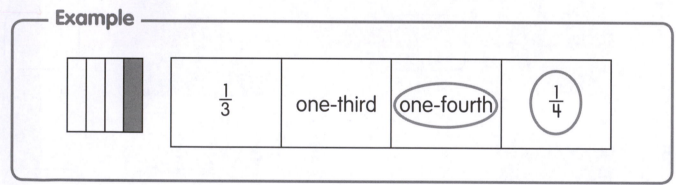

| $\frac{1}{3}$ | one-third | (one-fourth) | $\frac{1}{4}$ |

**9.**

| one-half | one-twos | $\frac{1}{2}$ | 1 |

**10.**

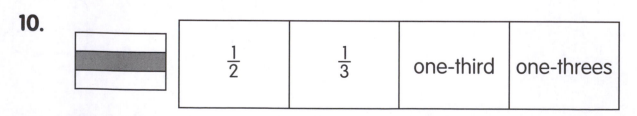

| $\frac{1}{2}$ | $\frac{1}{3}$ | one-third | one-threes |

## Mark with an x the fractional part that does not belong in each row.

┌─ **Example** ─────────────────────────────────────┐

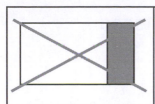 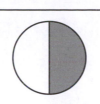 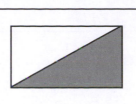 one-half

└──────────────────────────────────────────────────┘

**11.**

one-fourth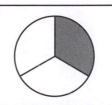

**12.**

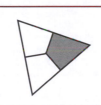 one-third

## Fill in the blanks.

┌─ **Example** ─────────────────────────────────────┐

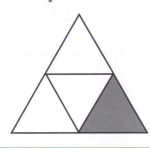  _____1_____ out of _____4_____ equal parts is shaded.

$\frac{1}{4}$ _____ of the figure is shaded.

└──────────────────────────────────────────────────┘

**13.**

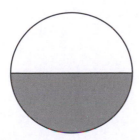  _____ out of _____ equal parts is shaded.

_____ of the figure is shaded.

**14.**

_____ out of _____ equal parts is shaded.

_____ of the figure is shaded.

**15.**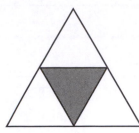

_____ out of _____ equal parts is shaded.

_____ of the figure is shaded.

## Write a fraction for each shaded part.

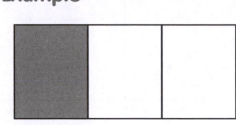

**Example**

. . . . . . . $\dfrac{1}{3}$ _____

**16.**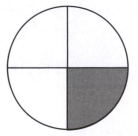

. . . . . . _____

**17.**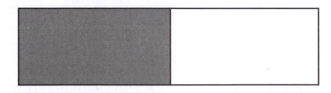

. . . . . . _____

**18.**

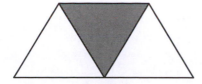

. . . . . . _____

**19.**

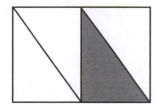

. . . . . . _____

## Shade part(s) of each figure to show the fraction.

**20.** $\frac{1}{3}$

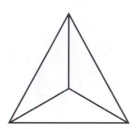
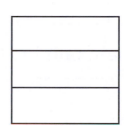

**21.** $\frac{1}{4}$

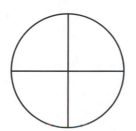
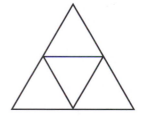

**22.** $\frac{1}{2}$

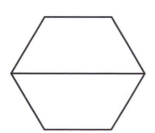
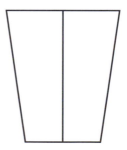

# Match the words and fractions to the figures.

**23.**

| one-half | • | • | 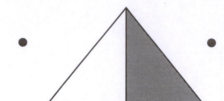 | • | • | $\frac{1}{4}$ |
| one-third | • | • |  | • | • | $\frac{1}{2}$ |
| one-fourth | • | • |  | • | • | $\frac{1}{3}$ |

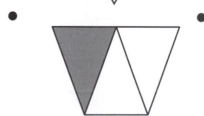

# Practice 2   Comparing Fractions

**Write the fraction of the shaded part or parts.**
**Then compare the fractions.**

**Example**

_____ $\frac{1}{4}$ is shaded.          _____ $\frac{1}{3}$ is shaded.

_____ $\frac{1}{3}$ is greater than _____ $\frac{1}{4}$ .

_____ $\frac{1}{4}$ is less than _____ $\frac{1}{3}$ .

1.

_____ is shaded.          _____ is shaded.

_____ is greater than _____ .

_____ is less than _____ .

**Compare.**
**Write > or < in ◯.**

2.

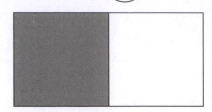

$\frac{1}{2}$ is shaded.

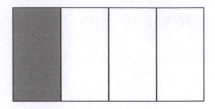

$\frac{1}{4}$ is shaded.

$\frac{1}{4}$ ◯ $\frac{1}{2}$

$\frac{1}{2}$ ◯ $\frac{1}{4}$

**Write a fraction for each shaded part.**
**Then arrange the fractions from the greatest to least.**

3.

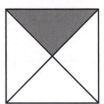

4.

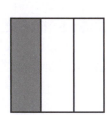

5.

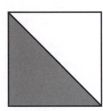

_____          _____                          _____

_____

greatest                                                    least

Name: _____     Date: _____

# Practice 3   Adding and Subtracting Like Fractions

**Write the fraction for the shaded parts.**

1.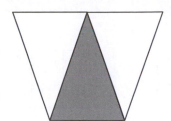

2.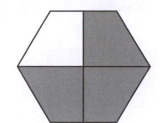

3.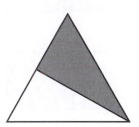

_____          _____          _____

**Shade the parts to show the sum.**

**Example**

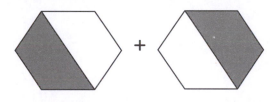

4.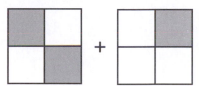

5.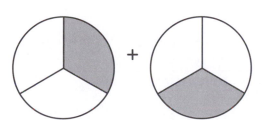

**Shade the parts to show the sum.**

**6.**

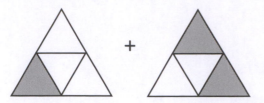 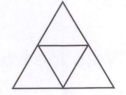

**7.**

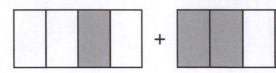 

## Add.
## Use models to help you.

┌─ **Example** ─────────────────┐

$\frac{1}{3} + \frac{1}{3} = \underline{\quad \frac{2}{3} \quad}$

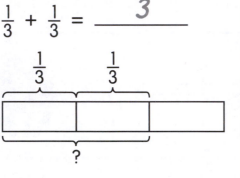

└──────────────────────────────┘

**8.**   $\frac{1}{4} + \frac{2}{4} = \underline{\qquad\qquad}$

## Add.
## Use models to help you.

**9.**   $\frac{1}{2} + \frac{1}{2} =$ _____

**10.**   $\frac{1}{3} +$ _____ $= 1$

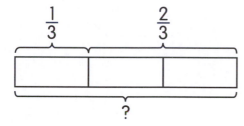

## Shade the parts to show the difference.

**Example**

**11.**

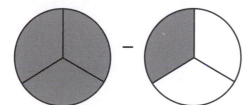

**12.**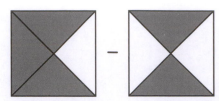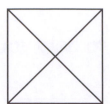

**13.**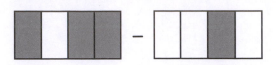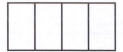

**14.**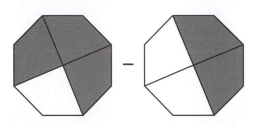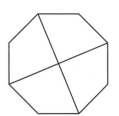

## Subtract.
## Use models to help you.

---
**Example**

$$1 - \frac{2}{3} = \underline{\quad \frac{1}{3} \quad}$$

---

**15.** $\frac{3}{4} - \frac{1}{4} = \underline{\qquad}$

## Subtract.
## Use models to help you.

16.  $\frac{2}{3} - \frac{1}{3} =$ _____

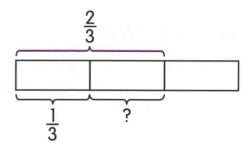

17.  $1 -$ _____ $= \frac{1}{4}$

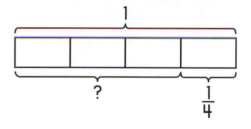

18.  $\frac{3}{4} - \frac{2}{4} =$ _____

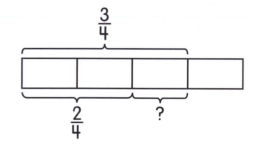

1.  _____ more parts need to be shaded to show $\frac{3}{4}$.

2.  _____ more part needs to be shaded to show $\frac{2}{3}$.

3.  _____ more parts need to be shaded to show $\frac{4}{4}$.

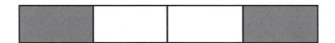

# Chapter Review/Test

## Vocabulary
**Fill in the blanks with words from the box.**

| whole |
| --- |
| equal |
| greater than |
| less than |

**1.**

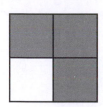

$\frac{3}{4}$ means 3 out of 4 _____ parts.

**2.**

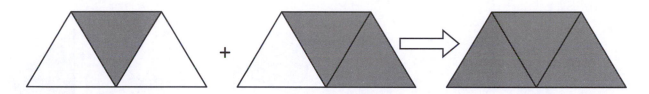

$\frac{1}{3}$ and $\frac{2}{3}$ make a _____.

**3.**

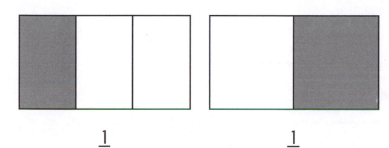

$\frac{1}{3}$      $\frac{1}{2}$

$\frac{1}{3}$ is _____ $\frac{1}{2}$.

**4.**

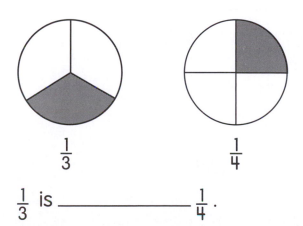

$\frac{1}{3}$      $\frac{1}{4}$

$\frac{1}{3}$ is _____ $\frac{1}{4}$.

# Concepts and Skills

**5.** **Match.**

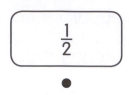

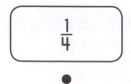

$\frac{1}{3}$

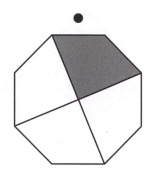

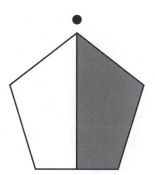

**Write > or < in** ◯**.**

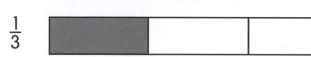

**6.** $\frac{1}{2}$

$\frac{1}{3}$

$\frac{1}{2}$ ◯ $\frac{1}{3}$

**7.** $\frac{1}{4}$

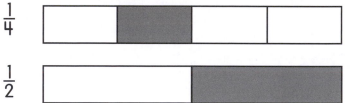

$\frac{1}{2}$

$\frac{1}{4}$ ◯ $\frac{1}{2}$

Name: _____    Date: _____

**Write > or < in** .

**8.** $\frac{1}{3}$

$\frac{1}{4}$     $\frac{1}{3}$  $\frac{1}{4}$

**9.** Now arrange the fractions in order from least to greatest.

⬭   ⬭   ⬭

**10. Match.**

$\frac{3}{4}$ •            •

$\frac{1}{2}$ •            •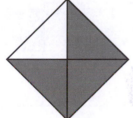

$\frac{2}{3}$ •            •

$\frac{1}{3}$ •            •

$\frac{1}{4}$ •            •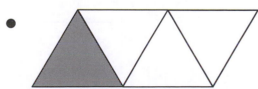

**Divide the drawings into equal parts.**

**11.**  2 equal parts

**12.**  3 equal parts

**13.**  4 equal parts

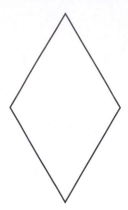
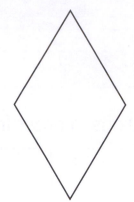
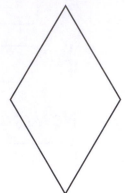

**Fill in the blanks.**

**14.**

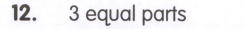
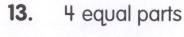
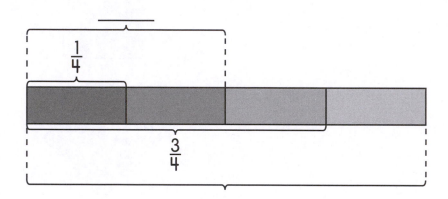

**Add or subtract.**
**Use the model in Exercise 14 to help you.**

**15.**  $\frac{1}{4} + \frac{3}{4} =$ _____

**16.**  $\frac{1}{4} + \frac{2}{4} =$ _____

**17.**  $1 - \frac{1}{4} =$ _____

**18.**  $\frac{3}{4} - \frac{2}{4} =$ _____

# Cumulative Review

## for Chapters 10 to 12

## Concepts and Skills

1.  Connect the cards to show the steps for mental math.

| 64 + 8 | 64 − 8 | 84 + 6 | 84 − 6 |

| Add 10 to 64 | Subtract 10 from 64 | Add 10 to 84 | Subtract 10 from 84 |

| Subtract 2 from the result | Subtract 4 from the result | Add 2 to the result | Add 4 to the result |

| 78 | 72 | 90 | 56 |

## Add mentally.

**2.** 352 + 4 = _____

**3.** 817 + 5 = _____

**4.** 143 + 30 = _____

**5.** 198 + 800 = _____

## Subtract mentally.

**6.** 916 – 5 = _____

**7.** 873 – 8 = _____

**8.** 477 – 60 = _____

**9.** 858 – 400 = _____

## Mark each number with an X on the number line. Then round each number to the nearest ten.

**10.** 76

**11.** 81

**12.** 123

**13.** 134

## Complete.

**14.** Write the numbers that give 50 when rounded to the nearest ten.

_____

**15.** What is the least number that rounds to 10? _____

**16.** What is the greatest number that rounds to 80? _____

**Add or subtract.**
**Round each number to the nearest ten.**
**Then estimate the sum or difference to check that your answer**
**is reasonable.**

**17.**     $874 + 67 =$ _____

874 is about _____.

67 is about _____.

_____ + _____ = _____.

So, $874 + 67$ is about _____.

Is the answer reasonable? Explain.

_____

_____

**18.**     $545 - 79 =$ _____

545 is about _____.

79 is about _____.

_____ − _____ = _____.

So, $545 - 79$ is about _____.

Is the answer reasonable? Explain.

_____

_____

## Circle the bills that make the amount shown.

**19.**

## Write the amount in numbers.

**20.** twenty-five cents                           $_____ or _____¢

**21.** thirty-nine dollars                          $_____

**22.** twelve dollars and ninety-seven cents   $_____

## Count the money.
## Then write the amount each way.

**23.**

dollars and cents _____

cents _____

words _____

**Name:** _____  **Date:** _____

**Circle the amount that is least.**

**24.**  $10.75   $7.98   $8.07

**Circle the greatest amount.**

**25.**  $96.50   $96.72   $96.09

**Shade the model to show the fraction.**

**26.**  $\frac{2}{3}$

**27.**  $\frac{1}{4}$

**Look at the model.**

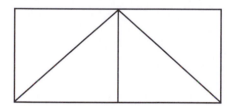

   Color $\frac{1}{4}$ blue.

   Color $\frac{2}{4}$ yellow.

**28.**  What fraction of the model is colored? _____

**29.**  What fraction of the model is not colored? _____

## Shade each strip.
## Then write the fractions in order from greatest to least.

**30.** $\frac{1}{3}$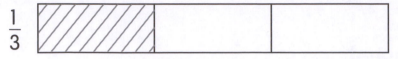

$\frac{1}{2}$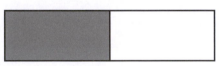

$\frac{1}{4}$

————, ————, ————
greatest

## Write a fraction for the shaded part.

**31.**
————

**32.**
————

**33.**
————

**Use your answers for Exercises 31 to 33. Fill in the blanks.**

**34.** _____ is 1 out of 2 equal parts.

**35.** _____ is 2 out of 3 equal parts.

**36.** $\frac{1}{2}$ is greater than _____.

**37.** $\frac{1}{2}$ is less than _____.

**38.** _____ is the least fraction.

**Find the missing fraction.**
**Use models to help you.**

**39.** Add $\frac{1}{3}$ and $\frac{1}{3}$.

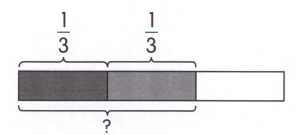

$$\frac{1}{3} + \frac{1}{3} = \underline{\hspace{2cm}}$$

**40.** Subtract $\frac{3}{4}$ from 1.

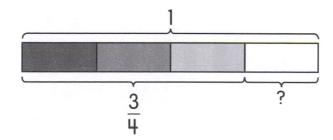

$$1 - \frac{3}{4} = \underline{\hspace{2cm}}$$

**Solve.**
**Draw bar models to help you.**
**Estimate to check your answers.**

**41.** Teri folds 32 pieces of paper.
Her sister folds 19 pieces.
How many pieces do they fold in all?

They fold _____ pieces in all.

**42.** Edwin has 83¢.
His father gives him 25¢ more.
How much does he have now?

He has $_____ now.

**43.** Jonas needs to deliver 34 newspapers.
He still has 11 newspapers left to deliver.
How many newspapers has he delivered?

He has delivered _____ newspapers.

**44.** Adam wants to buy a bat for $23 and a baseball glove for $17.
He has saved $19.
How much more money does he need?

He needs $_____ more.

**45.** An eraser costs 16¢ and a pencil costs 70¢.
Marian buys two erasers and a pencil.
How much does she spend?

Marian spends $_____.

**46.** Mrs. Barry has $200 to buy new clothes.
Round the cost of each item to the nearest ten.
Then estimate the total cost.

A pair of pants costs $44.

a. 44 is _____ when rounded to the nearest ten.

A pair of shoes costs $59.

b. 59 is _____ when rounded to the nearest ten.

A pair of socks costs $5.

c. 5 is _____ when rounded to the nearest ten.

A blouse costs $28.

d. 28 is _____ when rounded to the nearest ten.

Total cost is $_____.

Does Mrs. Barry have enough money to pay for all the items?
Explain your answer.

_____

_____

# CHAPTER 13 Customary Measurement of Length

## Practice 1   Measuring in Feet

**Look at the pictures.**
**Fill in the blanks with *more* or *less*.**

**1.**

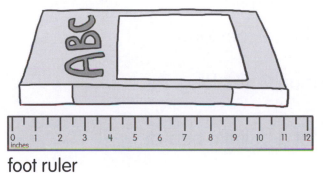

foot ruler

The length of the book

is _____ than 1 foot.

**2.**

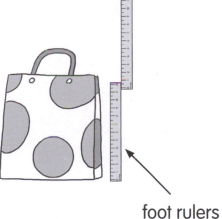

The height of the bag

is _____ than 1 foot.

foot rulers

**3.**

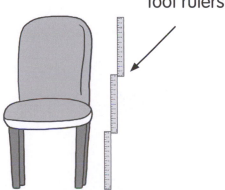

The height of the chair

is _____ than 2 feet.

## Fill in the blanks.

**4.** Foot rulers are placed against two ribbons.

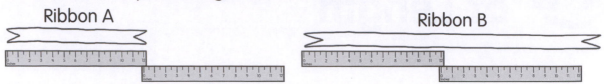

**a.** Which ribbon is about 1 foot long? _____

## Fill in the blanks with *more* or *less*.

**b.** Ribbon A is _____ than 2 feet long.

**c.** Ribbon B is _____ than 2 feet long.

**5.** Foot rulers are placed against a bulletin board.

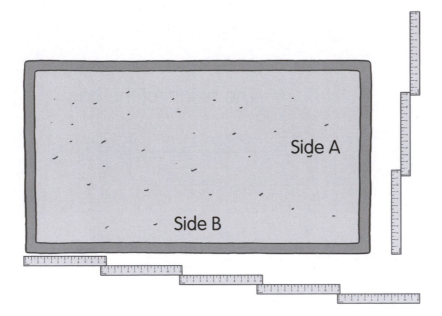

**a.** Which side of the board is about 5 feet long? _____

**b.** Side A is shorter than _____ feet.

**c.** Side B is shorter than _____ feet.

**Look at the list.**
**Check (✓) the columns that are true.**
**You will need a foot ruler to measure these items.**

| | Item | Less than 1 foot | More than 1 foot | More than 3 feet |
|---|---|---|---|---|
| **6.** | Umbrella | | | |
| **7.** | Blackboard | | | |
| **8.** | Shoe | | | |
| **9.** | Tissue box | | | |
| **10.** | Bookshelf | | | |

**Look around the classroom to find and name objects that match each length.**

11.

| Length | Object |
|---|---|
| Less than 1 foot long | |
| About 1 foot long | |
| More than 1 foot long | |

**Use a string and a foot ruler to measure.**
**Then fill in the blanks.**

12.   Mark on the string with a pencil how long you think 1 foot is.
Then use a ruler to measure this length.
Did you mark more or less than 1 foot on your string?

_____

13.   Next, mark on the string how long you think 2 feet is.
Then use a ruler to measure this length.
Did you mark more or less than 2 feet on your string?

_____

Name: _____  Date: _____

# Practice 2  Comparing Lengths in Feet

**Fill in the blanks.**

1.  Look at the two jump ropes.

 Jump Rope A: 10 ft

Jump Rope B: 5 ft

a.  Which jump rope is longer? Jump Rope _____

b.  How much longer is it? _____ ft

2.  Look at the trees.

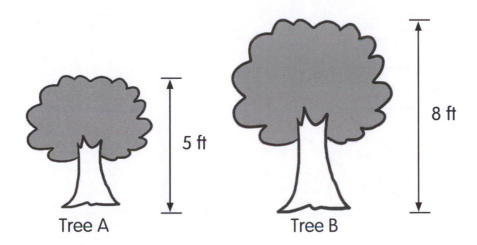

5 ft        8 ft

Tree A        Tree B

a.  Which tree is taller? Tree _____

b.  How much taller is it? _____ ft

## Answer the questions.
## Look at the sides of the rectangle.

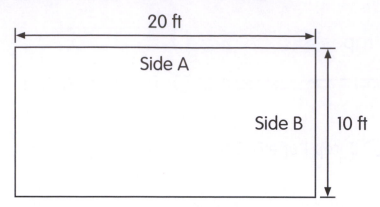

20 ft

Side A

Side B    10 ft

**3.**  Which is longer, Side A or Side B? Side _____

**4.**  How much longer is it? _____ ft

**5.**  Look at the paths.

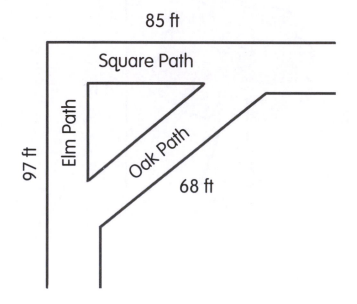

85 ft

Square Path

Elm Path

Oak Path

97 ft

68 ft

**a.**  Which path is the longest? _____

**b.**  How much longer is Elm Path than Square Path? _____ ft

**c.**  Elm Path is _____ feet longer than Oak Path.

# Practice 3   Measuring in Inches

**1.**     Check (✓) the correct way to measure the length of the pencil.

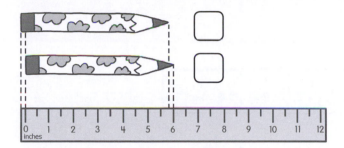

□

□

## Use an inch ruler to measure each part of a line.
## Then answer the questions.

Part of a line A |_____|

Part of a line B |_____|

**2.**     How long is Part of a line A? _____ in.

**3.**     How long is Part of a line B? _____ in.

## Use a string and an inch ruler to measure each curve.

**4.**

_____ in.

**5.**

_____ in.

## Fill in the blanks.

**6.**

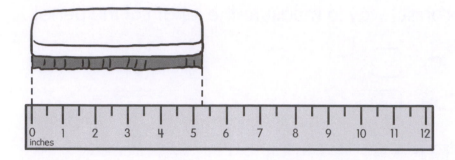

The eraser is about _____ inches long.

**7.**

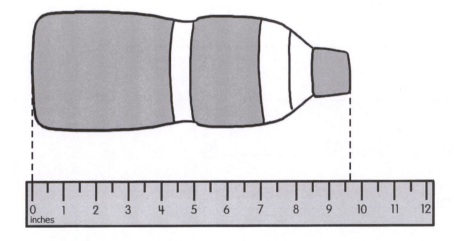

The bottle is about _____ inches long.

**8.**

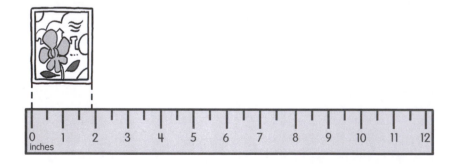

The sticker is about _____ inches long.

Name: _____    Date: _____

**Fill in the blanks.**

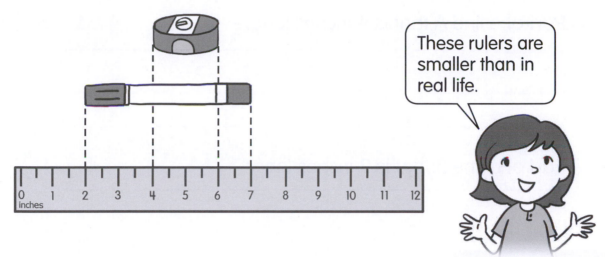

These rulers are smaller than in real life.

**9.**    The marker is _____ inches long.

**10.**    The pencil sharpener is _____ inches long.

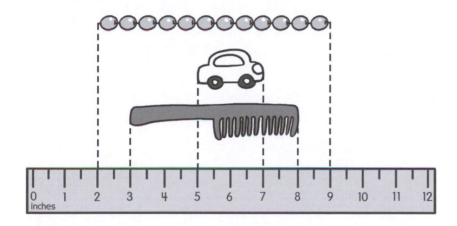

**11.**    The length of the comb is _____ inches.

**12.**    The length of the string of beads is _____ inches.

**13.**    The length of the toy car is _____ inches.

## Use your inch ruler to draw.

**14.**     Part of a line A that is 4 inches long.

**15.**     Part of a line B that is 2 inches long.

**16.**     Part of a line C that is 5 inches long.

**17.**     Part of a line D that is 1 inch long.

**18.**     Part of a line E that is 2 inches shorter than Part of a line C.

**19.**     Part of a Line F that is 3 inches longer than Part of a line D.

# Practice 4   Comparing Lengths in Inches and Feet

**Look at each drawing.**
**Then fill in the blanks.**

**1.**   Which is longer? Drawing _____

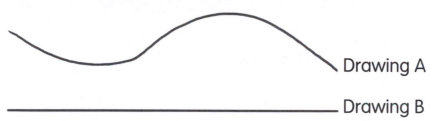

Drawing A

Drawing B

**2.**   Which is the longest?

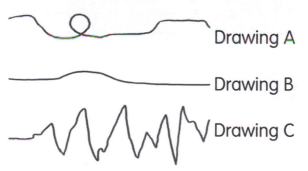

Drawing A

Drawing B

Drawing C

Drawing _____ is the shortest.

Drawing _____ is the longest.
Explain your answers.

_____

_____

_____

_____

**Fill in the blanks.**

**3.**

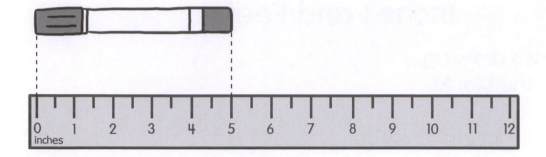

The marker is _____ inches long.

**4.**

The eraser is _____ inch long.

**5.**

The key is _____ inches long.

These rulers are smaller than in real life.

**Name:** _____   **Date:** _____

## Fill in the blanks.

**6.**

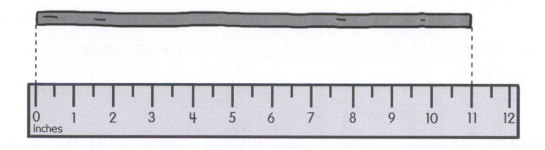

The stick is _____ inches long.

**7.**

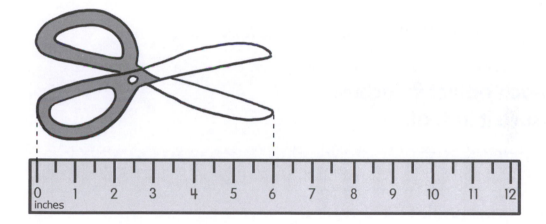

The pair of scissors is _____ inches long.

## Use your answers for Exercises 3 to 7.
## Fill in the blanks with *longer* or *shorter*.

**8.**   The stick is _____ than the eraser.

**9.**   The key is _____ than the scissors.

**10.**   The eraser is _____ than the marker.

**Use your answers for Exercises 3 to 7.**
**Fill in the blanks.**

11. The pair of scissors is _____ inches longer than the key.

12. The marker is _____ inches shorter than the stick.

13. The longest object is the _____.

14. The shortest object is the _____.

**Measure each object in inches.**
**Then measure it in feet.**

| | Measure (in.) | Measure (ft) |
|---|---|---|
| the length of your book | | |
| the width of your hand | | |
| the height of a bookshelf | | |
| the height of a chair | | |

15. Which objects are easier to measure in inches?

16. Which objects are easier to measure in feet?

17. Why are there more inches than feet when you measure the same object?

# Practice 5   Real-World Problems: Customary Length

**Solve.**

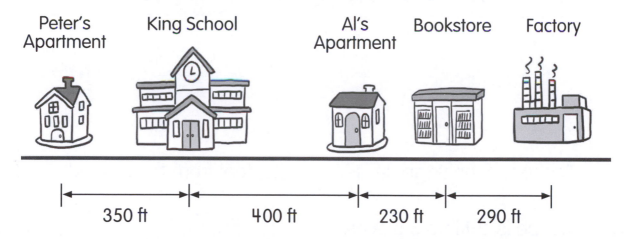

| Peter's Apartment | King School | Al's Apartment | Bookstore | Factory |

350 ft | 400 ft | 230 ft | 290 ft

**1.** How far does Al walk from his home to King School?                                        _____ ft

**2.** How far is Peter's Apartment from the Bookstore?          _____ ft

**3.** Who lives nearer to King School, Al or Peter?          _____

**4.** How much nearer?                                        _____ ft

**5.** Al goes to the Bookstore from his apartment, and then goes to school. How far does he walk?          _____ ft

**6.** Peter left his apartment to walk to Al's Apartment.
He has walked 400 feet.
How much farther does he have to walk?          _____ ft

**Solve.**

7. A flagpole is 6 feet tall.
   It stands on a building 26 feet tall.
   How high is the top of the flagpole from the ground?

   The top of the flagpole is _____ feet from the ground.

8. A rope is cut into 3 pieces.
   The rope pieces measure 14 feet, 16 feet, and 20 feet.
   How long was the rope before it was cut?

   The rope was _____ feet long.

9. A flagpole 156 inches tall is driven into the ground.
   38 inches of it is below the ground.
   How much of the flag pole is above the ground?

   _____ inches of the flagpole is above the ground.

**Solve.**
**Show your work.**
**Use bar models to help you.**

— **Example** —————————————————————————

The total length of two pieces of wood is 36 feet.
The first piece is 27 feet long.

**a.** What is the length of the second piece?

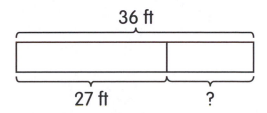

36 ft

27 ft          ?

The length of the second piece is ____*9*____ feet.

**b.** How much shorter is the second piece than the first piece?

27 − 9 = 18

The second piece is ____*18*____ feet shorter than the first piece.

**10.** James is 57 inches tall.
James is 8 inches taller than Ron.
Ron is taller than Brian by 2 inches.
How tall is Brian?

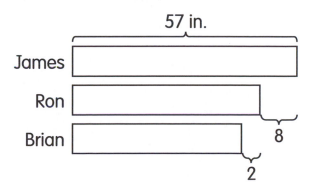

57 in.

James

Ron

Brian          8

2

Brian is _____ inches tall.

**11.** Marcus keeps 3 rolls of cable measuring 67 feet in all.
The first roll is 32 feet.
The second roll is 17 feet.
How long is the third roll?

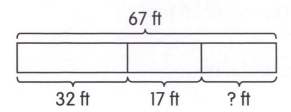

The third roll is _____ feet long.

**Solve.**
**Show your work.**
**Draw bar models to help you.**

**12.** A string is 500 inches long.
Nicole uses 142 inches of it to tie a package.
She gives 75 inches of it to Susan.
How long is the string that Nicole has left?

The string is _____ inches long.

Name: _____    Date: _____

# Put On Your Thinking Cap!
## Challenging Practice

1.  There are three drawings, A, B, and C.
    Drawing A is shown.

    |————————————————————————————| Drawing A

    Drawing B is 12 inches longer than Drawing A.
    Drawing C is 4 inches shorter than Drawing B.
    How long is Drawing C?

2.  Tom and Lionel climb a tree.
    They have to climb a ladder first, then up to the branches.
    The ladder is 6 feet long.
    Tom climbs 4 feet from the ladder to a branch.
    Lionel climbs 2 feet from the ladder to another branch.
    What is the total distance that Tom and Lionel have climbed?

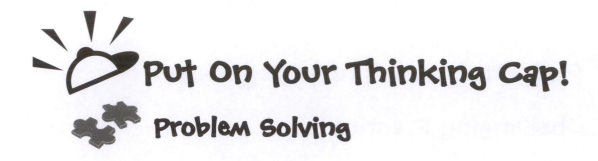

## Put On Your Thinking Cap!

### Problem Solving

**Solve.**

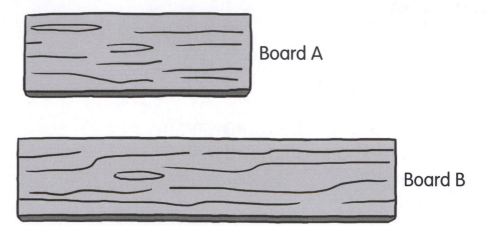

Board A

Board B

There are 2 boards, A and B.
The total length of both boards is 28 feet.
Board B is at least 5 feet longer than Board A, but the difference is not more than 12 feet.
What are the possible lengths of the two boards?

# Chapter Review/Test

## Vocabulary

**Fill in the blanks with words from the box.**

| |
|---|
| foot/feet |
| _____ |
| inch/inches |
| _____ |
| tallest |
| _____ |
| shorter |

1.   Measure short lengths in _____

and longer lengths in _____.

2.

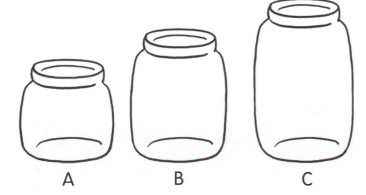

A          B          C

Cookie jar C is the _____.

3.   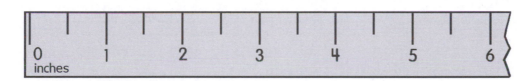 Simone's

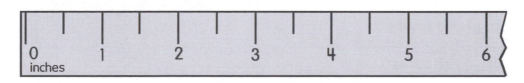 Annie's

Annie's string of beads is 2 inches _____ than Simone's.

# Concepts and Skills

## Check (✔) the correct answers.

**4.** What is the length of your math textbook?

| Length | Check |
|---|---|
| About 1 foot | |
| Less than 1 foot | |
| More than 1 foot | |

**5.** What is the height of your desk?

| Height | Check |
|---|---|
| About 2 feet | |
| Less than 2 feet | |
| More than 3 feet | |
| Less than 3 feet | |

**6.** What is the height of your classroom?

| Height | Check |
|---|---|
| About 20 feet | |
| Less than 20 feet | |
| More than 10 feet | |
| Less than 10 feet | |

**Name:** _____   **Date:** _____

## Look at the objects measured.
## Then fill in the blanks.

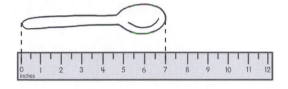

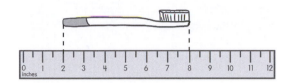

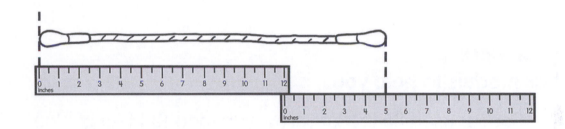

7.    spoon: _____ in.

8.    toothbrush: _____ in.

9.    rope: _____ ft _____ in.

10.   The rope is _____ foot longer than the spoon.

11.   The rope is longer than _____ foot.

12.

    The photo is about _____ inches long.

© Marshall Cavendish International (Singapore) Private Limited.

**13.** Use a ruler to draw a part of a line 7 inches long.

## Problem Solving

**Solve.**
**Show your work.**
**Draw bar models to help you.**

**14.** Ms. Cooper used 86 feet of yellow yarn and 123 feet of blue yarn to make a sweater.

    **a.** What is the total length of yarn that Ms. Cooper used to make a sweater?

       The total length of yarn is _____ feet.

    **b.** How much more blue yarn than yellow yarn did Ms. Cooper use?

       Ms. Cooper used _____ feet more blue yarn than yellow yarn.

**15.** A bookshelf is 50 inches tall.
It is 15 inches shorter than a step ladder.
How tall is the ladder?

       The step ladder is _____ inches tall.

Name: _____  Date: _____

# Time

## Practice 1   The Minute Hand

1.    Fill in the boxes with the number of minutes.

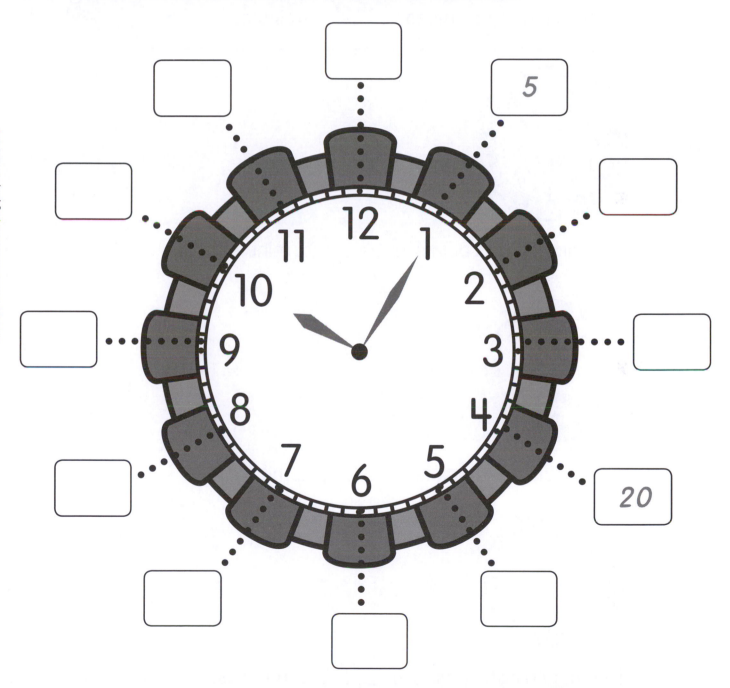

**Fill in the blanks.**

The minute hand is longer than the hour hand.

—— **Example** ——

The minute hand points to _____30_____ minutes.

**2.**

The minute hand points to _____ minutes.

**3.**

The minute hand points to _____ minutes.

**4.**

The minute hand points to _____ minutes.

Name: _____     Date: _____

## Write the time.

**5.**

_____     _____ minutes after 3 o'clock.

**6.**

_____     _____ minutes after 7 o'clock.

**7.**

_____     _____ minutes after 10 o'clock.

# Draw the minute hand to show the time.

**8.** 15 minutes after 4 o'clock

**9.** 40 minutes after 6 o'clock

**10.** 50 minutes after 1 o'clock

**11.** 35 minutes after 10 o'clock

# Practice 2   Reading and Writing Time

**Write the time in words.**

**Example**

*ten fifty or 50 minutes after 10*
_____

1.

_____

2.

_____

3.

_____

4.

_____

5.

_____

## Write the time.

**Example**

The time is ___7:40___.

**6.**

The time is _____.

**7.**

The time is _____.

**8.**

The time is _____.

**9.**

The time is _____.

**10.**

The time is _____.

# Draw the minute hand to show the time.

**Example**

The time is 3:55.

**11.**

The time is 6:30.

**12.**

The time is 10:15.

**13.**

The time is 8:00.

**14.**

The time is 12:40.

**15.**

The time is 9:05.

# Draw the hour hand to show the time.

**Example**

The time is 10:00.

**16.**

The time is 11:30.

**17.**

The time is 7:15.

**18.**

The time is 4:20.

**19.**

The time is 2:50.

**20.**

The time is 3:40.

# Draw the hands to show the time.

**Example**

The time is 7:15.

**21.**

The time is 4:30.

**22.**

The time is 1:20.

**23.**

The time is 9:25.

**24.**

The time is 7:00.

**25.**

The time is 9:50.

**Draw the hands to show the time.**
**Then write the time in words.**

**Example**

4:55
*four fifty-five*
*or 55 minutes after 4*

**26.**

5:10

_____

**27.**

11:40

_____

**28.**

6:55

_____

**29.**

1:25

_____

**30.**

12:15

_____

# Practice 3   Using A.M. and P.M.

**Write** A.M. **or** P.M.

**Example**

Sam wakes up at 6:30 ___A.M.___

**1.**

His grandparents begin their

daily exercise at 6:50 _____

**2.**

Sometimes, Sam rides his bike in

the afternoon at 2:50 _____

**Write** *A.M.* **or** *P.M.*

**3.** The sun sets at

about 7:25 _____

**4.**

At 6:30 _____, Sam eats

his dinner with his friend.

**5.**

His father likes to go jogging at night.

He usually jogs at 8:30 _____

© Marshall Cavendish International (Singapore) Private Limited.

**6.** Denise and her mother finished grocery shopping at 10:30 _____

**7.** The family had lunch at 12:30 _____

**8.** They reached home at 11:00 _____

**Write A.M. or P.M.**

**9.** Denise woke up at 7:30 _____

**10.** Denise and her mother left for the grocery store at 9:30 _____

**11.** Denise helped her mother put away the groceries.
Then they started preparing lunch at 11:30 _____

**12.** **List the times of events in Practice 6–11.**
**Arrange them in order from the beginning of the day.**

_____

Beginning

# Practice 4   Elapsed Time

Fill in the blanks with the time.

Check your answer by drawing the hands on the clock.

**Example**

is 1 hour after

5:00 ............    4:00 ............

---

**1.**

is 1 hour before

11:00    _____

---

**2.**

is 1 hour after

8:00    _____

# Write *before* or *after*.

**Example**

 is 1 hour ___before___

**3.**

 is 1 hour _____

**4.**

 is 1 hour _____

**5.**

 is 1 hour _____

Name: _____     Date: _____

## Fill in the blanks with the time.

## Check your answer by drawing the hands on the clock.

     is 30 minutes before

_1:30_     _2:00_

**6.**

     is 30 minutes after

_____     8:00

**7.**

     is 30 minutes before

_____     10:00

# Write *before* or *after*.

is 30 minutes ___*after*___

**8.**

is 30 minutes _____

**9.**

is 30 minutes _____

**10.**

is 30 minutes _____

**Name:** _____   **Date:** _____

## Draw the hands on the clock.
## Then write the time.

**11.**

    is 30 minutes after

_____                                    _____

**12.**

    is 1 hour after

_____                                    _____

**13.**

    is 30 minutes before

_____                                    _____

**Write *before* or *after*.**

**Then draw the hands on the clock.**

**14.**

7:00

is 1 hour _____

6:00

**15.**

6:30

is 1 hour _____

7:30

**16.**

6:00

is 30 minutes _____

6:30

**Fill in the blanks with the number of minutes or hours.**

**17.**  Captain James left the dock at 8.00 A.M. and arrived on shore at 8:30 A.M.

Start                                    End

How long was the trip? _____

**18.**  Peter played basketball from 6.00 P.M. to 7.00 P.M.

Start                                    End

How long did he play? _____

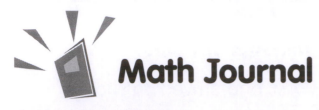

# Math Journal

**Find the mistakes.**
**Circle the mistakes.**
**Then correct them.**

**1.**

Albert wrote: The time is 4:25.

_____

**2.** Keisha drew the hands on the clock
to show 7:55.
This is how she did it.

  # Put On Your Thinking Cap!

## Challenging Practice

Look at the picture.
Where can the hour hand be?
Draw it on the clock face.
Explain.

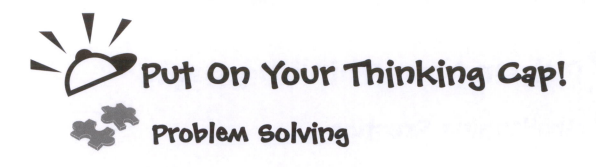

# Put On Your Thinking Cap!

## Problem Solving

What time did Kyle finish his homework?
Use the clues below to find out.

Kyle spent 1 hour writing his story.
He took another 30 minutes to color the pictures.
Kyle started his homework at 6.00 P.M.

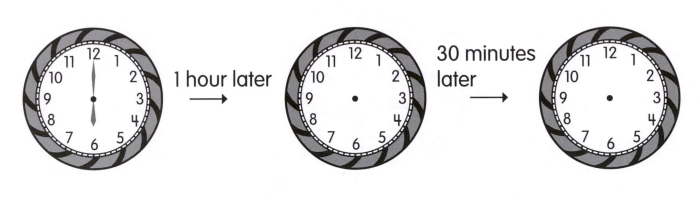

1 hour later

30 minutes later

6:00 P.M.

_____          _____          _____

**Name:** _____   **Date:** _____

# Chapter Review/Test

## Vocabulary

**Fill in the blanks with words from the box.**

> minutes        hours        A.M.        P.M.

**1.** 60 _____ is equal to 1 hour.

**2.** Use _____ to talk about time just after midnight to just before noon.

**3.** Use _____ to talk about time just after noon to just before midnight.

**4.** Use a clock to tell time in _____ and minutes.

## Concepts and Skills

**Write the time in numbers and in words.**

**5.**

_____

_____

**6.**

_____

_____

## Draw the hands on the clock to show the time.

**7.**

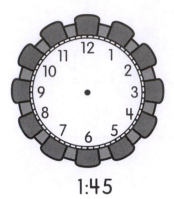

1:45

**8.**

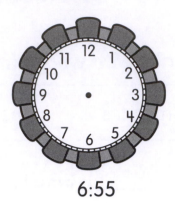

6:55

## Write A.M. or P.M.

**9.** Katy goes to school at 7:15 _____

**10.** She goes home after school at 3:00 _____

## Find the time.

**11.** 30 minutes before 6:00 P.M. is _____

**12.** 30 minutes after noon is _____

**13.** 1 hour before 3:30 A.M. is _____

**14.** 1 hour after midnight is _____

# Problem Solving

## Solve.

**15.** Annie spent 30 minutes on her math homework.
She started at 6:30 P.M.
What time did she finish? _____

**16.** Pedro has swimming lesson from 5:00 P.M.
to 6:00 P.M. How long is his swimming lesson? _____

Name: _____    Date: _____

# Cumulative Review
## for Chapters 13 and 14

## Concepts and Skills

**Fill in the blanks.**

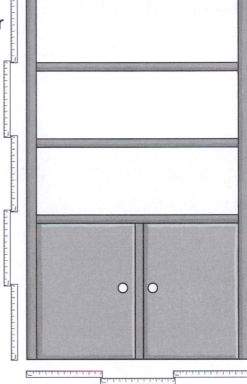

foot ruler

1.  The bookshelf is _____ feet tall.

2.  The bookshelf is _____ feet wide.

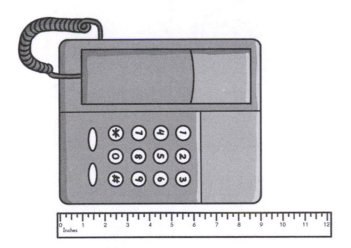

3.  The telephone is _____ inches long.

**Fill in the blanks with *feet* or *inches*.**

**4.** A car is about 8 _____ long.

**5.** The grip on a bicycle handle bar is about 6 _____ long.

**Look at each drawing.**
**Then fill in the blanks.**

Drawing A
5 ft

Drawing B
2 ft

**6.** Which drawing is shorter? _____

**7.** How much shorter? _____ feet

**Fill in the blanks.**

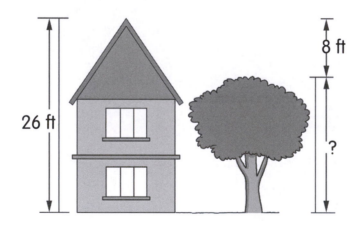

26 ft

8 ft

?

**8.** The tree is about _____ feet shorter than the house.

**9.** The tree is about _____ feet tall.

Name: _____     Date: _____

Side A
12 in.

Side B
7 in.

**10.** Side A is _____ inches longer than Side B.

**11.** The total length of the two sides is _____.

## Use the picture to answer each question.

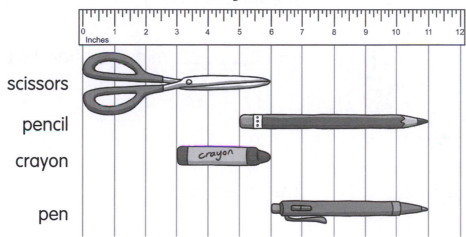

**12.** What is the length of the pen? _____

**13.** Which is longer, the scissors or the pen? _____

**14.** The shortest item is the _____.

**15.** Which two items have the same length? _____

**16.** The total length of 2 pens and 3 crayons is _____ inches.

**17.** The length of _____ crayons is more than the length of 2 pens.

## Draw the hands to show the time.
## Then fill in the blanks.

**18.**

The time is 4:15.

It is 15 minutes after _____ o'clock.

**19.**

The time is 9:55.

It is _____ minutes after 9 o'clock.

**20.**

The time is 6:45.

It is _____ minutes after 6 o'clock.

**21.**

The time is 11:15.

It is 15 minutes after _____ o'clock.

## Match.
## Then write the time in words under each digital clock.

**22.**

6:45

**23.**

5:30

_____

**24.**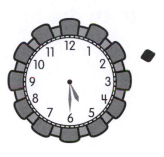

_____

2:20

**25.**

3:10

_____

**26.**

1:15

**27.**

_____

4:05

_____

**Fill in the blanks with A.M. or P.M.**

**28.** On Saturdays, Marjorie usually wakes up at 8:00 _____

**29.** She has lunch at her grandparents' house at 12:30 _____

**30.** She helps her mother do house chores at 9:30 _____

**31.** She plays board games with her grandpa at 3:00 _____

**32.** She goes home at 5:00 _____

**Now list the times in Exercises 28 to 32 in order from the beginning of the day.**

**33.** _____ _____ _____
Beginning

_____ _____

**Fill in the blanks with the time.**
**Check your answer by drawing the hands on the clock.**

**34.**

is 1 hour after

1:00                                    _____

**35.**

is 1 hour before

_____

10:30

**36.**

is 30 minutes after

_____

11:00

**37.**

is 30 minutes before

2:00

_____

## Fill in the blanks with *before* or *after*.

**38.**  is 1 hour _____

**39.**  is 1 hour _____

**40.**  is 30 minutes _____

**41.**  is 30 minutes _____

# Problem Solving

## Solve.
## Draw bar models to help you.

**42.**   Ben uses a piece of rope to form a triangle.

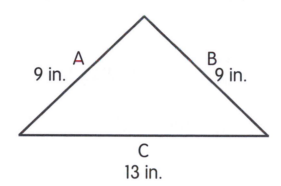

**a.**   What is the length of the rope?

**b.**   How much longer is the sum of the two shorter sides than the longest side of the triangle?

**a.**   The rope is _____ inches long.

**b.**   The sum of the two shorter sides is _____ inches longer than the longest side.

**43.**   Rope A is 56 feet long.
Rope B is 47 feet longer than Rope A.
Rope C is 71 feet shorter than Rope B.

**a.**   How long is Rope B?

**b.**   How long is Rope C?

**a.**   Rope B is _____ feet long.

**b.**   Rope C is _____ feet long.

**44.** Jason is 71 inches tall.
Rodney is 12 inches shorter than Jason.
Marco is 18 inches taller than Rodney.

    **a.**  How tall is Rodney?
    **b.**  How tall is Marco?


    **a.**  Rodney is _____ inches tall.

    **b.**  Marco is _____ inches tall.

**45.**

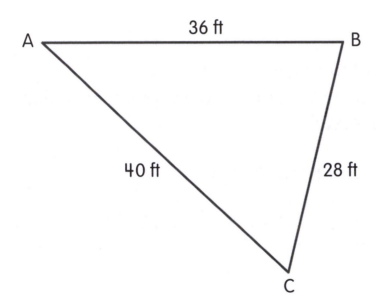

    **a.**  Adam walks from Point A to Point C through Point B.

        How far does he walk? _____

    **b.**  Susan walks from Point B to Point C through Point A.

        How far does she walk? _____

    **c.**  Who walks farther? _____

        How much farther? _____

Name: _____ Date: _____

# Multiplication Tables of 3 and 4

## Practice 1    Multiplying 3: Skip-Counting

Match the shapes that have the same value.

6 × 3

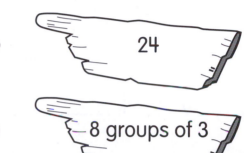
24

8 groups of 3

**1.** 4 × 3

18

**2.** 5 × 3

30

**3.** 10 × 3

12

15

**4.** 8 × 3

10 groups of 3

4 groups of 3

## Count by 3s.
## Then fill in the blanks.

**Example**

3, 6, 9, 12, _____15_____, 18

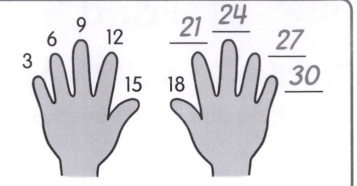

**5.** 9, 12, 15, _____, _____, _____, _____

**6.** 12, _____, 18, 21, _____, _____, 30

## Fill in the blanks.

**7.** 4 × 3 = _____

**8.** 2 × 3 = _____

**9.** 6 × 3 = _____

**10.** 8 × 3 = _____

**11.** 9 × 3 = _____

**12.** 7 × 3 = _____

**13.** 3 × 3 = _____

**14.** 10 × 3 = _____

## Solve.

**15.** Andrea has 5 flower vases.
Each vase has 3 roses.
How many roses are there in all?

5 × 3 = _____

There are _____ roses in all.

Name: _____  Date: _____

# Practice 2 Multiplying 3: Using Dot Paper

**Use dot paper to solve.**

---
**Example**

Sally buys 4 lanterns.
Each lantern costs $3.
How much does Sally pay for the lanterns?

$3   $3   $3   $3

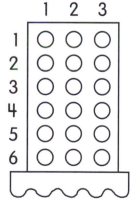

1 2 3

$4 \times \$3 = \$\underline{\quad 12 \quad}$

Sally pays $\$\underline{\quad 12 \quad}$ for the lanterns.

---

1.   Nicole buys 6 soup bowls.
Each soup bowl costs $3.
How much does she pay for all the soup bowls?

$3   $3   $3   $3   $3   $3

1 2 3

$\underline{\qquad} \times \$3 = \$\underline{\qquad}$

She pays $\$\underline{\qquad}$ for all the soup bowls.

**Use dot paper to solve.**

2. There are 7 tricycles.
Each tricycle has 3 wheels.
How many wheels are there in all?

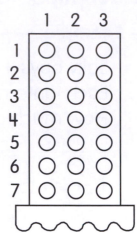

_____ × _____ = _____

There are _____ wheels in all.

3. There are 8 groups of children in the class.
There are 3 children in each group.
How many children are there in the class?

_____ × _____ = _____

There are _____ children in the class.

**Name:** _____ **Date:** _____

## Use dot paper to help you fill in the blanks.

─ **Example** ─

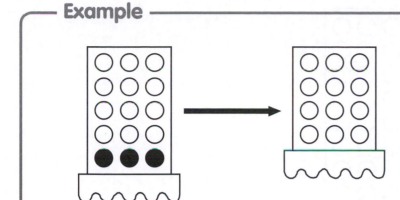

$5 \times 3 =$ _____ *15*

$4 \times 3 = 5$ groups of 3 – 1 group of 3

$= \underline{\quad 15 \quad} - 3$

$= \underline{\quad 12 \quad}$

**4.**

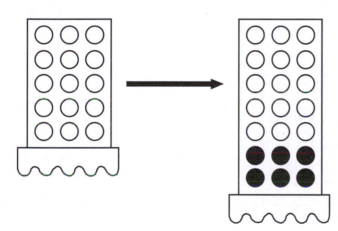

$5 \times 3 =$ _____

$7 \times 3 = 5$ groups of 3 + _____ groups of 3

$= \underline{\qquad} + \underline{\qquad}$

$= \underline{\qquad}$

## Use dot paper to help you fill in the blanks.

**5.**

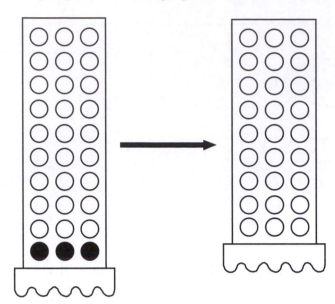

10 × 3 = _____          9 × 3 = 10 groups of 3 – _____ group of 3

= _____ – _____

= _____

**6.**

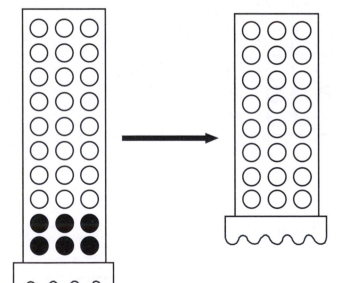

10 × 3 = _____          8 × 3 = 10 groups of 3 – _____ groups of 3

= _____ – _____

= _____

## Use dot paper to help you fill in the blanks.

**Example**

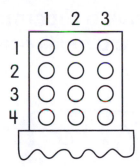 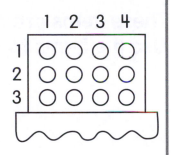

_____4_____ × 3 = 12

3 × _____4_____ = 12

7.  _____ × 3 = 18

3 × _____ = 18

8.  _____ × 3 = 21

3 × _____ = 21

9.  8 × 3 = _____

3 × 8 = _____

10.  _____ × 3 = 27

3 × _____ = 27

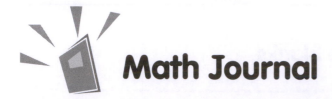

# Math Journal

These items are sold in a supermarket.
Use the items to write a multiplication story.

$3

$4

**Example**

I want to buy 4 boxes of cereal.

I will have to give the cashier $16.

**Story**

# Practice 3   Multiplying 4: Skip-Counting

**Match.**

8 × 4

**1.**

7 × 4

**2.**

2 × 4

**3.**

4 × 4

4 groups of 4

2 groups of 4

7 groups of 4

8 groups of 4

## Count by 4s.
## Then fill in the blanks.

**Example**

4, 8, 12, 16, ___20___

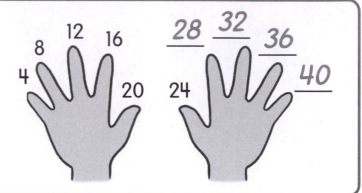

**4.**   12, 16, 20, _____, _____, _____, _____

**5.**   16, _____, 24, 28, _____, _____, 40

## Fill in the blanks.

**6.**   3 × 4 = _____

**7.**   6 × 4 = _____

**8.**   2 × 4 = _____

**9.**   8 × 4 = _____

**10.**   9 × 4 = _____

**11.**   4 × 4 = _____

**12.**   10 × 4 = _____

**13.**   7 × 4 = _____

## Solve.

**14.**   There are 5 pencil cases.
4 erasers are in each pencil case.
How many erasers are there in all?

5 × 4 = _____

There are _____ erasers in all.

# Practice 4  Multiplying 4: Using Dot Paper

**Solve.**

---

**Example**

There are 3 boxes of crayons.
There are 4 crayons in each box.
How many crayons are there in all?

   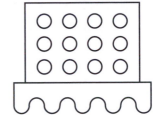

$3 \times 4 = \underline{\quad 12 \quad}$

There are $\underline{\quad 12 \quad}$ crayons in all.

---

1.  There are 6 toy cars in a toy box.
    Each car has 4 wheels.
    How many wheels are there in all?

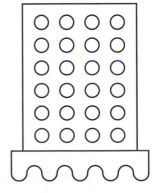

$\underline{\qquad} \times 4 = \underline{\qquad}$

There are $\underline{\qquad}$ wheels in all.

## Use dot paper to solve.

**2.**     Mrs. Jones buys 5 T-shirts.
Each T-shirt costs $4.
How much does Mrs. Jones spend in all?

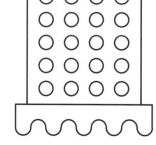

_____ × $4 = $_____

Mrs. Jones spends $_____ in all.

**3.**     There are 8 bags.
Each bag has 4 muffins.
How many muffins are there in all?

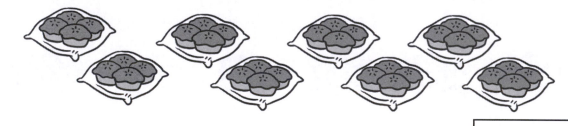

_____ × _____ = _____

There are _____ muffins in all.

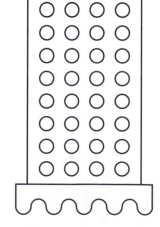

## Use dot paper to help you fill in the blanks.

**Example**

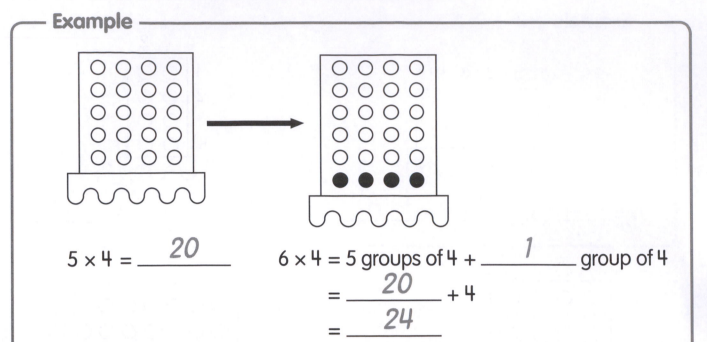

$5 \times 4 =$ _____20_____ 　　 $6 \times 4 = 5$ groups of $4 +$ _____1_____ group of $4$

$= $ _____20_____ $+ 4$

$= $ _____24_____

**4.**

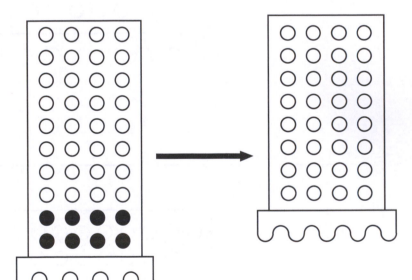

$10 \times 4 =$ _____ 　　 $8 \times 4 = 10$ groups of $4 -$ _____ groups of $4$

$= $ _____ $- 8$

$= $ _____

**5.** 　 $7 \times 4 =$ _____ $+ 8$ 　　　 **6.** 　 $9 \times 4 =$ _____ $- 4$

$= $ _____ 　　　　　　　　　 $= $ _____

# Use dot paper to help you fill in the blanks.

**Example**

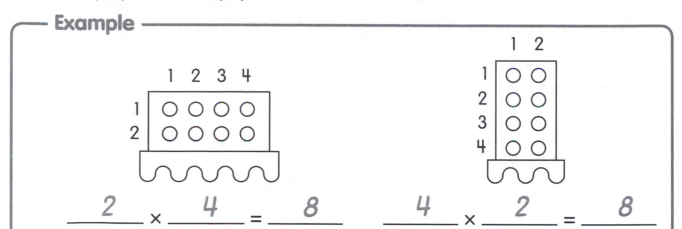

$\underline{\quad 2 \quad} \times \underline{\quad 4 \quad} = \underline{\quad 8 \quad}$

$\underline{\quad 4 \quad} \times \underline{\quad 2 \quad} = \underline{\quad 8 \quad}$

**7.**

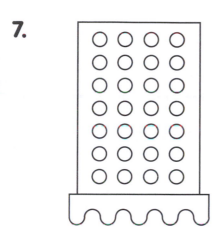

$\underline{\qquad} \times \underline{\qquad} = \underline{\qquad}$

$\underline{\qquad} \times \underline{\qquad} = \underline{\qquad}$

**8.**

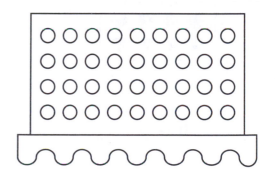

$\underline{\qquad} \times \underline{\qquad} = \underline{\qquad}$

$\underline{\qquad} \times \underline{\qquad} = \underline{\qquad}$

# Practice 5　Divide Using Related Multiplication Facts

**Complete the multiplication sentences.**
**Then complete the division sentences.**

---

**Example**

$24 \div 4 =$ ___6___

$24 \div 3 =$ ___8___

$6 \times 4 = 24$
$8 \times 3 = 24$

---

**1.** $4 \times$ _____ $= 8$

_____ $\times 4 = 8$

$8 \div 2 =$ _____

$8 \div 4 =$ _____

**2.** $4 \times$ _____ $= 12$

_____ $\times 4 = 12$

$12 \div 3 =$ _____

$12 \div 4 =$ _____

**3.** $5 \times$ _____ $= 15$

_____ $\times 5 = 15$

$15 \div 3 =$ _____

$15 \div 5 =$ _____

**4.** $5 \times$ _____ $= 20$

_____ $\times 5 = 20$

$20 \div 4 =$ _____

$20 \div 5 =$ _____

## Use related multiplication facts to solve.

---
**Example**

The teacher divides 21 books equally among 3 children.
How many books does each child get?

$$\underline{\quad 21 \quad} \div \underline{\quad 3 \quad} = \underline{\quad 7 \quad}$$

Each child gets __7__ books.

---

**5.** Mr. Holtz gives $24 to 4 workers.
The workers share the money equally among themselves.
How much money does each worker get?

$$\$\underline{\qquad} \div \underline{\qquad} = \$\underline{\qquad}$$

Each worker gets $_____.

**6.** Rita has 27 stuffed toys.
She puts them on 3 shelves.
She puts the same number on each shelf.
How many stuffed toys are on each shelf?

$$\underline{\qquad} \div \underline{\qquad} = \underline{\qquad}$$

There are _____ stuffed toys on each shelf.

**Name:** _____   **Date:** _____

## Use related multiplication facts to solve.

**7.**   Phil puts 36 pencils equally into 4 boxes.
How many pencils are in each box?


_____ ÷ _____ = _____


There are _____ pencils in each box.


**8.**   Angie uses 9 craft sticks to make 3 triangles of the same size.
How many craft sticks are needed to make one triangle?


_____ ÷ _____ = _____


_____ craft sticks are needed to make one triangle.


**9.**   Sammy fixes 8 tires on his cars.
He fixes 4 tires on each car.
How many cars are there?


_____ ÷ _____ = _____


There are _____ cars.


**10.**   Mr. Yuma has 18 pieces of bread.
He puts 3 pieces in each basket.
How many baskets does he use?


_____ ÷ _____ = _____


He uses _____ baskets.

**11.** A photo album contains 20 photos.
Each filled page of the album has 4 photos.
How many pages are filled?

_____ ÷ _____ = _____

_____ pages are filled.

**12.** Keisha has 9 fish.
She puts 3 fish in each fish tank.
How many fish tanks does she need?

_____ ÷ _____ = _____

She needs _____ fish tanks.

# Put On Your Thinking Cap!

## Challenging Practice

1. Steve starts reading a book at page 7.
   He reads the book for 4 days.
   He reads 3 pages each day.
   Which page will Steve stop at on the 4th day?

   (Hint: Use a diagram to help you solve.)

2. The music teacher is selecting children to sit in the
   front row at a concert.
   100 children are given numbers 1 to 100.
   The teacher first picks the child with the number 3.
   He then skip-counts by tens to pick the other children.
   What are the numbers of the other children who are picked?

   The numbers are _____.

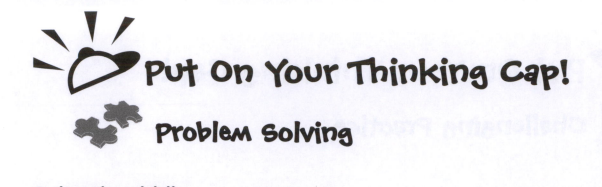

# Put On Your Thinking Cap!

## Problem Solving

**Solve the riddle.**

I am a two-digit number.
I am more than 20 but less than 30.
I can be found in both the multiplication tables
of 3 and 4.
What number am I?

# Chapter Review/Test

## Vocabulary
**Fill in the blanks with words from the box.**

**1.**

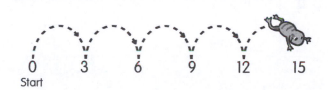

| skip-counting |
|---|
| dot paper |
| related multiplication facts |

_____ is fun!

**2.**

$6 \times 3 = 18$   $3 \times 6 = 18$   are examples of

_____.

## Concepts and Skills

**Skip count to find the missing numbers.**

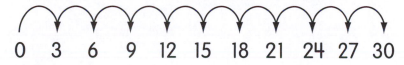

0   3   6   9   12   15   18   21   24   27   30

**3.**   $9 \times 3 = $ _____

**4.**   _____ $\times 3 = 24$

0   4   8   12   16   20   24   28   32   36   40

**5.**   _____ $\times 4 = 16$

**6.**   _____ $\times 4 = 36$

**Find the missing numbers.**

**7.**    8 groups of 3 = _____ × 3

            = _____

**8.**    7 groups of 4 = _____ × 4

            = _____

**Use dot paper to find the missing numbers.**

**9.**    6 × 4 = 5 groups of 4 + _____ group of 4

            = _____ + 4

            = _____

# Problem Solving

**Use skip-counting or dot paper to solve.**

**10.**    Caleb ties sets of 3 medals with a piece of ribbon.
          He ties 10 sets of medals.
          How many medals does Caleb have in all?

**Use related multiplication facts to solve.**

**11.**    Gail has 32 star-shaped key chains.
          She puts 4 key chains equally into some boxes.
          How many boxes are there?

# CHAPTER 16  Using Bar Models: Multiplication and Division

## Practice 1  Real-World Problems: Multiplication

**Solve.**
**Use bar models to help you.**

---

**Example**

Aaron has 3 baskets of oranges.
There are 5 oranges in each basket.
How many oranges does Aaron have?

_____3_____ groups
of 5 oranges

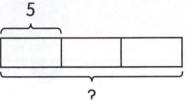

5

?

_____3_____ × 5 = _____15_____

Aaron has _____15_____ oranges.

---

1.  Susan has 4 bunches of roses.
    There are 8 roses in each bunch.
    How many roses does Susan have?

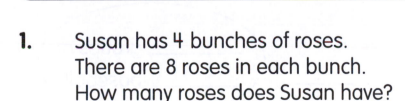

_____ groups
of 8 roses

8

?

_____ × 8 = _____

Susan has _____ roses.

© Marshall Cavendish International (Singapore) Private Limited.

**Solve.**
**Draw bar models to help you.**

2. Willie reads 10 pages of his book each day.
How many pages does he read in 3 days?

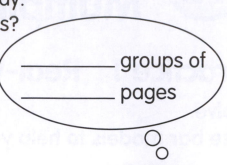

_____ groups of
_____ pages

_____ × _____ = _____

Willie reads _____ pages in 3 days.

3. There are 7 boxes.
There are 5 baseballs in each box.
How many baseballs are there in all?

_____ groups of
_____ baseballs

_____ × _____ = _____

There are _____ baseballs in all.

© Marshall Cavendish International (Singapore) Private Limited.

**Solve.**
**Draw bar models to help you.**

4.  There are 3 tricycles in a shop.
    Each tricycle has 3 wheels.
    How many wheels do the tricycles have in all?

    The tricycles have _____ wheels in all.

5.  Carlos buys 5 boxes of markers.
    There are 10 markers in each box.
    How many markers does Carlos buy?

    Carlos buys _____ markers.

**Solve.**
**Draw bar models to help you.**

6.　There are 9 boxes of rocks.
　　There are 3 rocks in each box.
　　How many rocks are there in all?




　　There are _____ rocks in all.


7.　Samuel makes 6 shapes using craft sticks.
　　He uses 5 craft sticks for each shape.
　　How many craft sticks does Samuel use in all?




　　Samuel uses _____ craft sticks in all.

Name: _____     Date: _____

**Solve.**
**Draw bar models to help you.**

**8.**     Farah has 8 vases.
         She puts 5 flowers in each vase.
         How many flowers does Farah have in all?

Farah has _____ flowers in all.

**9.**     Benny has 7 fish tanks.
         There are 4 goldfish in each tank.
         How many goldfish does Benny have?

Benny has _____ goldfish.

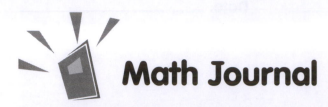

# Math Journal

**Fill in the blanks, circles, and ovals.**

To show 3 groups of 6 strawberries,

**Step 1**  I draw _____ strips of equal lengths in a row to represent 3 groups.

**Step 2**  I write the number _____ in the oval above one strip

and a _____ in the oval below the strips.

**Step 3**  I write the number sentence.

_____ ◯ _____ = ?

**Step 4**  I _____ to find the answer.

_____ ◯ _____ = _____

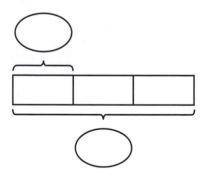

# Practice 2   Real-World Problems: Division

**Circle the correct bar model.**

**Example**

Divide 15 children into 5 groups.
How many children are in each group?

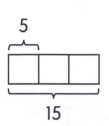   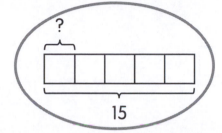   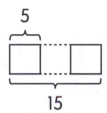

**1.**   Place 20 strawberries equally on 4 plates.
How many strawberries are on each plate?

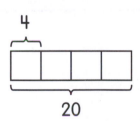   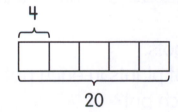   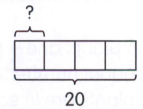

**2.**   There are 21 buttons to sew on some shirts.
Each shirt needs 3 buttons.
How many shirts are there?

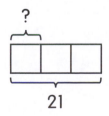   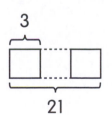   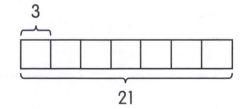

**Solve.**
**Use the bar model to help you.**

> ## Example
>
> A baker has 12 rolls.
> He divides the rolls equally among 4 children.
> How many rolls does each child get?
>
>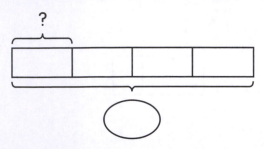
>
> ___12___ ÷ ___4___ = ___3___
>
> Each child gets ___3___ rolls.

3. Zach has 36 plants and 4 pots.
   He puts an equal number of plants in each pot.
   How many plants are in each pot?

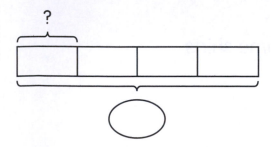

_____ ÷ _____ = _____

There are _____ plants in each pot.

**Solve.**
**Use the bar model to help you.**

**Example**

Ben has 35 leather strips.
He uses 5 strips for each necklace he makes.
How many necklaces does he make?

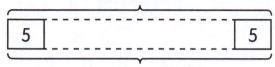

? necklaces

35 leather strips

_____35_____ ÷ _____5_____ = _____7_____

Ben makes _____7_____ necklaces.

---

**4.**  Lily sews 24 dresses for her dolls.
Each doll gets 3 dresses.
How many dolls does Lily have?

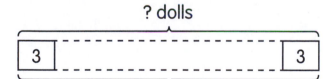

? dolls

24 dresses

_____ ÷ _____ = _____

Lily has _____ dolls.

**Solve.**
**Draw bar models to help you.**

5.   Gina has 40 stamps.
     She pastes them equally on 4 pages in her album.
     How many stamps are on each page?

     There are _____ stamps on each page.

6.   Ryan has read 28 pages of a book.
     He reads 4 pages each day.
     How many days has Ryan been reading the book?

     Ryan has been reading for _____ days.

# Practice 3　Real-World Problems: Measurement and Money

**Tell whether you need to multiply or divide.**
**Then solve.**
**Use bar models to help you.**

┌─ **Example** ─────────────────────────────────

Jen walks along an 8-meter path.
She walks along the path 3 times each day.
How far does she walk each day?

8 m

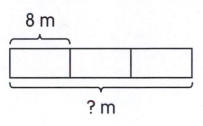

? m

$8 \times 3 =$ ___24___

Jen walks ___24___ meters each day.

Multiply to find the answer.

└──────────────────────────────────────────────

**1.**　Raul cuts 6 strips of paper.
Each strip is 5 centimeters long.
He tapes them together to make a long strip.
How long is the strip he makes?

5 cm

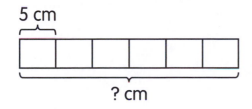

? cm

$5 \times 6 =$ _____

The strip is _____ centimeters long.

**Tell whether you need to multiply or divide.**
**Then solve.**
**Use bar models to help you.**

2.  Helen has a ribbon that is 21 inches long.
    She cuts it into 3 equal pieces.
    How long is each piece?

? in.

21 in.

21 ÷ 3 = _____

Each piece is _____ inches long.

3.  Jessica has a string that is 30 feet long.
    She cuts it into equal pieces.
    Each piece is 5 feet long.
    How many pieces does she cut the string into?

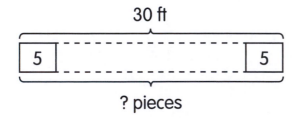

30 ft

| 5 | | 5 |

? pieces

She cuts the string into _____ pieces.

**Name:** _____  **Date:** _____

**Tell whether you need to multiply or divide.**
**Then solve.**
**Draw bar models to help you.**

**4.**   A strip of paper is 40 centimeters long.
        It is cut into 4 equal pieces.
        How long is each piece?

Each piece is _____ centimeters long.

**5.**   Sara is making curtains.
        She needs 5 meters of cloth for each curtain.
        She has 45 meters of cloth.
        How many curtains can she make?

She can make _____ curtains.

**Tell whether you need to multiply or divide.**
**Then solve.**
**Use bar models to help you.**

6. The mass of 5 bags of potatoes is 30 kilograms.
   Each bag has the same mass.
   What is the mass of each bag?

   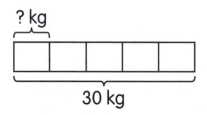
   ? kg

   30 kg

   The mass of each bag is _____ kilograms.

7. There are 6 bricks.
   Each brick has a mass of 3 kilograms.
   What is the total mass of the 6 bricks?

   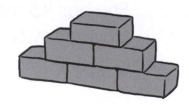

   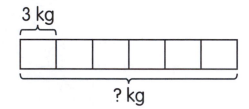
   3 kg

   ? kg

   The total mass of the 6 bricks is _____ kilograms.

**Tell whether you need to multiply or divide.**
**Then solve.**
**Draw bar models to help you.**

8.      A pencil sharpener has a mass of 10 grams.
        What is the total mass of 7 pencil sharpeners?




        The total mass of 7 pencil sharpeners is _____ grams.

9.      The total mass of 3 bags of flour is 6 kilograms.
        Each bag has the same mass.
        What is the mass of each bag of flour?




        The mass of each bag of flour is _____ kilograms.

**Tell whether you need to multiply or divide.**
**Then solve.**
**Draw bar models to help you.**

10. 32 kilograms of rice is divided equally into some bags.
Each bag has a mass of 8 kilograms.
How many bags of rice are there?

There are _____ bags of rice.

11. Mrs. Evan's family drinks 5 liters of milk in a week.
How many liters of milk does her family drink in 7 weeks?

Her family drinks _____ liters of milk in 7 weeks.

**Tell whether you need to multiply or divide.**
**Then solve.**
**Draw bar models to help you.**

**12.** Alberto pours 18 liters of water equally into 3 tanks.
How much water is there in each tank?

There are _____ liters of water in each tank.

**13.** Barry collects 16 liters of water from a well.
He pours the water into some pails.
Each pail contains 4 liters of water.
How many pails are there in all?

There are _____ pails in all.

**Tell whether you need to multiply or divide.**
**Then solve.**
**Draw bar models to help you.**

14. Mariam gives $40 to her grandchildren.
    Each of them gets $5.
    How many grandchildren does she have?

    She has _____ grandchildren.

15. Mrs. Tan buys 4 bottles of sauce.
    Each bottle costs $4.
    How much does she pay?

    She pays $_____.

16. Linda has $50.
    She spends all of it on some bags.
    Each bag costs $10.
    How many bags are there in all?

    There are _____ bags in all.

# Put On Your Thinking Cap!

## Challenging Practice

Macy has some ropes, each 2 feet long.
Nellie has some ropes, each 3 feet long.
Oscar has some ropes, each 5 feet long.
What is the length of each line of ropes when they are of the same length?

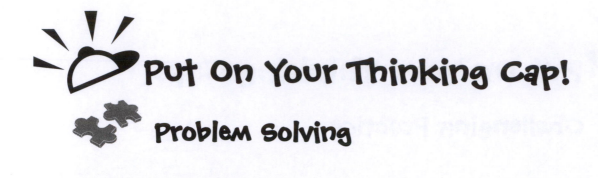

## Put On Your Thinking Cap!

### Problem Solving

Sheena bakes 100 muffins.
She shares them equally with 4 other girls.
How many muffins does each girl get?
How many more muffins are needed so that each one
gets two more muffins?

# Chapter Review/Test

## Concepts and Skills

**Match each bar model to a word problem.**
**Then solve the problem.**

**1.**  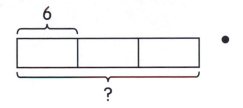   •          •   Ken has 18 strawberries. He divides them equally into 3 baskets. How many strawberries are in each basket?

_____ strawberries in each basket

**2.**  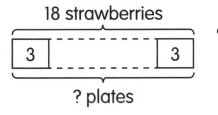   •          •   Ken has 18 strawberries. He puts 3 onto some plates. How many plates does he need?

_____ plates

**3.**  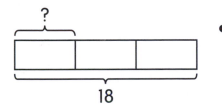   •          •   Ken has 3 plates. He puts 6 strawberries onto each plate. How many strawberries does he have in all?

_____ strawberries in all

## Problem Solving

**Write whether you need to multiply or divide.**
**Then solve.**
**Draw bar models to help you.**

**4.**  Jason has 5 apricots on each tray.
He has a total of 50 apricots.
How many trays are there?

There are _____ trays.

**5.**  Claire paints 90 masks.
She divides the masks equally and puts them in baskets.
She puts 10 masks in each basket.
How many baskets are there in all?

There are _____ baskets in all.

**Write whether you need to multiply or divide.**
**Then solve.**
**Draw bar models to help you.**

**6.** Sonny helps his mother pack old books in 6 boxes.
Each box has a mass of 4 kilograms.
What is the total mass of 6 boxes of books?

The total mass of 6 boxes of books is _____ kilograms.

**7.** Sarah is making necklaces for her friends.
She needs 12 feet of string for the necklaces.
Each necklace needs a string 2 feet long.
How many necklaces is Sarah making?

Sarah is making _____ necklaces.

**Tell whether you need to multiply or divide.**
**Then solve.**
**Draw bar models to help you.**

8. Billy's cats drink 4 liters of milk in a week.
How much milk do the cats drink in 4 weeks?

The cats drink _____ liters of milk.

9. Mr. Andres has 4 grandsons.
He gives each of them $5.
How much does he give his grandsons in all?

He gives $_____ to his grandsons.

# Graphs and Line Plots

## Practice 1  Reading Picture Graphs with Scales

**Fill in the blanks. Use the picture graph to help you.**

The picture graph shows the food a team ate after a softball game.

**Food Eaten After the Game**

| Hot dogs | 🥘 🥘 🥘 |
| Salad | 🥘 🥘 🥘 🥘 |
| Oranges | 🥘 🥘 |
| Carrots | 🥘 🥘 🥘 |
| Apples | 🥘 🥘 |

Key: Each 🥘 stands for 2 helpings of food.

---

**Example**

They had ____6____ helpings of hot dogs.

---

1.  They had the same number of helpings of _____ as hot dogs.

2.  They had _____ more helpings of salad than apples.

3.  They had _____ helpings of salad and apples in all.

Jane and her classmates chose their favorite fairy tale character.
This picture graph shows their choices.

## Favorite Fairy Tale Characters

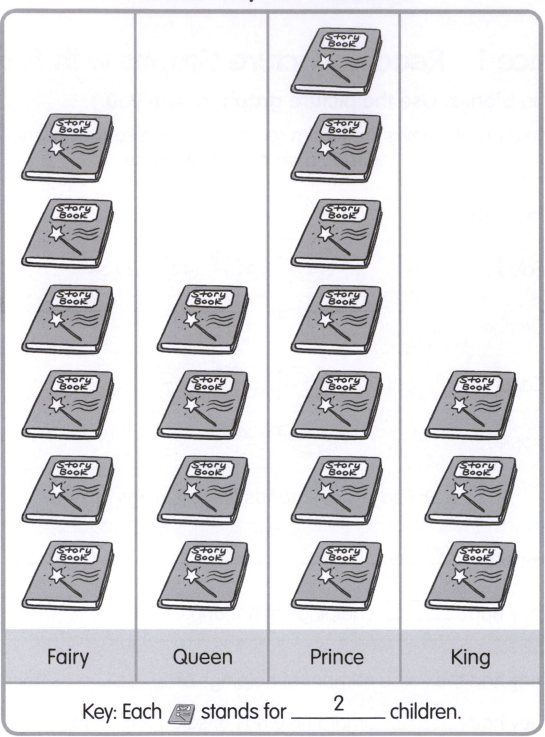

| Fairy | Queen | Prince | King |
|-------|-------|--------|------|

Key: Each 📖 stands for ___2___ children.

**Fill in the blanks.**
**Use the picture graph on page 182 to help you.**

> **Example**
>
> How many characters are shown?
>
> _____4_____

4. Which is the most common favorite character?

   _____

5. Which is the least common favorite character?

   _____

6. 8 children like the Queen.

   What does each  stand for?

   _____

7. How many children chose the Prince?

   _____ children

8. How many more children chose the Fairy than the Queen
   as their favorite character?

   _____ more children

9. The total number of children who chose _____

   or _____ as their favorite character is the same as the
   number of children who chose the Prince.

**Fill in the blanks.**
**Use the picture graph to help you.**

Randy's home is near a School, a Bus Stop, a Store, and a Post Office.
He draws a picture graph to show how far his home is from these places.

### Number of Steps from Home

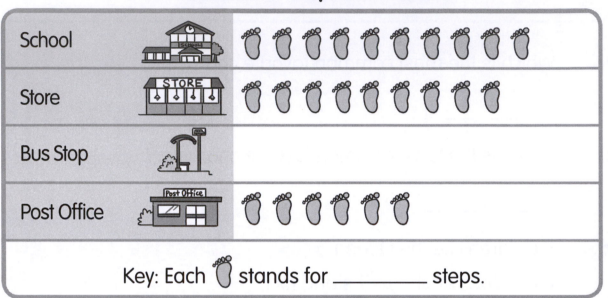

Key: Each 🦶 stands for _____ steps.

**Example**

The School is 100 steps from Randy's home.

Each 🦶 stands for ____10____ steps.

10. The Store is _____ steps from Randy's home.

11. Randy's home is 50 steps from the Bus Stop.

    He will draw _____ 🦶 on the graph.

12. The Post Office is 80 steps from Randy's home.

    He will draw _____ more 🦶 on the graph.

# Practice 2   Making Picture Graphs

1. **Count the boxes of fruit juice on the shelves. Complete the tally chart.**

| Fruit Juice | Tally | Number of Boxes of Fruit Juice |
|---|---|---|
| Apple | ℍℍ ℍℍ ℍℍ ℍℍ | |
| Orange | | |
| Pear | | |
| Grape | | |

**2.** **Fill in the missing numbers.**

| Fruit Juice | Apple | Orange | Pear | Grape |
|---|---|---|---|---|
| Number of Boxes of Fruit Juice | 20 | | | |

**3.** **Then complete the graph.**

### Number of Boxes of Fruit Juice

Key: Each ☐ stands for 2 boxes of fruit juice.

| Apple | Orange | Pear | Grape |
|---|---|---|---|

## Fill in the blanks.

**4.** There are _____ boxes of apple juice.

**5.** There are _____ boxes of fruit juice in all.

**Name:** _____     **Date:** _____

6.      **Look at the picture.**
            **Count the animals in the picture.**
            **Then complete the tally chart.**

| Animals | Tally | Number of Animals |
|---------|-------|-------------------|
| 🐱 | | |
| 🐦 | | |
| 🐰 | | |
| 🐹 | | |

**7.** Use the picture and your answer on page 187. Show the number of animals by coloring the ⬭ in the graph.

### Animals in the Picture

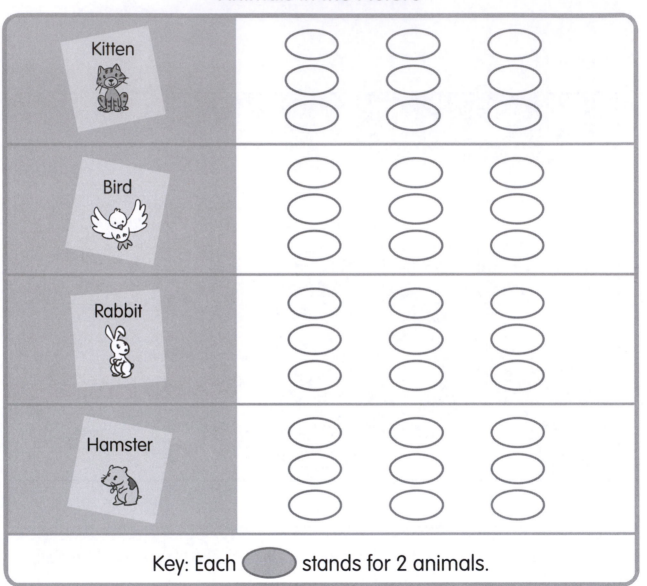

Key: Each ⬭ stands for 2 animals.

Name: _____     Date: _____

**8.**  **These are five kinds of stickers Amy has.**
**Count the number of stickers and complete the tally chart.**

Flowers

Seashells

Puppies

Hearts

Stars

| Stickers | Tally | Number of Stickers |
|---|---|---|
| Flower | | |
| Puppy | | |
| Heart | | |
| Star | | |
| Seashell | | |

## Now fill in the blanks.

9.   Amy's stickers show _____ flowers,

_____ seashells, _____ puppies,

_____ hearts, and _____ stars.

10.  **Then complete the picture graph.
     Give it a title.**

Title: _____

| | |
|---|---|
| Seashell | |
| Puppy | |
| Star | ⬭ ⬭ ⬭ ⬭ ⬭<br>⬭ ⬭ ⬭ ⬭ ⬭ |
| Flower | |
| Heart | |

Key: Each ⬭ stands for 3 stickers.

## Look at the pictures.
## Then fill in the blanks.

Peter, Roy, Shantel, and Amy are friends.
They made up a story that takes place in outer space.
Each drew pictures of his or her favorite thing for the story.

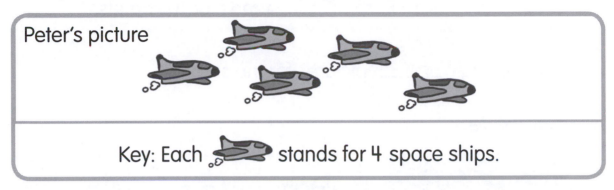

Peter's picture

Key: Each 🚀 stands for 4 space ships.

**11.**  Peter drew _____ pictures for the story.

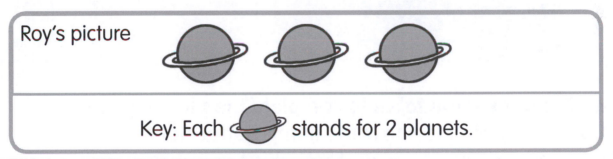

Roy's picture

Key: Each 🪐 stands for 2 planets.

**12.**  Roy drew _____ pictures for the story.

Shantel's picture

Key: Each ⭐ stands for 4 stars.

**13.**  Shantel drew _____ pictures for the story.

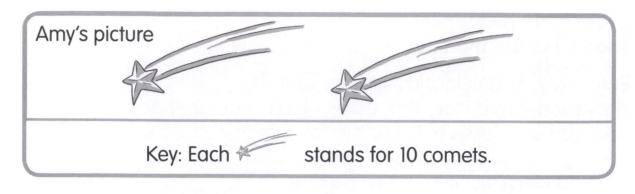

Amy's picture

Key: Each  stands for 10 comets.

**14.** Amy drew _____ pictures for the story.

**15. Complete.**

| Kinds of Things in the Story | ✈ | 🪐 | ⭐ | ☄ |
|---|---|---|---|---|
| **Number of Favorite Things** | | | | |

**Use the data in the table to complete the picture graph.**
**Choose a symbol to show the things in the story.**
**Put a key under the graph. Then give the graph a title.**

Title: _____

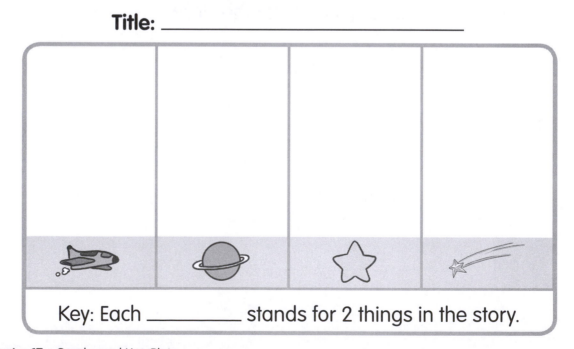

Key: Each _____ stands for 2 things in the story.

# Practice 3   Real-World Problems: Picture Graphs

**Use the picture graph to answer the questions.**

Dora and her friends compare their sticker collections.
She draws a picture graph to show the number of stickers they have.
However, she accidentally spills her drink on part of the graph.

**Number of Stickers**

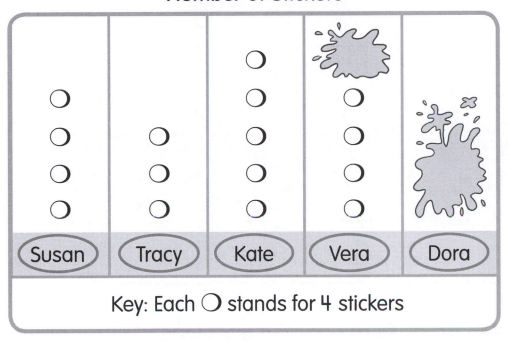

Key: Each ○ stands for 4 stickers

1.      How many stickers does Susan have? _____

2.      How many more stickers does Kate have than Tracy? _____

3.      Dora has 8 stickers.

        How many ○ should there be on the graph? _____

4.      Vera has 24 stickers.
        How many more ○ must be on the graph? _____

5.      How many stickers do Susan and Tracy have in all? _____

**The graph shows the number of children playing each game at a fair.**

## Number of Children Playing Games

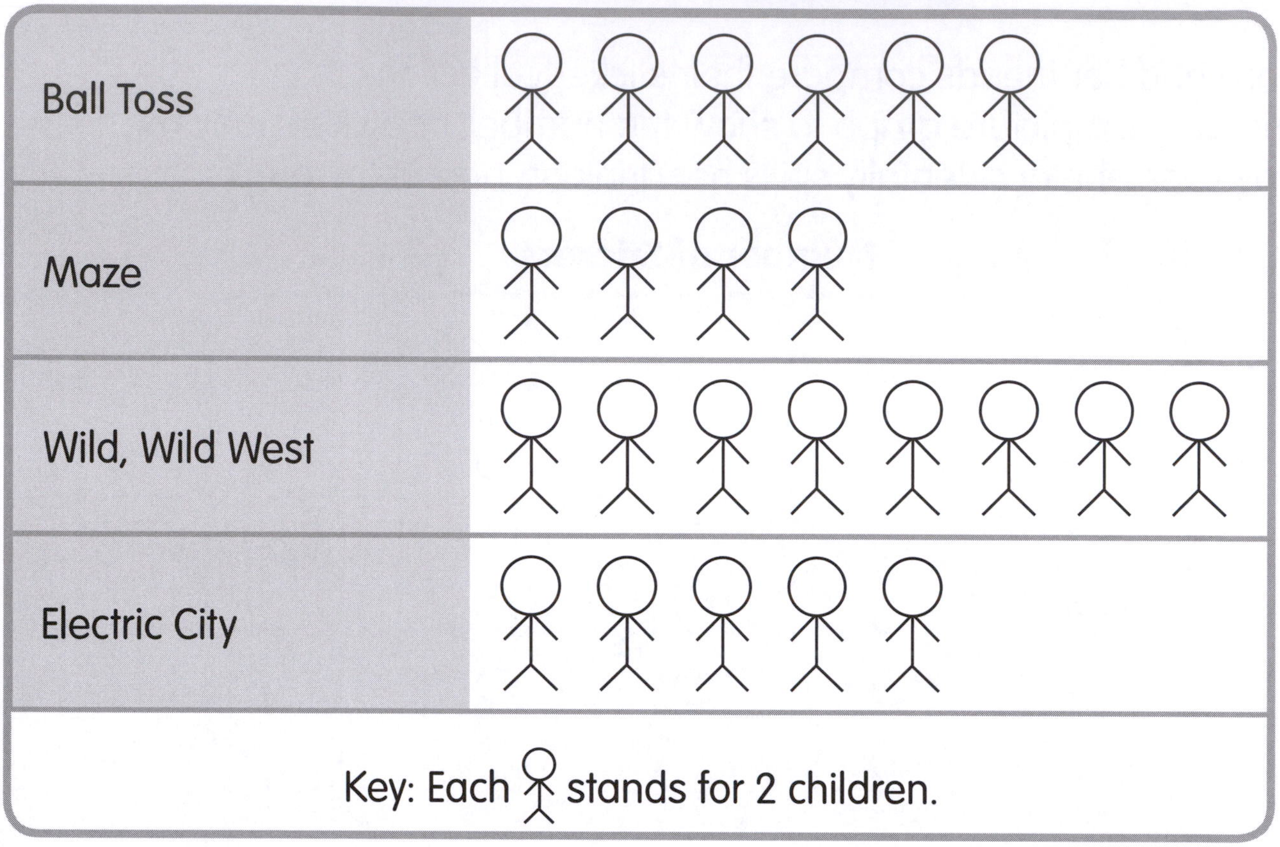

| | |
|---|---|
| Ball Toss | 🧍🧍🧍🧍🧍 |
| Maze | 🧍🧍🧍🧍 |
| Wild, Wild West | 🧍🧍🧍🧍🧍🧍🧍🧍 |
| Electric City | 🧍🧍🧍🧍🧍 |

Key: Each 🧍 stands for 2 children.

**Use the picture graph to answer the questions.**

6.    There are 6 boys at the Electric City stall.
      How many girls are at the Electric City stall? _____

7.    6 of the children who play Wild, Wild West are girls.

      How many are boys? _____

8.    2 girls are at the Maze.
      4 boys are at the Ball Toss.
      How many girls are at the Maze or Ball Toss in all? _____

**9.** Abigail visits a pet store and sees different kinds of fish. Use the data given to finish the graph.

Use a 🐟 to stand for 4 fish.

**a.** There are 16 clown fish.

**b.** There are 12 more barb fish than clown fish.

**c.** There are 4 more goldfish than barb fish.

**d.** There are 8 fewer guppies than goldfish.

**e.** There are the same number of discus fish as clown fish and guppies together.

## Fishes in a Pet Store

| | | | | |
|---|---|---|---|---|
| | | | | |
| Goldfish | Guppy | Clown fish | Discus fish | Barb fish |

Key: Each _____ stands for 4 fish.

10. **Gita made banana muffins for her family. Use the data given to complete the graph.**

Use △ **to stand for 2 cups.**

a. Gita used 2 cups of sugar.
   She used the same number of cups of oil.

b. She used 4 cups of milk.
   She used 2 more cups of oatmeal than the number of cups of milk.

c. She used 6 cups of mashed bananas.

### Banana Muffin Ingredients

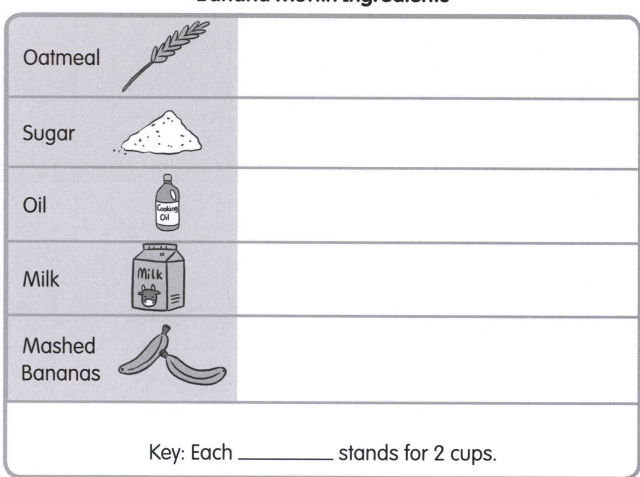

Key: Each _____ stands for 2 cups.

Name: ______________________________ Date: ____________________

# Practice 4 Bar Graphs and Line Plots

Ms. Rafael's students took a Science quiz.
Each student answered 10 questions.
Each correct answer earned 1 point.
The tally chart below shows the scores.

**Complete.**

**1.** Complete the tally chart.

| Scores | Tally | Number of Students |
|---|---|---|
| 1 | | |
| 2 | | |
| 3 | //// | |
| 4 | / | |
| 5 | /// | |
| 6 | 𝍸 | |
| 7 | 𝍸 / | |
| 8 | // | |
| 9 | / | |
| 10 | /// | |

**2.**  Complete the bar graph to show the data.
Label your graph.

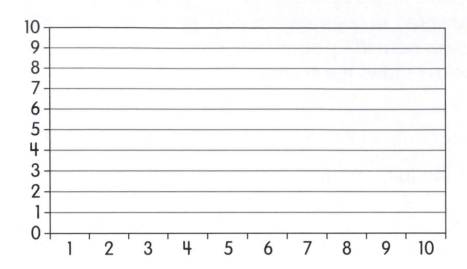

**3.**  Use the data in the bar graph to create a line plot.

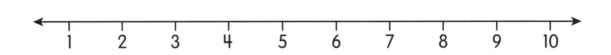

## Use the bar graph or line plot to answer the questions.

**4.**  How many students scored 6 points? _____ students

**5.**  How many students scored more than 5 points? _____ students

**6.**  How many students took the Science quiz? _____ students

**7.**  Ms. Rafael awarded a sticker to each student who scored more than
7 points.

How many stickers did she give out? _____ stickers

# Put On Your Thinking Cap!

## Challenging Practice

Tricia read a story book.
She recorded the number of pages she read every day for 3 days.

She drew a ☐ for every 2 pages she read.

| 1st day | 2nd day | 3rd day | 4th day |

Key: Each ☐ stands for 2 pages.

The number of pages Tricia read follows a pattern.
If this pattern continues, how many pages will Tricia read on the 4th day?

Tricia will read _____ pages on the 4th day.

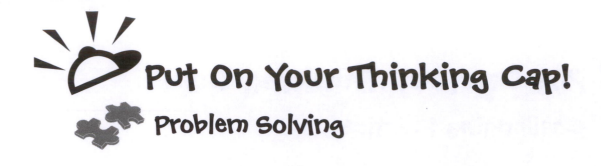

## Put On Your Thinking Cap!

### Problem Solving

The graph shows the number of points 5 children scored on a science test.
The total score for the test is 40.
Complete the graph using the information given.

Ariel scored all the points she could.
Tyrone scored 8 points less than Ariel.
Nicole and Vera had the same number of points.

**Points Scored on a Science Test**

| Ariel  |                                    |
|--------|------------------------------------|
| Edwin  | ✓ ✓ ✓ ✓ <br> ✓ ✓ ✓                 |
| Nicole |                                    |
| Vera   | ✓ ✓ ✓ ✓ ✓ <br> ✓ ✓ ✓ ✓             |
| Tyrone |                                    |

Each ✓ stands for 4 points.

# Chapter Review/Test

## Vocabulary

**Fill in the blanks with words from the box.**

1. The _____ shows what a picture or symbol stands for.

2. A _____ shows data using pictures or symbols.

3. You record the number of things in a _____.

## Concepts and Skills

4. Tammy went to a bird park.
   Help her make a tally chart of the birds she saw on page 202.

## Tally Chart

| Birds | Tally | Number of birds |
|---|---|---|
| | | |
| | | |
| | | |
| | | |
| | | |

5. Then complete the picture graph of the data in exercise 4. Give it a title.

**Title:** _____

| | | | | |
|---|---|---|---|---|
| | | | | |
| Jay | Swallow | Robin | Flamingo | Peacock |

Key: Each O stands for 3 birds.

**Name:** _____    **Date:** _____

## The graph shows how much money each child has saved in a month.

### Money Saved in One Month

Key: Each 💰 stands for $2.

## Use the graph to find the missing numbers.

**6.**  How much has Keith saved?

There are _____ 💰 for Keith.

_____ × $_____ = $_____.

Keith has saved $_____

**7.**  How much have Michelle and Alberto saved in all? _____

There are 7 💰 for Michelle.

_____ × $_____ = $_____

There are 6 💰 for Alberto.

_____ × $_____ = $_____

$_____ + $_____ = $_____

Michelle and Alberto saved $_____ in all.

**8.** How much more has Michelle saved than Gloria?

There are 7  for Michelle.

_____ × $_____ = $_____

There are 5  for Gloria.

_____ × $_____ = $_____

$_____ − $_____ = $_____

Michelle has saved $_____ more than Gloria.

**9.** Grace has 2  .

How much less has she saved than Gloria?

_____ × $_____ = $_____

$_____ − $_____ = $_____

Grace has saved $_____ less than Gloria.

The chart shows the number of beads that each child used to make a bracelet.

| | Number of beads |
|---|---|
| Andrea | 9 |
| Abby | 7 |
| Zoe | 7 |
| Lorie | 5 |
| Bob | 8 |
| Mike | 4 |
| Shelly | 7 |
| Angel | 6 |

**Use the data to complete the bar graph below.
Give your graph a title.**

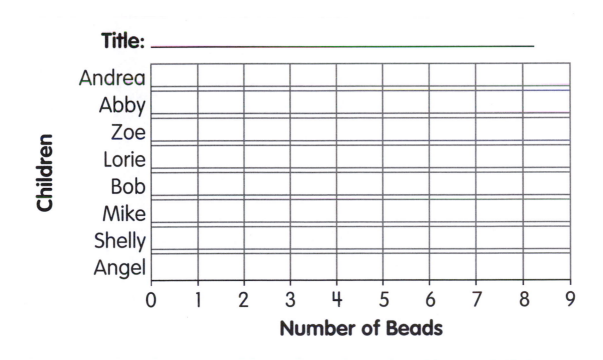

Title: _____

**Make a line plot using the data on the bar graph on page 205. Then answer the questions.**

10. How many children used 6 beads? _____

11. How many children used fewer than 7 beads? _____

12. How many children made bracelets? _____

13. How many children used more than 7 beads? _____

14. How many beads did the children use in all? _____

Name: _____     Date: _____

## Cumulative Review
### for Chapters 15 to 17

## Concepts and Skills

**Skip-count.**

1.  3, 6, 9, _____, _____, _____, _____, _____,

    _____, _____

2.  4, 8, 12, _____, _____, _____, _____, _____,

    _____, _____

## Fill in the blanks.

3.  4 groups of 3 = _____ × _____ = _____
4.  8 groups of 3 = _____ × _____ = _____
5.  3 groups of 4 = _____ × _____ = _____
6.  9 groups of 4 = _____ × _____ = _____

## Use dot paper to find the missing numbers.

7.

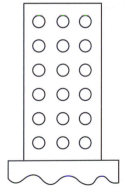
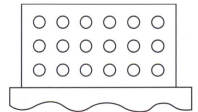

_____ × 3 = _____     _____ × _____ = _____

**8.**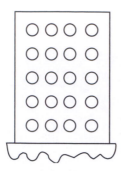

_____ × _____ = _____     _____ × _____ = _____

## Complete the multiplication sentences.
## Use dot paper to help you.

**9.**   9 × 3 = _____

3 × 9 = _____

**10.**   7 × 3 = _____

3 × 7 = _____

**11.**   10 × 4 = _____

4 × 10 = _____

**12.**   6 × 4 = _____

4 × 6 = _____

## Fill in the blanks.

**13.**   10 × 4 = _____

7 × 4 = 10 groups of 4 − 3 groups of 4

= _____ − 12

= _____

**14.**   5 × 3 = _____

7 × 3 = 5 groups of 3 + 2 groups of 3

= _____ + 6

= _____

## Complete the multiplication and division sentences.

**15.**   _____ × 3 = 15          15 ÷ 3 = _____

**16.**   _____ × 4 = 20          20 ÷ 4 = _____

**Fill in the blanks.**
**Use the picture graphs to help you.**

A large bottle contains different kinds of nuts.
The graph shows the number of each kind of nut in the jar.

**Kinds of Nuts in a Jar**

| Almond | ◯ ◯ ◯ ◯ ◯ ◯ |
| Peanut | ◯ ◯ ◯ ◯ ◯ ◯ ◯ ◯ ◯ ◯ |
| Cashew | ◯ ◯ ◯ ◯ |
| Walnut | ◯ ◯ ◯ |
| Pecan | ◯ ◯ ◯ ◯ |

Key: Each ◯ stands for 2 nuts.

**17.**   There are _____ peanuts in the jar.

**18.**   The number of _____ and _____ in the jar is the same.

**19.**   There are _____ fewer walnuts than almonds.

**20.**   There are _____ more peanuts than cashews.

**21.**   There are _____ almonds and pecans in all.

## Count the vegetables in a bin.
## Then complete the tally chart.

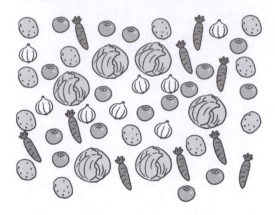

| Vegetable | Tally |
|-----------|-------|
| Onion | |
| Cabbage | |
| Carrot | |
| Potato | |
| Tomato | |

**22.**    Use the picture and the tally chart to make a bar graph.

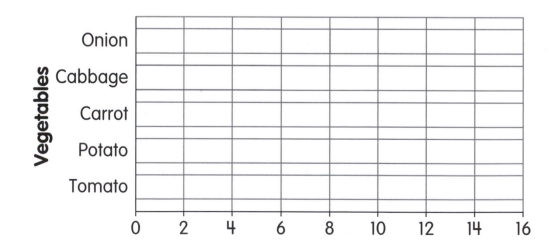

## Complete.
## Use your bar graph to help you.

**23.** How many carrots are there? _____

**24.** How many tomatoes are there? _____

**25.** How many cabbages are there? _____

## Problem Solving
**Solve.**
**Draw bar models to help you.**

**26.** Alicia has 3 bags.
She puts 10 beads in each bag.
How many beads does she have?

There are _____ beads in all.

**Solve.**

**Draw bar models to help you.**

27.    Peter has 18 crayons.
       He divides them into 3 equal groups.
       How many crayons are in each group?

       There are _____ crayons in each group.

28.    Yasmin buys 30 stickers.
       She distributes the stickers equally among her 5 friends.
       How many stickers does each of her friends get?

       Each friend gets _____ stickers.

29.    A day camp has 12 soccer balls.
       Each team uses 3 balls.
       How many teams are there?

       There are _____ teams.

**30.**  5 bags of food for a food drive have a mass of 25 kilograms.
Each bag has the same mass.
What is the mass of each bag?

The mass of each bag is _____ kilograms.

**31.**  The total length of a piece of lace is 28 feet.
It is cut into equal pieces 4 feet long.
How many pieces are there?

There are _____ pieces.

**32.**  Andrew uses 6 liters of water to water his plants every day.
How many liters of water does he use in 4 days?

He uses _____ liters of water.

**Complete the picture graph using Exercises 33 and 34.**
**Then use the graph to solve Exercises 35 and 36.**
A group of people attended a workshop.
They were divided into 5 groups.
The number of people in each group is shown in the graph.

### Groups at the Workshop

| Group 1 | ☺☺☺☺☺☺☺ |
| Group 2 | ☺☺☺ |
| Group 3 | ☺☺☺☺☺ |
| Group 4 | ☺☺☺☺☺ |
| Group 5 | |

Key: Each ☺ stands for _____ people.

**33.** There were 15 people in Group 2.

What does each ☺ stand for? _____

**34.** Draw ☺ to show 20 people in Group 5.

**35.** 7 people in Group 3 were women.

How many were men? _____

**36.** There were 50 men in Group 1 and Group 4. How many women were there in Group 1 and Group 4?

_____

#  Lines and Surfaces

## Practice 1   Parts of Lines and Curves

Trace the correct figures.

**1.**   Parts of lines only

**2.**   Curves only

**3.**   Parts of lines and curves

**Look at these letters.**

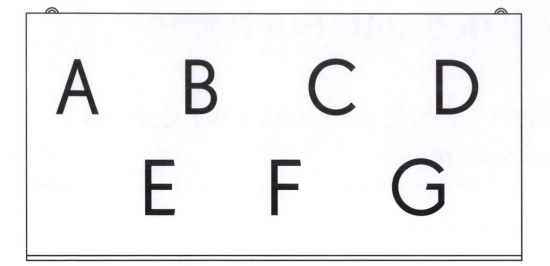

Which of these letters have

**4.** parts of lines only? _____

**5.** curves only? _____

**6.** parts of lines and curves? _____

Draw three other letters using parts of lines only.

**7.**

Draw three other letters using parts of lines and curves.

**8.**

**Julie drew pictures with parts of lines and curves.**
**Count the parts of lines and curves she used.**

**Example**

_____*7*_____ parts of lines and _____*1*_____ curve.

**9.**

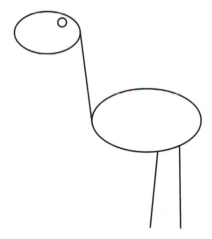

_____ parts of lines and _____ curves.

**10.**

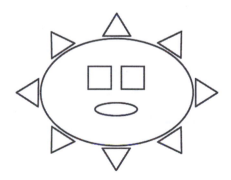

_____ parts of lines and _____ curves.

Count the number of parts of lines in each figure.
Count the number of curves.
Sort the figures into two groups.
Sort using the numbers of parts of lines and curves.
Color each group a different color.

11.

## Draw a picture with

**12.**   more than 5 parts of lines.

**13.**   fewer than 8 curves.

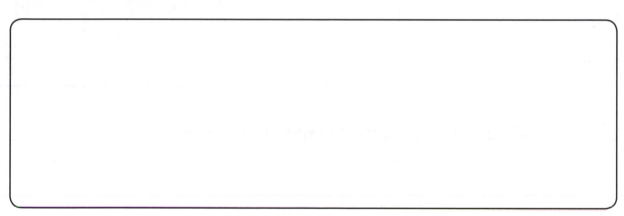

**14.**   more than 10 parts of lines and curves.

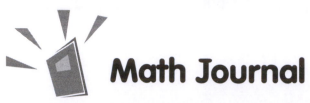 **Math Journal**

**Draw a happy face using curves only.**

**Draw a sad face using parts of lines and curves.**

Name: _____    Date: _____

# Practice 2   Flat and Curved Surfaces

**Look at the objects.**
**Then fill in the blanks.**

**— Example —**

An orange has _____0_____ flat surfaces.

_____1_____ curved surface.

**1.**

Milk

A can has _____ flat surfaces.

_____ curved surface.

**2.**

A plastic cup has _____ flat surface.

_____ curved surface.

**3.**

CEREAL

The cereal box has _____ flat surfaces.

_____ curved surfaces.

**Look around your home.**
**Find two objects that have only flat surfaces.**
**Name and draw them.**

4. _____

5. _____

6. **Circle the solids that you can stack.**

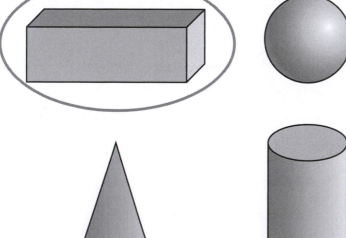

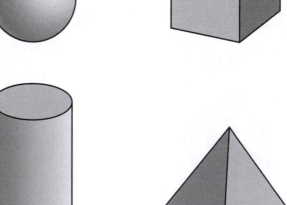

**7.** **Circle the solids that you can roll.**

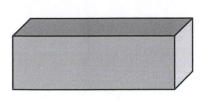

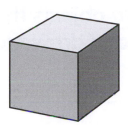

**8.** **Circle the solids that you can slide.**

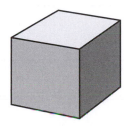

**Look around your home.**
**Find two objects that have only curved surfaces.**
**Name and draw them.**

9. _____

10. _____

**How many flat and curved surfaces does each object have?**
**Write your answers in the table.**

tissue box

egg

piece of paper

basketball

library card

cereal box

vase

| | | |
|---|---|---|
| **11.** | 0 flat surfaces | |
| **12.** | 1 flat surface | |
| **13.** | 1 curved surface | |
| **14.** | 2 flat surfaces | |
| **15.** | 6 flat surfaces | |

Cut out pictures of objects in newspapers or magazines.
Paste them here.
Count the flat and curved surfaces in each object.
Write your answers next to the picture.

16.

# Put On Your Thinking Cap!

## Challenging Practice

The shapes at the bottom of this page can be combined to make a square.
Color the pieces yellow.
Cut them out and paste them below to make the square.

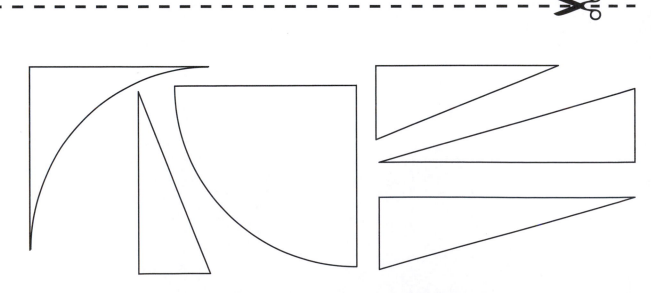

# Chapter Review/Test

## Vocabulary

**Fill in the blanks with words from the box.**

| curved | stack | roll | flat |
|--------|-------|------|------|

1. A ball has a _____ surface.

   It can _____ on the ground.

2. A picture has a _____ surface.

   You can _____ pictures on top of each other.

## Concepts and Skills

**Circle the correct answer.**

3.

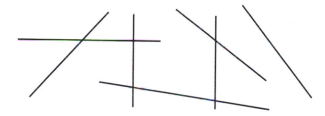

These are (parts of lines, curves).

4.

These are (parts of lines, curves).

**Draw.**

| | |
|---|---|
| **5.** A figure that has five parts of lines and three curves | **6.** A figure that has only parts of lines |
| **7.** An object that has only curved surfaces | **8.** An object that has two flat surfaces and one curved surface |

## Problem Solving

**Each pattern is made of curves and straight lines.**
**Find the pattern.**
**Then complete the pattern.**

**9.**

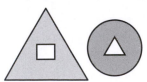  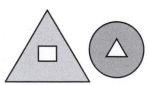  _____

Name: _____    Date: _____

## CHAPTER 19 Shapes and Patterns

## Practice 1   Plane Shapes

**Look at the shapes.**

1.  Color the circles green, the triangles yellow, the rectangles purple, the trapezoids blue, the hexagons red, and the pentagons orange.

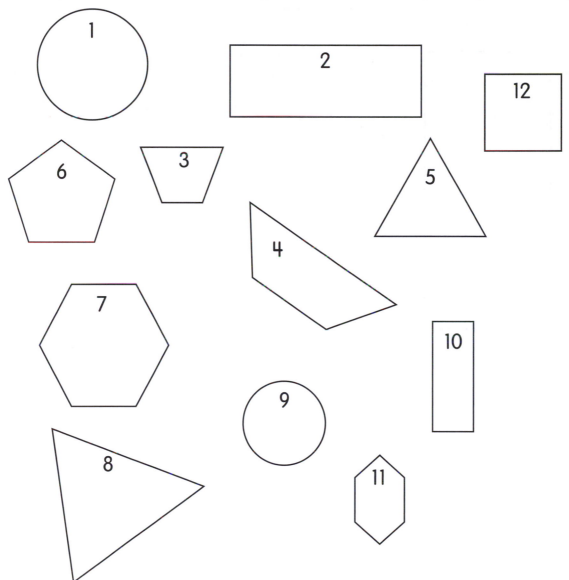

2.  Which of these are quadrilaterals? Write the numbers: _____

# Draw lines on each shape to show the smaller shapes.

**Example**

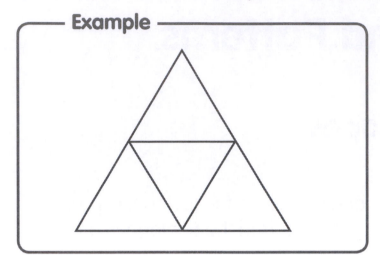

**2.**

**3.**

**4.**  **Cut out the shapes.**
**Then glue them on top of the shape given.**
**Here are two simple rules to follow:**
**a) All cut-outs must be used.**
**b) Cut-outs cannot overlap.**

| Plane Shape | Cut-outs |
| --- | --- |
| | |
| | |

**5.** Draw lines on each figure to show how it is made with these shapes: triangle, square, rectangle, trapezoid, hexagon, and pentagon.

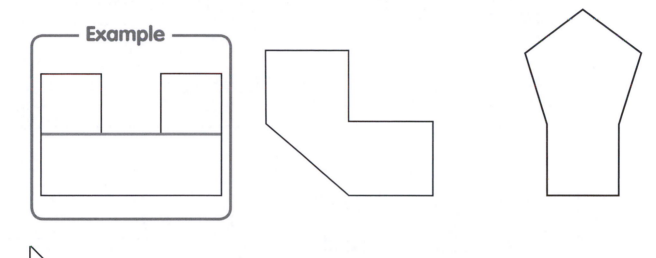

Example

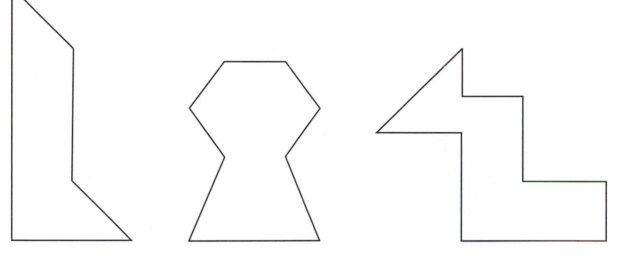

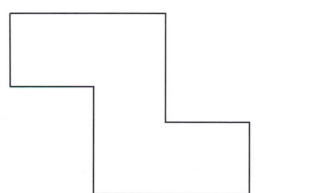

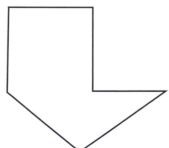

## Each figure is made with two shapes.
## Name the shapes.

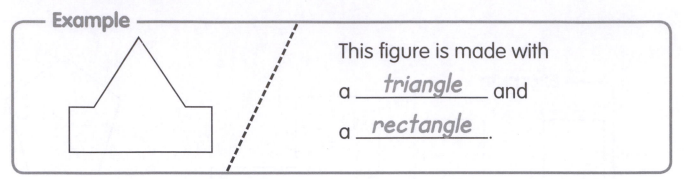

Example

This figure is made with

a ___triangle___ and

a ___rectangle___.

6.

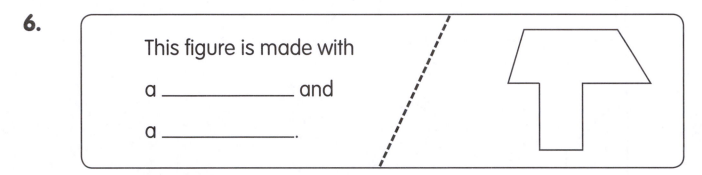

This figure is made with

a _____ and

a _____.

7.

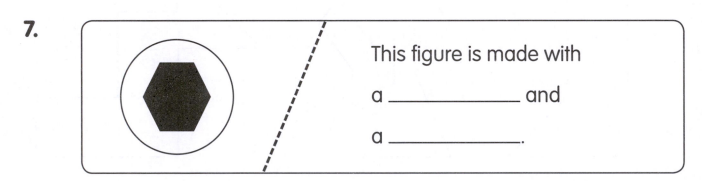

This figure is made with

a _____ and

a _____.

8.

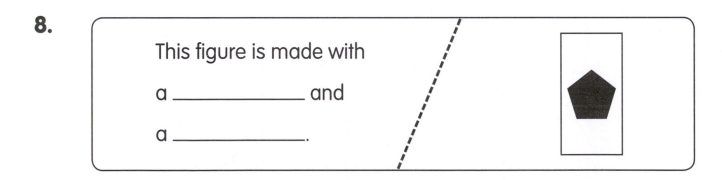

This figure is made with

a _____ and

a _____.

**Name:** _____  **Date:** _____

# A part is missing from each figure.
# Color the shape that makes the figure complete.

**Example**

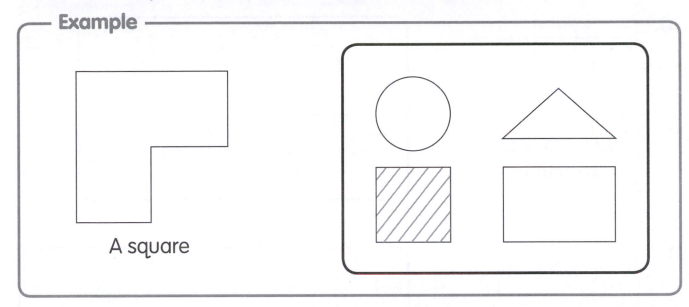

A square

**9.**

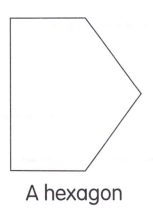

A hexagon

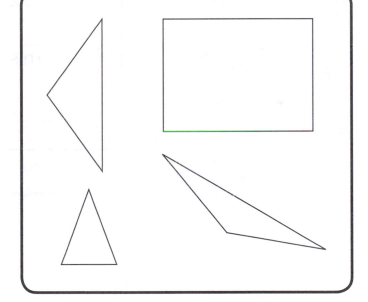

**A part is missing from each figure.**
**Color the shape that makes the figure complete.**

**10.**

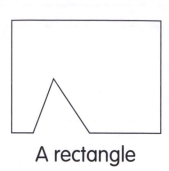

A rectangle

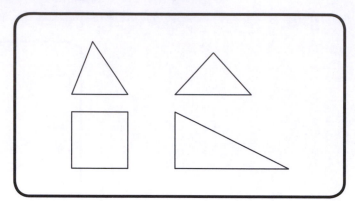

**11.**

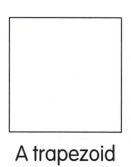

A trapezoid

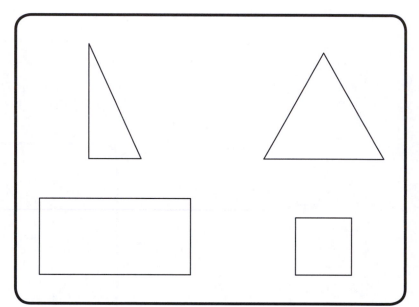

**12.**

A pentagon

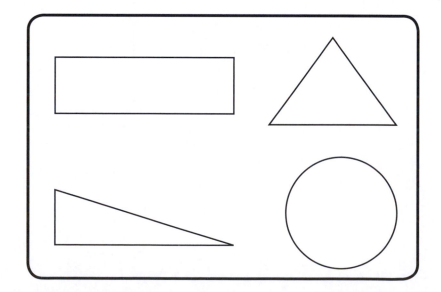

Name: _____   Date: _____

**13.**   Cut out the shapes.
Then glue them on top of the figure.

Here are two simple rules to follow.
(a) All cut-outs must be used.
(b) Cut-outs cannot overlap.

| Figure | Cut-outs ✂ |
|---|---|
| | |

| Figure | Cut-outs ✂ |
|---|---|
| | |

# Practice 2   Solid Shapes

**Write the number of solid shapes used in each model.**

**1.**

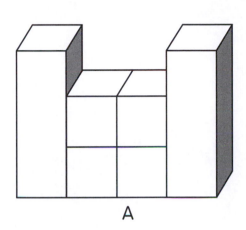

A

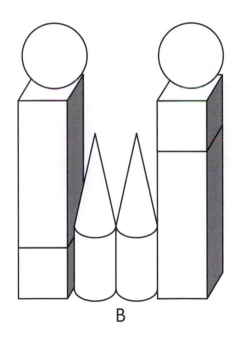

B

| Object | A | B |
|---|---|---|
| Rectangular prism | 2 | 2 |
| Cube | | |
| Cone | | |
| Cylinder | | |
| Sphere | | |

**Look at the cube.**

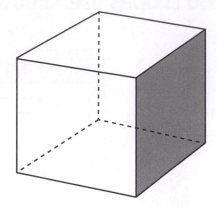

**2.** How many faces can you see on the cube?

**3.** What do you notice about the faces on the cube?

**4.** Name some objects in your classroom or home that are cubes.

Name: _____    Date: _____

# Practice 3   Making Patterns

**Look at the pattern.**
**Draw what comes next.**

**Example**

1. ◯ ● ◦ ⬤ ◯ ◑ ◦ ⬤ ◯ _____

2. [pattern of boxes with circles and shading] _____

3. △ ▢ ◯ △ ▢ ◯ _____

# Circle the correct shapes or figures made of shapes to complete the pattern.

**Example**

**4.**

**5.**

**6.**

**7.**

## Circle the correct shapes or figures made of shapes to complete the pattern.

**8.**

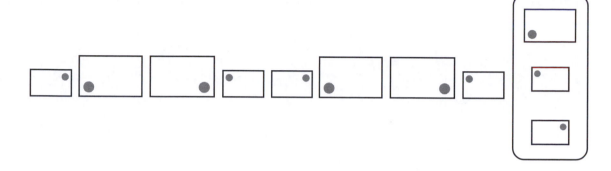

**9.**

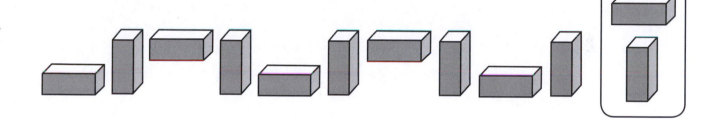

**10.**

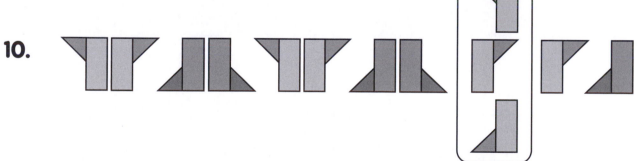

## Circle the correct shapes or figures made of shapes to complete the pattern.

**11.**

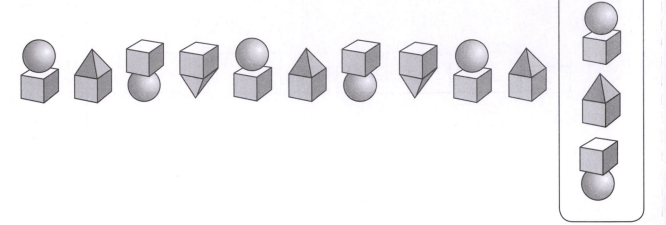

**12.**

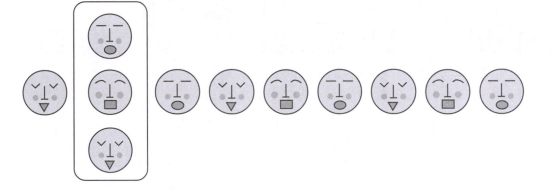

**13.**

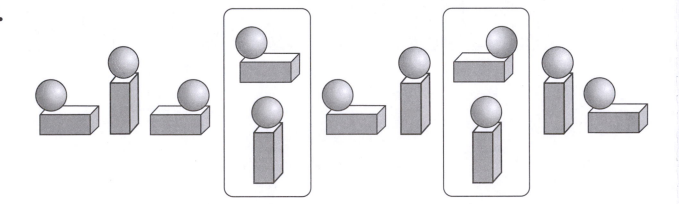

**Name:** _____  **Date:** _____

# Math Journal

This pattern is made with plane shapes.
Circle the mistake in the pattern.
Name the correct shape.
Then draw the repeating pattern unit.

The correct plane shape is a _____.

This pattern is made with solid shapes.
Circle the mistake in the pattern.
Write what the correct shape is.
Then draw or describe the repeating unit.

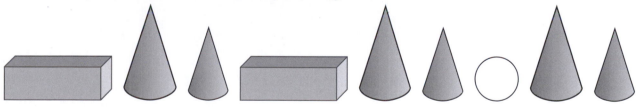

The correct solid shape is a _____.

**Use plane shapes to make a pattern**

**1.** using shapes of different types.

**2.** using the same shape of different colors.

**3.** by turning the shape.

**Name:** _____ **Date:** _____

# Chapter Review/Test

## Vocabulary
**Fill in the blanks with words from the box.**

| |
|---|
| hexagon |
| trapezoid |
| pattern |
| turning |

1. You can form a repeating _____ using

   different shapes, colors, sizes, and

   by _____ the shapes.

2. A _____ has six sides.

3. A _____ is four-sided like the square and the rectangle.

## Concepts and Skills
**Match the shape to its name.**

4.

_____

5.

_____

6.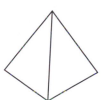

_____

7.

_____

8.

_____

9.

_____

a. pentagon     b. cylinder     c. hexagon

d. pyramid      e. rectangular prism     f. trapezoid

**Use this shape to make another bigger shape.**
**Write how many of this shape you used.**
**Name the shape you made.**

10.

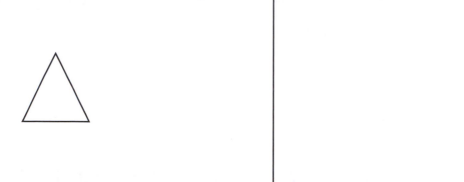

**Draw lines to separate this rectangle into several copies of the same smaller shape.**

11.

**Copy the shape onto the dot grid.**
**Circle one of the angles of the shape.**

12.

**Name:** _____ **Date:** _____

**Write the number of plane shapes that make up this figure.**

**13.**

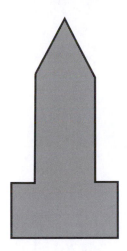

| Solid shape | How many? |
|---|---|
| Rectangle | |
| Triangle | |

**Write the number of solid shapes that make up this model.**

**14.**

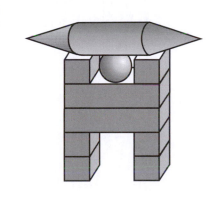

| Solid shape | How many? |
|---|---|
| Cube | |
| Rectangular prism | |
| Cone | |
| Sphere | |
| Cylinder | |

**Draw the next figure in each pattern.**

**15.**

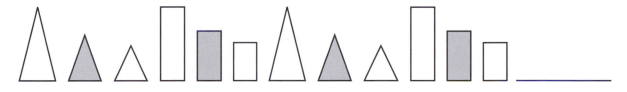

**16.**

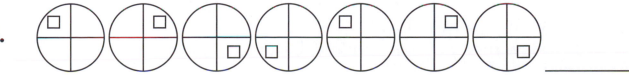

**Complete the pattern.**
**Circle the correct solid or model.**

**17.**

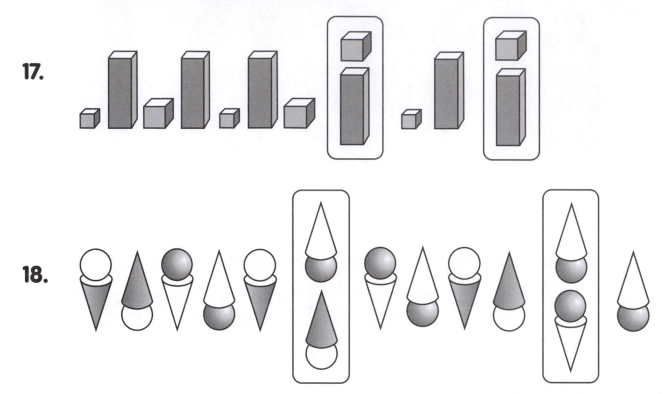

**18.**

## Problem Solving

**Look at the pattern.**
**Draw what comes next.**

**19.**

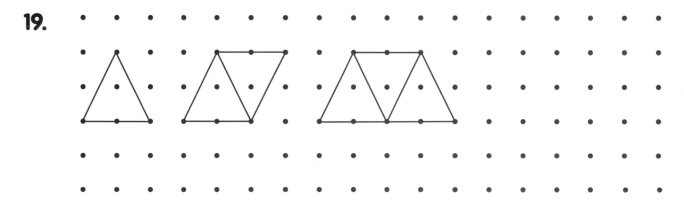

**20.** Susan wants to make a hexagon using the least number of one shape.
    **a.** Which can she use?
    **b.** How many of this shape will she use?

Name: _____   Date: _____

## Cumulative Review
### for Chapters 18 and 19

## Concepts and Skills

**Look at the letters.**
**Then fill in the blanks.**

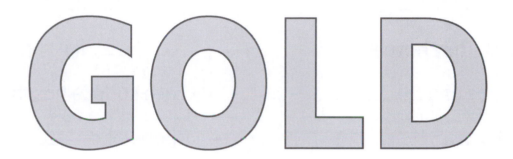

1.  Letter G has _____ parts of lines and _____ curves.

2.  Letter _____ has curves only.

3.  Letters _____ and _____ have the most parts of lines.

4.  The total number of curves in the first and last letters is _____.

5.  The total number of parts of lines in all the letters is _____.

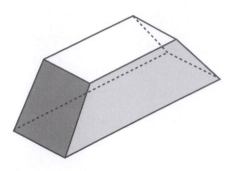

**6.** This solid has _____ faces. They have the shapes of a _____ and a _____.

**7.** This solid has _____ flat surfaces. Each surface has the shape of a _____.

**Look at the drawings.**
**Count the number of curves and parts of lines in each.**
**Complete the table.**

**8.**

**9.**

**10.**

| Drawing | Parts of Lines | Curves |
|---------|---------------|--------|
| 8 | | |
| 9 | | |
| 10 | | |

Name: _____    Date: _____

**Draw dotted lines within each figure to show the shapes it is made of.**

**11.**

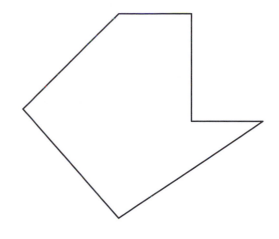

**12.**

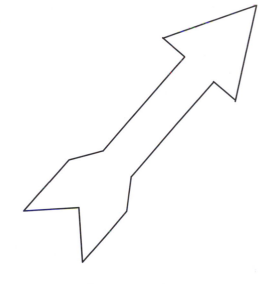

**13.**

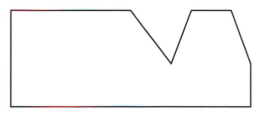

**14.**

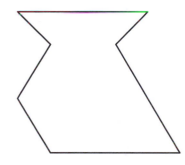

**Look at the picture.**
**Count and write the number of shapes you see.**

**15.**

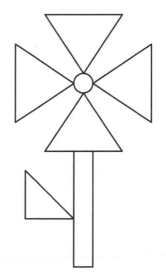

| Shape | Number |
|---|---|
| Circle | |
| Triangle | |
| Rectangle | |

**Copy on dot grid paper.**

**16.**

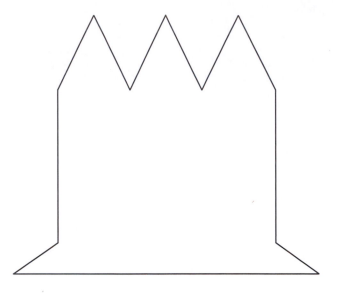

. . . . . . . . . .

. . . . . . . . . .

. . . . . . . . . .

. . . . . . . . . .

. . . . . . . . . .

. . . . . . . . . .

. . . . . . . . . .

. . . . . . . . . .

. . . . . . . . . .

## Problem Solving.

**Look at the pattern.**
**What comes next?**
**Fill in the blank.**

**17.**

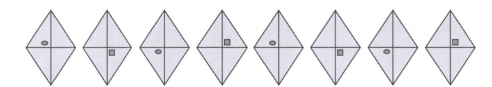

_____

**Circle what comes next.**

**18.**

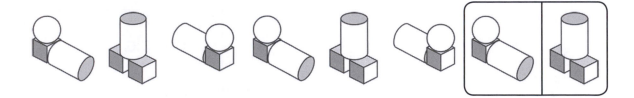

## End-of-Year Review
### Test Prep

**Multiple Choice**

**Fill in the circle next to the correct answer.**

1. Which of the following is correct?

   (A) In 345, the digit 3 is in the ones place.

   (B) In 345, the digit 5 is in the ones place.

   (C) In 345, the digit 5 is in the tens place.

   (D) In 345, the digit 4 is in the hundreds place.

2. What comes next? 5, 15, 25 _____.

   (A) 0          (B) 10          (C) 35          (D) 50

3. The sum of 500 and 43 is _____.

   (A) 345      (B) 354      (C) 435      (D) 543

4. Farmer Ben has 456 chickens.
   He has 336 ducks.
   What is the difference between the number of chickens and ducks?

   (A) 130      (B) 120      (C) 576      (D) 932

5.

   How many groups of 5 can you make?

   (A) 2          (B) 4          (C) 5          (D) 10

**6.** Rope A is 45 feet long.
Rope B is 71 feet long.
How much longer is Rope B than Rope A?

(A) 26 ft   (B) 34 ft   (C) 36 ft   (D) 116 ft

**7.** Roma weighs about _____ kilograms.

(A) 3 kg   (B) 442 kg   (C) 81 g   (D) 4300 g

**8.** 137 + 40 = _____.

(A) 177   (B) 187   (C) 237   (D) 277

**9.**

Which is the correct amount of money shown?

(A) $16.00   (B) $20.50   (C) $16.24   (D) $19.34

Name: _____     Date: _____

**10.**   Angeline got home at 6:20 P.M.
Which clock shows the time Angeline got home?

Ⓐ

Ⓑ

Ⓒ

Ⓓ

**11.**   Which has only flat surfaces?

Ⓐ a banana

Ⓑ a bottle

Ⓒ a balloon

Ⓓ a square box

**12.** Yumi buys a violin for $287.
She gives the cashier $300.
How much change does she get?

(A) $20    (B) $17    (C) $23    (D) $13

**13.**

Zach makes some juice. How much does he make?

(A) 1 L    (B) 10 L    (C) 5 L    (D) 12 L

**14.** Which is a part of a line?

(A)     (B)     (C)     (D)

**15.** Which is not divided into equal parts?

(A)

(B)

(C)

(D)

## Short Answer

**Read the questions carefully.**
**Write your answers in the space provided.**

**16.**   What is 345 + 70?                                 _____

**17.**   ☆ stands for 4 people.

What does ☆ ☆ ☆ ☆ ☆ ☆ stand for?  _____

**18.**   What is 920 − 80?                                 _____

**19.**   Write an odd number bigger than 80 but smaller than 100.  _____

**20.**   How many parts of lines and curves are there?

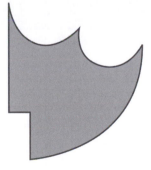

_____ parts of lines

_____ curves

**21.** Joy and Andrew share a pie equally.
What fraction of the pie does Andrew eat?

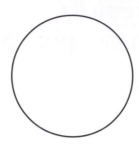

Andrew eats _____ of the pie.

**22.** Joe has $2.
He buys a toy for 75¢.
How much does he have left?
$_____

**23.** How many of each shape are there?

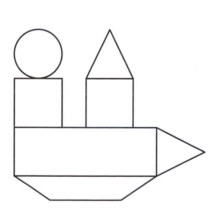

| Shape | How many? |
|-------|-----------|
| ○ | |
| ▢ | |
| △ | |
| ▭ | |
| ⏢ | |

**Fill in the blanks.**

**24.** 789 = 7 hundreds _____ tens 9 ones

**25.** The mass of Mary's bag is about 3 _____ g/kg.

**26.** Subtract 73 from 100.

_____

**27.** **Draw the hands on the clock to show 9:10.**

**Draw a part of a line, 4 inches long.**

**28.**

**Complete the number pattern.**

**29.**  820, 840, 860, _____, _____, _____, 940

**Draw what comes next.**

**30.** ●▲○△●▲○△●▲○ _____

**Look at the pattern. Check (✓) what comes next.**

**31.**

**32.**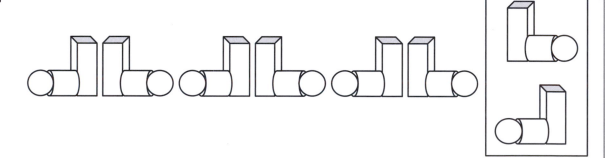

Name: ______________________ Date: ______________________

## Extended Response

**The picture graph shows the number of storybooks each boy has.**

| | |
|---|---|
| Greg | ○ ○ ○ |
| Albert | ○ ○ ○ ○ |
| Mario | ○ ○ ○ ○ ○ |
| Anthony | ○ ○ |
| Each ○ stands for 3 books. | |

**Use the picture graph to fill in the blanks.**

**33.** How many books does Greg have?

There are __________ ○ for Greg.

__________ × __________ = __________

Greg has __________ storybooks.

**34.** How many books do Albert and Anthony have in all?

There are _____ ◯ for Albert and Anthony.

_____ × _____ = _____

Albert and Anthony have _____ books in all.

**35.** How many storybooks does the boy with the greatest number of books have?

There are _____ ◯ for _____.

_____ × _____ = _____

He has _____ books in all.

**36.** How many more books does Mario have than Anthony?

Mario has 5 ◯.

_____ × _____ = _____

Anthony has _____ ◯.

_____ × _____ = _____

_____ − _____ = _____

Mario has _____ more books than Anthony.

**Solve.**
**Show your work.**

**37.** Sam has 300 books.
He sells 118 books.
He lends 55 books to friends.
How many books does he have left?

He has _____ books left.

**38.** Alexandra adds 200 grams of flour.
She adds 100 grams of butter.
She adds 150 grams of sugar.
Then she adds enough milk to make the total mass
1,000 grams.
How much milk does she add?

She adds _____ grams of milk.

**Solve.**
**Show your work.**
**Use bar models to help you.**

**39.** Abigail has $300. Mabel has $12 more than Abigail.

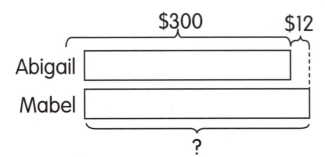

How much money does Mabel have?

Mabel has $_____.

**40.** 381 boys take part in a game.
78 fewer girls than boys take part in the game.

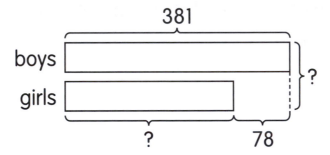

**a.** How many girls take part in the game?

_____ girls take part in the game.

**b.** How many children take part in the game?

_____ children take part in the game.